2009 EDITION

NATIONAL SAFETY COUNCIL

INJURY FACTS®

FORMERLY
ACCIDENT FACTS®

The National Safety Council, chartered by an act of Congress, is a nongovernmental, not-for-profit, public service organization with a mission to educate and influence people to prevent accidental injury and death.

Injury Facts®, the Council's annual statistical report on unintentional injuries and their characteristics and costs, was prepared by:

Research and Statistical Services Group
Mei-Li Lin, Executive Director
Alan F. Hoskin, Manager, Statistics Department, retired
Kenneth P. Kolosh, Manager, Statistics Department
Kevin T. Fearn, Sr. Statistical Associate
Kathleen T. Porretta, Production Manager

Questions or comments about the content of *Injury Facts*® should be directed to the Research and Statistics Department, National Safety Council, 1121 Spring Lake Drive, Itasca, IL 60143, or telephone 630-775-2322, or fax 630-285-0242, or E-mail rssdept@nsc.org.

For price and ordering information, visit www.nsc.org or write Customer Relations, National Safety Council, 1121 Spring Lake Drive, Itasca, IL 60143, or telephone 800-621-7619, or fax 630-285-0797.

Acknowledgments
The information presented in *Injury Facts*® was made possible by the cooperation of many organizations and individuals, including state vital and health statistics authorities, state traffic authorities, state workers' compensation authorities, trade associations, Bureau of the Census, Bureau of Labor Statistics, Consumer Product Safety Commission, Federal Highway Administration, Federal Railroad Administration, International Labour Office, National Center for Health Statistics, National Fire Protection Association, National Highway Traffic Safety Administration, National Transportation Safety Board, National Weather Service, Mine Safety and Health Administration, and the World Health Organization. Specific contributions are acknowledged in footnotes and source notes throughout the book.

Visit the National Safety Council's website:
http://www.nsc.org

Suggested citation: National Safety Council. (2009). *Injury Facts*®, *2009 Edition*. Itasca, IL: Author.

Library of Congress Catalog Card Number: 99-74142

Printed in U.S.A.   ISBN 978-0-87912-282-9   NSC Press Product No. 02312-0000

TABLE OF CONTENTS

Unintentional-injury deaths were down 0.4% in 2007 compared to the revised 2006 total. Unintentional-injury deaths were estimated to total 120,000 in 2007 and 120,500 in 2006.

The resident population of the United States was 301,621,000 in 2007, an increase of less than 1% from 2006. The death rate in 2007 was 39.8 per 100,000 population—down 1% from 2006 but still 17% greater than the lowest rate on record, which was 34.0 in 1992.

The National Safety Council has identified four areas where the greatest number of people are being hurt and killed. These areas are:

Motor vehicle safety—Teen drivers, mature drivers, speeding, impaired driving, distracted driving, and occupant restraints are the areas we focus on. Too many lives are changed forever by injuries and deaths in these areas.

Falls—At work and at home, falls are a rapidly increasing concern, especially falls among older adults. Bring attention to this issue by helping others know how to create safe environments and develop best practices.

Unintentional drug overdoses—Non-medical use of prescription pain relievers is taking the lives of thousands of people each year. On a search to get high, people are using pills from friends and family members. Help bring attention to this growing issue.

Overexertion—Overexertion is a leading cause of sprains and strains, resulting in a significant number of back injuries.

The first graph on page *v* shows that motor vehicles, poisonings (representing drug overdoses as well as other unintentional poisonings), and falls are the leading events resulting in fatalities. The second graph highlights that falls and overexertion are the leading events resulting in medically attended nonfatal injuries. To learn more about how you can work with the Council on these issues as a Safety Ambassador please visit our web site (www.nsc.org).

Changes in the 2009 Edition

Once again, some important improvements have been made to *Injury Facts*. In addition to the changes listed below, motor vehicle fleet benchmarking rates are back after a seven year hiatus. The fleet benchmarking program intends to provide a source that organizations can use to compare their fleet's safety performance with other organizations operating similar vehicles (see page 118 for all the motor fleet vehicle rates).

Look for *new* data on …

- Nature of work injury
- Outdoor recreational injuries
- Ladder related injuries
- Home and community historical trends
- Global burden of unintentional injuries and deaths
- And more

and *updated* or *expanded* data on …

- General mortality
- Occupational injury and illness incidence rates by industry
- Occupational injury and illness profile data by industry sector
- Workers' compensation claims and costs
- Disasters
- Comparing safety of transportation modes
- Traffic safety issues – alcohol, occupant protection, speeding, distracted driving, and others
- Consumer product-related injuries
- Accidental deaths by state
- And more

For more information on the full *Injury Facts* family of products, visit the Council's web site (www.nsc.org), call Customer Service at 800-621-7619, or contact your local council.

Your comments and suggestions to improve *Injury Facts* are welcome. Information on how to contact us is given on page *ii*.

FATAL INJURIES BY EVENT, 2006

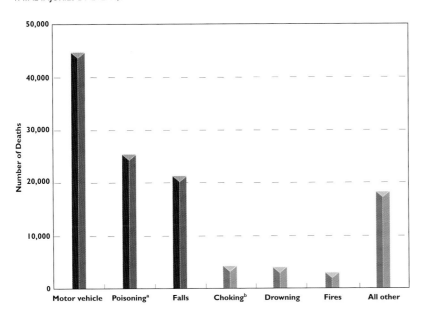

Source: National Safety Council estimates. See the Technical Appendix.
aPoisoning includes unintentional drug overdoses.
bInhalation or ingestion of food or object obstructing breathing.

MEDICALLY ATTENDED NONFATAL INJURIES BY EVENT, 2006

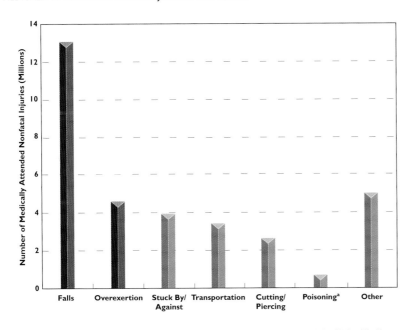

Source: Adams, P. F., & Barnes, P. M. (2008, January). Summary health statistics for the U. S. population: National Health Interview Survey, 2006. National Center for Health Statistics. Vital Health Statistics, Series 10 (No. 236).
aPoisoning includes unintentional drug overdoses.

NATIONAL SAFETY COUNCIL

INJURY FACTS®

Unintentional-injury deaths were down 0.4% in 2007 compared to the revised 2006 estimate. Unintentional-injury deaths were estimated to total 120,000 in 2007 and 120,500 in 2006. The 2007 estimate is 2% greater than the 2005 final count of 117,809. **The 2007 estimate is 38% greater than the 1992 total of 86,777 (the lowest annual total since 1924) and 3% greater than the previous highest total of 116,385 deaths in 1969.**

The death rate in 2007 was 39.8 per 100,000 population—17% greater than the lowest rate on record, which was 34.0 in 1992. The 2007 death rate was down 1% from the 2006 revised rate.

Comparing 2007 to 2006, motor-vehicle, home, and work deaths decreased while public deaths increased. The population death rate in the motor-vehicle, home, and work classes declined while the public rate increased.

The motor-vehicle death total was down 3% in 2007. The 2007 mileage death rate of 1.44 per 100,000,000 vehicle miles was down 3% from the revised 2006 rate of 1.48, and is the lowest on record. The 2007 rate is down 5% from the revised 2005 rate of 1.52.

According to the latest final data (2005), unintentional injuries continued to be the fifth leading cause of death, exceeded only by heart disease, cancer, stroke, and chronic lower respiratory diseases. Preliminary death certificate data for 2006 indicate that unintentional injuries will remain in fifth place.

Nonfatal injuries also affect millions of Americans. In 2006, 33.2 million people—about 1 out of 9—sought medical attention for an injury and 3.0 million people were hospitalized for injuries. About 27.6 million were treated in hospital emergency departments and about 6.4 million visits to hospital outpatient departments were for unintentional injuries. About 49.2 million visits to physicians' offices were for unintentional injuries.

The economic impact of these fatal and nonfatal unintentional injuries amounted to $684.4 billion in 2007. This is equivalent to about $2,300 per capita, or about $5,900 per household. These are costs that every individual and household pays whether directly out of pocket, through higher prices for goods and services, or through higher taxes.

Between 1912 and 2007, unintentional-injury deaths per 100,000 population were reduced 49% (after adjusting for the classification change in 1948) from 82.4 to 39.8. The reduction in the overall rate during a period when the nation's population tripled has resulted in 5,300,000 fewer people being killed due to unintentional injuries than there would have been if the rate had not been reduced.

ALL UNINTENTIONAL INJURIES, 2007

Class	Deaths	Change from 2006	Deaths per 100,000 Persons	Disabling Injuries[a]
All Classes[b]	**120,000**	**−0.4%**	**39.8**	**26,300,000**
Motor-vehicle	43,100	−3%	14.3	2,300,000
Public nonwork	40,955			2,200,000
Work	1,945			100,000
Home	200			([c])
Work	4,689	−8%	1.6	3,500,000
Nonmotor-vehicle	2,744			3,400,000
Motor-vehicle	1,945			100,000
Home	43,500	−11%	14.4	10,400,000
Nonmotor-vehicle	43,300			10,400,000
Motor-vehicle	200			([c])
Public	30,500	+26%	10.1	10,200,000

Source: National Safety Council estimates (rounded) based on data from the National Center for Health Statistics, state departments of health, and state traffic authorities, except for the work figures which are from the Bureau of Labor Statistics, Census of Fatal Occupational Injuries (CFOI). The National Safety Council adopted the CFOI count for work-related unintentional injuries beginning with 1992. See the Glossary for definitions and the Technical Appendix for estimating procedures. Beginning with 1999 data, deaths are classified according to the 10th revision of the International Classification of Diseases. Caution should be used in comparing data classified under the two systems.
[a]Disabling beyond the day of injury. Disabling injuries are not reported on a national basis, so the totals shown are approximations based on ratios of disabling injuries to deaths developed by the National Safety Council. The totals are the best estimates for the current year. They should not, however, be compared with totals shown in previous editions of this book to indicate year-to-year changes or trends. See the Glossary for definitions and the Technical Appendix for estimating procedures.
[b]Deaths and injuries above for the four separate classes add to more than the All Classes figures due to rounding and because some deaths and injuries are included in more than one class. For example, 1,945 work deaths involved motor vehicles and are in both the work and motor-vehicle totals and 200 motor-vehicle deaths occurred on home premises and are in both home and motor-vehicle. The total of such duplication amounted to about 2,145 deaths and 100,000 injuries in 2007.
[c]Less than 10,000.

UNINTENTIONAL-INJURY DEATHS BY CLASS, UNITED STATES, 2007

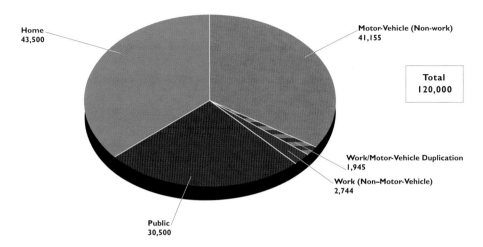

Home
43,500

Motor-Vehicle (Non-work)
41,155

Total
120,000

Work/Motor-Vehicle Duplication
1,945

Work (Non–Motor-Vehicle)
2,744

Public
30,500

UNINTENTIONAL DISABLING INJURIES BY CLASS, UNITED STATES, 2007

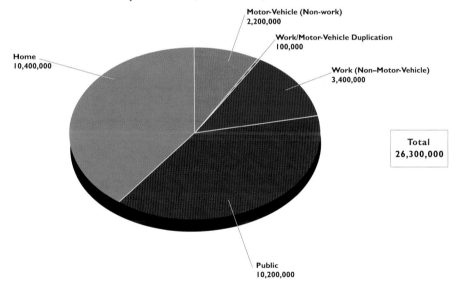

Motor-Vehicle (Non-work)
2,200,000

Work/Motor-Vehicle Duplication
100,000

Home
10,400,000

Work (Non–Motor-Vehicle)
3,400,000

Total
26,300,000

Public
10,200,000

COSTS OF UNINTENTIONAL INJURIES
BY CLASS, 2007

4

The total cost of unintentional injuries in 2007, $684.4 billion, includes estimates of economic costs of fatal and nonfatal unintentional injuries together with employers' uninsured costs, vehicle damage costs, and fire losses. Wage and productivity losses, medical expenses, administrative expenses, and employers' uninsured costs are included in all four classes of injuries. Cost components unique to each class are identified below.

Motor-vehicle crash costs include property damage from motor-vehicle accidents. Work costs include the value of property damage in on-the-job motor-vehicle accidents and fires. Home and public costs include estimated fire losses, but do not include other property damage costs.

Besides the estimated $684.4 billion in economic losses from unintentional injuries in 2007, lost quality of life from those injuries is valued at an additional $3,292.5 billion, making the comprehensive cost $3,976.9 billion in 2007.

Several cost benchmarks were updated for the 2005–2006 edition making 2004 and later costs not comparable to previous years. The method for estimating the number of medically attended injuries by class was revised to use the latest National Health Interview Survey data. Estimated property damage costs in motor-vehicle crashes were rebenchmarked using National Highway Traffic Safety Administration data. The value of a statistical life also was updated, which affects only the comprehensive cost mentioned in the paragraph above.

CERTAIN COSTS OF UNINTENTIONAL INJURIES BY CLASS, 2007 ($ BILLIONS)

Cost	Total[a]	Motor-Vehicle	Work	Home	Public Nonmotor-Vehicle
Total	**$684.4**	**$257.7**	**$175.3**	**$164.7**	**$108.3**
Wage and productivity losses	344.4	88.5	84.1	104.4	71.1
Medical expenses	134.0	38.5	35.3	38.1	24.3
Administrative expenses[b]	129.2	86.1	40.4	8.3	8.1
Motor-vehicle damage	42.6	42.6	1.7	(c)	(c)
Employers' uninsured costs	19.5	2.0	10.4	4.8	2.6
Fire loss	14.7	(c)	3.4	9.1	2.2

Source: National Safety Council estimates. See the Technical Appendix. Cost estimating procedures were revised extensively for the 1993 edition of Accident Facts®. In general, cost estimates are not comparable from year to year. As additional data or new benchmarks become available, they are used from that point forward. Previously estimated figures are not revised.
[a]Duplication between work and motor-vehicle, which amounted to $21.6 billion, was eliminated from the total.
[b]Home and public insurance administration costs may include costs of administering medical treatment claims for some motor-vehicle injuries filed through health insurance plans.
[c]Not included; see comments above.

COSTS OF UNINTENTIONAL INJURIES BY CLASS, 2007

TOTAL COST $684.4 BILLION

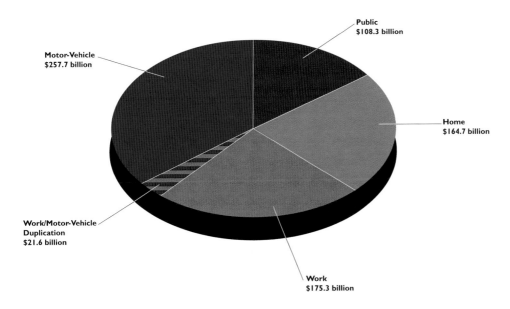

Public
$108.3 billion

Motor-Vehicle
$257.7 billion

Home
$164.7 billion

Work/Motor-Vehicle
Duplication
$21.6 billion

Work
$175.3 billion

Wage and Productivity Losses

A person's contribution to the wealth of the nation usually is measured in terms of wages and household production. The total of wages and fringe benefits together with an estimate of the replacement-cost value of household services provides an estimate of this lost productivity. Also included is travel delay for motor-vehicle accidents.

Medical Expenses

Doctor fees, hospital charges, the cost of medicines, future medical costs, and ambulance, helicopter, and other emergency medical services are included.

Administrative Expenses

Include the administrative cost of public and private insurance, and police and legal costs. Private insurance administrative costs are the difference between premiums paid to insurance companies and claims paid out by them. It is their cost of doing business and is a part of the cost total. Claims paid by insurance companies are not identified separately, as every claim is compensation for losses such as wages, medical expenses, property damage, etc.

Motor-Vehicle Damage

Includes the value of damage to vehicles from motor-vehicle crashes. The cost of normal wear and tear to vehicles is not included.

Employers' Uninsured Costs

This is an estimate of the uninsured costs incurred by employers, representing the dollar value of time lost by uninjured workers. It includes time spent investigating and reporting injuries, giving first aid, hiring and training of replacement workers, and the extra cost of overtime for uninjured workers.

Fire Loss

Includes losses from both structure fires and nonstructure fires such as vehicles, outside storage, crops, and timber.

Work–Motor-Vehicle Duplication

The cost of motor-vehicle crashes that involve persons in the course of their work is included in both classes but the duplication is eliminated from the total. The duplication in 2007 amounted to $21.6 billion and was made up of $3.7 billion in wage and productivity losses, $2.2 billion in medical expenses, $13.7 billion in administrative expenses, $1.7 billion in vehicle damage, and $0.3 billion in employers' uninsured costs.

COSTS OF UNINTENTIONAL INJURIES BY COMPONENT, 2007

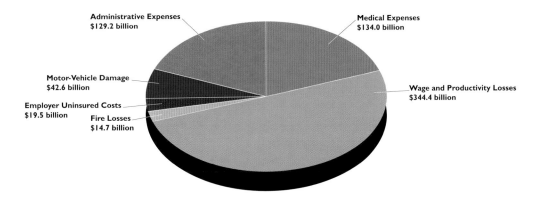

TOTAL COST $684.4 BILLION

Administrative Expenses
$129.2 billion

Medical Expenses
$134.0 billion

Motor-Vehicle Damage
$42.6 billion

Wage and Productivity Losses
$344.4 billion

Employer Uninsured Costs
$19.5 billion

Fire Losses
$14.7 billion

COST EQUIVALENTS

The costs of unintentional injuries are immense—billions of dollars. Since figures this large can be difficult to comprehend, it is sometimes useful to reduce the numbers to a more understandable scale by relating them to quantities encountered in daily life. The table below shows how the costs of unintentional injuries compare to common quantities such as taxes, corporate profits, or stock dividends.

COST EQUIVALENTS, 2007

The Cost of ...	Is Equivalent to ...
... **All Injuries** ($684.4 billion)	... 59 cents of every dollar paid in federal personal income taxes, **or** ... 51 cents of every dollar spent on food in the U.S.
... **Motor-Vehicle Crashes** ($257.7 billion)	... purchasing 360 gallons of gasoline for each registered vehicle in the U.S., **or** ... more than $1,300 per licensed driver.
... **Work Injuries** ($175.3 billion)	... 22 cents of every dollar of corporate dividends to stockholders, **or** ... 9 cents of every dollar of pre-tax corporate profits, **or** ... exceeds the combined profits reported by the 20 largest Fortune 500 companies.
... **Home Injuries** ($164.7 billion)	... a $135,200 rebate on each new single-family home built, **or** ... 42 cents of every dollar of property taxes paid.
... **Public Injuries** ($108.3 billion)	... a $11.8 million grant to each public library in the U.S., **or** ... a $96,200 bonus for each police officer and firefighter.

Source: National Safety Council estimates.

DEATHS DUE TO UNINTENTIONAL INJURIES, 2007

TYPE OF EVENT AND AGE OF VICTIM

All Unintentional Injuries

The term "unintentional" covers most deaths from injury and poisoning. Excluded are homicides (including legal intervention), suicides, deaths for which none of these categories can be determined, and war deaths.

	Total	Change from 2006	Death Rate[a]
Deaths	120,000	(d)	39.8

Age	0–4	5–14	15–24	25–44	45–64	65–74	75+
Deaths	2,500	2,300	15,800	30,300	30,300	9,000	29,800

Motor-Vehicle Accidents

Includes deaths involving mechanically or electrically powered highway-transport vehicles in motion (except those on rails), both on and off the highway or street.

	Total	Change from 2006	Death Rate[a]
Deaths	43,100	−3%	14.3

Age	0–4	5–14	15–24	25–44	45–64	65–74	75+
Deaths	600	1,200	10,500	13,300	10,800	2,900	3,800

Poisoning

Includes deaths from drugs, medicines, other solid and liquid substances, and gases and vapors. Excludes poisonings from spoiled foods, salmonella, etc., which are classified as disease deaths.

	Total	Change from 2006	Death Rate[a]
Deaths	22,700	−10%	7.5

Age	0–4	5–14	15–24	25–44	45–64	65–74	75+
Deaths	50	50	2,500	10,400	8,600	600	500

Falls

Includes deaths from falls from one level to another or on the same level. Excludes falls in or from transport vehicles, or while boarding or alighting from them.

	Total	Change from 2006	Death Rate[a]
Deaths	21,700	+10%	7.2

See footnotes on page 9.

Age	0–4	5–14	15–24	25–44	45–64	65–74	75+
Deaths	90	60	300	950	2,900	2,500	14,800

Drowning

Includes nontransport-related drownings such as those resulting from swimming, playing in the water, or falling in. Excludes drownings in floods and other cataclysms, which are classified to the cataclysm, and boating-related drownings.

	Total	Change from 2006	Death Rate[a]
Deaths	4,700	+34%	1.6

Age	0–4	5–14	15–24	25–44	45–64	65–74	75+
Deaths	750	350	800	1,100	1,000	250	450

Choking

Includes deaths from unintentional ingestion or inhalation of food or other objects resulting in the obstruction of respiratory passages.

	Total	Change from 2006	Death Rate[a]
Deaths	3,700	+6%	1.2

Age	0–4	5–14	15–24	25–44	45–64	65–74	75+
Deaths	90	10	100	300	900	500	1,800

Fires, flames, and smoke

Includes deaths from exposure to fires, flames, and smoke, and from injuries in fires--such as falls and struck by falling objects. Excludes burns from hot objects or liquids.

	Total	Change from 2006	Death Rate[a]
Deaths	2,700	−18%	0.9

Age	0–4	5–14	15–24	25–44	45–64	65–74	75+
Deaths	200	250	200	350	600	400	700

Mechanical suffocation

Includes deaths from hanging and strangulation, and suffocation in enclosed or confined spaces, cave-ins, or by bed clothes, plastic bags, or similar materials.

	Total	Change from 2006	Death Rate[a]
Deaths	1,200	0%	0.4

Age	0–4	5–14	15–24	25–44	45–64	65–74	75+
Deaths	500	110	110	170	180	70	60

All Other Types

Most important types included are: natural heat and cold, firearms, struck by or against object, machinery, electric current, and air, water, and rail transport.

	Total	Change from 2006	Death Rate[a]
Deaths	20,300	(e)	6.7

Age	0–4	5–14	15–24	25–44	45–64	65–74	75+
Deaths	200	300	1,300	3,800	5,300	1,700	7,700

Note: Category descriptions have changed due to adoption of ICD-10. See Technical Appendix for comparability.
[a]Deaths per 100,000 population.
[b]Deaths per 100,000 population in each age group.
[c]Death rate less than 0.05.
[d]Change less than 0.5%.
[e]Direct comparison is not possible. Starting in 2007 all other includes natural heat and cold.

LEADING CAUSES OF DEATH

Unintentional injuries are the fifth leading cause of death overall and first among persons in age groups from 1 to 44. By single years of age, unintentional injuries are the leading cause from 1 to 41.

Causes are ranked for both sexes combined. Some leading causes for males and females separately may not

be shown. Beginning with 1999 data, deaths are classified according to the 10th revision of the International Classification of Diseases. See the Technical Appendix for comparability.

DEATHS AND DEATH RATES BY AGE AND SEX, 2005

Cause	Number of Deaths			Death Rates[a]		
	Total	Male	Female	Total	Male	Female
All Ages[b]						
All Causes	2,448,017	1,207,675	1,240,342	825.6	827.3	824.0
Heart disease	652,091	322,841	329,250	219.9	221.2	218.7
Cancer (malignant neoplasms)	559,312	290,422	268,890	188.6	199.0	178.6
Stroke (cerebrovascular disease)	143,579	56,586	86,993	48.4	38.8	57.8
Chronic lower respiratory diseases	130,933	62,435	68,498	44.2	42.8	45.5
Unintentional injuries	**117,809**	**76,375**	**41,434**	**39.7**	**52.3**	**27.5**
Motor-vehicle	45,343	31,631	13,712	15.3	21.7	9.1
Poisoning	23,618	15,884	7,734	8.0	10.9	5.1
Falls	19,656	10,154	9,502	6.6	7.0	6.3
Choking[c]	4,386	2,209	2,177	1.5	1.5	1.4
Drowning	3,582	2,818	764	1.2	1.9	0.5
All other unintentional injuries	21,224	13,679	7,545	7.2	9.4	5.0
Diabetes mellitus	75,119	36,538	38,581	25.3	25.0	25.6
Alzheimer's disease	71,599	20,559	51,040	24.1	14.1	33.9
Influenza and pneumonia	63,001	28,052	34,949	21.2	19.2	23.2
Nephritis and nephrosis	43,901	21,268	22,633	14.8	14.6	15.0
Septicemia	34,136	15,322	18,814	11.5	10.5	12.5
Under 1 Year						
All Causes	28,440	16,018	12,422	692.9	763.1	619.5
Congenital anomalies	5,552	2,965	2,587	135.3	141.3	129.0
Short gestation, low birth weight, n.e.c.	4,714	2,644	2,070	114.9	126.0	103.2
Sudden infant death syndrome	2,230	1,372	858	54.3	65.4	42.8
Maternal complications of pregnancy	1,776	943	833	43.3	44.9	41.5
Complications of placenta, cord, membranes	1,110	611	499	27.0	29.1	24.9
Unintentional injuries	**1,083**	**578**	**505**	**26.4**	**27.5**	**25.2**
Mechanical suffocation	700	397	303	17.1	18.9	15.1
Motor-vehicle	146	74	72	3.6	3.5	3.6
Drowning	64	27	37	1.6	1.3	1.8
Choking[c]	48	21	27	1.2	1.0	1.3
Fires and flames	34	16	18	0.8	0.8	0.9
All other unintentional injuries	91	43	48	2.2	2.0	2.4
Respiratory distress	860	518	342	21.0	24.7	17.1
Bacterial sepsis	834	478	356	20.3	22.8	17.8
Neonatal hemorrhage	665	398	267	16.2	19.0	13.3
Necrotizing enterocolitis	546	316	230	13.3	15.1	11.5
1 to 4 Years						
All Causes	4,756	2,765	1,991	29.3	33.4	25.1
Unintentional injuries	**1,664**	**1,027**	**637**	**10.3**	**12.4**	**8.0**
Motor-vehicle	617	351	266	3.8	4.2	3.4
Drowning	493	336	157	3.0	4.1	2.0
Fires and flames	204	124	80	1.3	1.5	1.0
Mechanical suffocation	64	38	26	0.4	0.5	0.3
Choking[c]	62	40	22	0.4	0.5	0.3
All other unintentional injuries	224	138	86	1.4	1.7	1.1
Congenital anomalies	522	264	258	3.2	3.2	3.3
Cancer (malignant neoplasms)	377	217	160	2.3	2.6	2.0
Homicide	375	214	161	2.3	2.6	2.0
Heart disease	151	81	70	0.9	1.0	0.9
Influenza and pneumonia	110	56	54	0.7	0.7	0.7
Septicemia	85	47	38	0.5	0.6	0.5
Stroke (cerebrovascular disease)	62	41	21	0.4	0.5	0.3
Certain conditions originating in the perinatal period	58	36	22	0.4	0.4	0.3
Chronic lower respiratory diseases	56	33	23	0.3	0.4	0.3

See source and footnotes on page 12.

DEATHS AND DEATH RATES BY AGE AND SEX, 2005, Cont.

Cause	Number of Deaths			Death Rates[a]		
	Total	Male	Female	Total	Male	Female
5 to 14 Years						
All Causes	**6,602**	**3,853**	**2,749**	**16.3**	**18.6**	**13.9**
Unintentional injuries	**2,415**	**1,493**	**922**	**6.0**	**7.2**	**4.7**
Motor-vehicle	1,447	848	599	3.6	4.1	3.0
Drowning	253	184	69	0.6	0.9	0.3
Fires and flames	222	125	97	0.5	0.6	0.5
Mechanical suffocation	69	57	12	0.2	0.3	0.1
Firearms	52	39	13	0.1	0.2	0.1
All other unintentional injuries	372	240	132	0.9	1.2	0.7
Cancer (malignant neoplasms)	1,000	557	443	2.5	2.7	2.2
Congenital anomalies	396	195	201	1.0	0.9	1.0
Homicide	341	204	137	0.8	1.0	0.7
Suicide	272	204	68	0.7	1.0	0.3
Heart disease	252	131	121	0.6	0.6	0.6
Influenza and pneumonia	106	53	53	0.3	0.3	0.3
Chronic lower respiratory diseases	104	63	41	0.3	0.3	0.2
Stroke (cerebrovascular disease)	95	55	40	0.2	0.3	0.2
Septicemia	81	49	32	0.2	0.2	0.2
15 to 24 Years						
All Causes	**34,234**	**25,509**	**8,725**	**81.3**	**117.8**	**42.7**
Unintentional injuries	**15,753**	**11,827**	**3,926**	**37.4**	**54.6**	**19.2**
Motor-vehicle	10,908	7,904	3,004	25.9	36.5	14.7
Poisoning	2,484	1,940	544	5.9	9.0	2.7
Drowning	649	588	61	1.5	2.7	0.3
Falls	236	198	38	0.6	0.9	0.2
Firearms	203	190	13	0.5	0.9	0.1
All other unintentional injuries	1,273	1,007	266	3.0	4.6	1.3
Homicide	5,466	4,765	701	13.0	22.0	3.4
Suicide	4,212	3,498	714	10.0	16.1	3.5
Cancer	1,717	1,035	682	4.1	4.8	3.3
Heart disease	1,119	770	349	2.7	3.6	1.7
Congenital anomalies	504	326	178	1.2	1.5	0.9
Diabetes mellitus	202	115	87	0.5	0.5	0.4
Stroke (cerebrovascular disease)	196	94	102	0.5	0.4	0.5
Complicated pregnancy	183	0	183	0.4	0.0	0.9
Influenza and pneumonia	172	117	55	0.4	0.5	0.3
25 to 34 Years						
All Causes	**41,925**	**29,283**	**12,642**	**104.4**	**143.6**	**64.0**
Unintentional injuries	**13,997**	**10,665**	**3,332**	**34.9**	**52.3**	**16.9**
Motor-vehicle	7,239	5,501	1,738	18.0	27.0	8.8
Poisoning	4,386	3,193	1,193	10.9	15.7	6.0
Drowning	385	328	57	1.0	1.6	0.3
Falls	295	256	39	0.7	1.3	0.2
Fires and flames	224	137	87	0.6	0.7	0.4
All other unintentional injuries	1,468	1,250	218	3.7	6.1	1.1
Suicide	4,990	4,066	924	12.4	19.9	4.7
Homicide	4,752	4,008	744	11.8	19.7	3.8
Cancer	3,601	1,805	1,796	9.0	8.9	9.1
Heart disease	3,249	2,206	1,043	8.1	10.8	5.3
Human immunodeficiency virus infection	1,318	809	509	3.3	4.0	2.6
Diabetes mellitus	617	372	245	1.5	1.8	1.2
Stroke (cerebrovascular disease)	546	301	245	1.4	1.5	1.2
Congenital anomalies	436	244	192	1.1	1.2	1.0
Influenza and pneumonia	354	196	158	0.9	1.0	0.8
35 to 44 Years						
All Causes	**84,785**	**53,309**	**31,476**	**193.3**	**243.2**	**143.4**
Unintentional injuries	**16,919**	**12,026**	**4,893**	**38.6**	**54.9**	**22.3**
Motor-vehicle	6,748	4,869	1,879	15.4	22.2	8.6
Poisoning	6,729	4,423	2,306	15.3	20.2	10.5
Falls	607	489	118	1.4	2.2	0.5
Drowning	497	410	87	1.1	1.9	0.4
Fires and flames	334	226	108	0.8	1.0	0.5
All other unintentional injuries	2,004	1,609	395	4.6	7.3	1.8
Cancer	14,566	6,338	8,228	33.2	28.9	37.5
Heart disease	12,688	8,931	3,757	28.9	40.7	17.1
Suicide	6,550	5,063	1,487	14.9	23.1	6.8
Human immunodeficiency virus infection	4,363	3,146	1,217	9.9	14.4	5.5
Homicide	3,109	2,317	792	7.1	10.6	3.6
Chronic liver disease and cirrhosis	2,688	1,786	902	6.1	8.1	4.1
Stroke (cerebrovascular disease)	2,260	1,148	1,112	5.2	5.2	5.1
Diabetes mellitus	2,045	1,270	775	4.7	5.8	3.5
Influenza and pneumonia	934	540	394	2.1	2.5	1.8

See source and footnotes on page 12.

LEADING CAUSES OF DEATH (CONT.)

DEATHS AND DEATH RATES BY AGE AND SEX, 2005, Cont.

Cause	Number of Deaths			Death Rates[a]		
	Total	Male	Female	Total	Male	Female
45 to 54 Years						
All Causes	**183,530**	**114,472**	**69,058**	**432.0**	**548.0**	**319.8**
Cancer	50,405	25,403	25,002	118.6	121.6	115.8
Heart disease	38,103	27,486	10,617	89.7	131.6	49.2
Unintentional injuries	**18,339**	**13,002**	**5,337**	**43.2**	**62.2**	**24.7**
Poisoning	6,983	4,537	2,446	16.4	21.7	11.3
Motor-vehicle	6,397	4,631	1,766	15.1	22.2	8.2
Falls	1,181	897	284	2.8	4.3	1.3
Fires and flames	497	325	172	1.2	1.6	0.8
Drowning	492	393	99	1.2	1.9	0.5
All other unintentional injuries	9,772	6,756	3,016	23.0	32.3	14.0
Chronic liver disease and cirrhosis	7,517	5,423	2,094	17.7	26.0	9.7
Suicide	6,991	5,269	1,722	16.5	25.2	8.0
Stroke (cerebrovascular disease)	6,381	3,446	2,935	15.0	16.5	13.6
Diabetes mellitus	5,691	3,467	2,224	13.4	16.6	10.3
Human immunodeficiency virus infection	4,516	3,417	1,099	10.6	16.4	5.1
Chronic lower respiratory diseases	3,977	2,034	1,943	9.4	9.7	9.0
Viral hepatitis	2,314	1,697	617	5.4	8.1	2.9
55 to 64 Years						
All Causes	**275,301**	**165,429**	**109,872**	**907.0**	**1,131.3**	**698.4**
Cancer	99,240	54,039	45,201	326.9	369.5	287.3
Heart disease	65,208	44,895	20,313	214.8	307.0	129.1
Chronic lower respiratory diseases	12,747	6,589	6,158	42.0	45.1	39.1
Diabetes mellitus	11,301	6,570	4,731	37.2	44.9	30.1
Unintentional injuries	**10,853**	**7,507**	**3,346**	**35.8**	**51.3**	**21.3**
Motor-vehicle	4,454	3,055	1,399	14.7	20.9	8.9
Poisoning	2,007	1,269	738	6.6	8.7	4.7
Falls	1,451	1,023	428	4.8	7.0	2.7
Choking[c]	417	248	169	1.4	1.7	1.1
Fires and flames	398	244	154	1.3	1.7	1.0
All other unintentional injuries	2,126	1,668	458	7.0	11.4	2.9
Stroke (cerebrovascular disease)	10,028	5,636	4,392	33.0	38.5	27.9
Chronic liver disease and cirrhosis	7,126	5,094	2,032	23.5	34.8	12.9
Suicide	4,210	3,250	960	13.9	22.2	6.1
Nephritis and nephrosis	4,141	2,352	1,789	13.6	16.1	11.4
Septicemia	3,912	2,074	1,838	12.9	14.2	11.7
65 to 74 Years						
All Causes	**398,355**	**222,807**	**175,548**	**2,136.0**	**2,610.9**	**1,735.3**
Cancer	138,446	76,685	61,761	742.3	898.6	610.5
Heart disease	96,729	59,050	37,679	518.7	692.0	372.5
Chronic lower respiratory diseases	29,910	15,414	14,496	160.4	180.6	143.3
Stroke (cerebrovascular disease)	18,839	9,688	9,151	101.0	113.5	90.5
Diabetes mellitus	16,183	8,505	7,678	86.8	99.7	75.9
Unintentional injuries	**8,632**	**5,343**	**3,289**	**46.3**	**62.6**	**32.5**
Motor-vehicle	3,110	1,976	1,134	16.7	23.2	11.2
Falls	2,319	1,384	934	12.4	16.2	9.2
Choking[c]	566	318	248	3.0	3.7	2.5
Poisoning	435	228	207	2.3	2.7	2.0
Fires and flames	390	224	166	2.1	2.6	1.6
All other unintentional injuries	1,812	1,213	600	9.7	14.2	5.9
Nephritis and nephrosis	7,320	3,733	3,587	39.2	43.7	35.5
Influenza and pneumonia	6,623	3,648	2,975	35.5	42.7	29.4
Septicemia	6,073	3,095	2,978	32.6	36.3	29.4
Chronic liver disease and cirrhosis	5,066	3,052	2,014	27.2	35.8	19.9
75 Years and Older[b]						
All Causes	**1,390,089**	**574,230**	**815,859**	**7,664.4**	**8,352.9**	**7,244.1**
Heart disease	434,234	179,094	255,140	2,394.2	2,605.1	2,265.4
Cancer	249,885	124,298	125,587	1,377.8	1,808.1	1,115.1
Stroke (cerebrovascular disease)	105,046	36,104	68,942	579.2	525.2	612.1
Chronic lower respiratory diseases	82,810	37,632	45,178	456.6	547.4	401.1
Alzheimer's disease	67,046	18,588	48,458	369.7	270.4	430.3
Influenza and pneumonia	48,832	20,007	28,825	269.2	291.0	255.9
Diabetes mellitus	39,039	16,224	22,815	215.2	236.0	202.6
Nephritis and nephrosis	29,096	13,215	15,881	160.4	192.2	141.0
Unintentional injuries	**28,154**	**12,907**	**15,247**	**155.2**	**187.7**	**135.4**
Falls	13,485	5,857	7,628	74.4	85.2	67.7
Motor-vehicle	4,277	2,422	1,855	23.6	35.2	16.5
Choking[c]	2,581	1,144	1,437	14.2	16.6	12.8
Fires and flames	726	362	364	4.0	5.3	3.2
Poisoning	502	240	262	2.8	3.5	2.3
All other unintentional injuries	6,583	2,882	3,701	36.3	41.9	32.9
Septicemia	20,173	8,063	12,110	111.2	117.3	107.5

Source: National Safety Council analysis of National Center for Health Statistics mortality data and Bureau of the Census population data.
[a] Deaths per 100,000 population in each age group.
[b] Includes 255 deaths where the age is unknown.
[c] Inhalation or ingestion of food or other objects.

Falls are the leading cause of nonfatal unintentional injuries that are treated in hospital emergency departments (ED) according to data from the All Injury Program, a cooperative program involving the National Center for Injury Prevention and Control, CDC, and the Consumer Product Safety Commission. Nearly eight million people were treated in an ED for fall-related injuries in 2006. Falls were the leading cause of nonfatal injuries for all age groups except for the 10–14 and 15–24 year old age groups, for which struck by or against an object or person was the leading cause. Struck by or against, overexertion, and motor-vehicle crashes involving vehicle occupants were also leading causes for most age groups.

LEADING CAUSES OF NONFATAL UNINTENTIONAL INJURIES TREATED IN HOSPITAL EMERGENCY DEPARTMENTS BY AGE GROUP, UNITED STATES, 2006

Rank	All Ages	Age Group									
		<1	1–4	5–9	10–14	15–24	25–34	35–44	45–54	55–64	65+
1	Falls 7,934,840	Falls 124,747	Falls 860,281	Falls 635,912	Struck by/against 608,658	Struck by/against 1,071,586	Falls 748,064	Falls 784,154	Falls 817,043	Falls 633,428	Falls 1,840,117
2	Struck by/against 4,663,517	Struck by/against 30,872	Struck by/against 390,563	Struck by/against 420,693	Falls 602,415	Falls 888,138	Overexertion 726,511	Overexertion 656,632	Overexertion 468,164	Struck by/against 223,447	Struck by/against 225,785
3	Overexertion 3,474,597	Other bite/sting[a] 12,456	Other bite/sting[a] 153,553	Cut/pierce 116,918	Overexertion 279,148	Motor-vehicle occupant 833,189	Struck by/against 693,006	Struck by/against 570,882	Struck by/against 427,588	Overexertion 214,793	Overexertion 178,808
4	Motor-vehicle occupant 2,723,465	Foreign body 10,903	Foreign body 125,543	Other bite/sting[a] 99,452	Cut/pierce 144,366	Overexertion 782,425	Motor-vehicle occupant 551,875	Motor-vehicle occupant 436,807	Motor-vehicle occupant 338,731	Motor-vehicle occupant 196,080	Motor-vehicle occupant 175,219
5	Cut/Pierce 2,215,211	Fire/burn 10,378	Overexertion 81,923	Pedalcyclist 88,734	Pedalcylist 110,506	Cut/pierce 500,646	Cut/pierce 437,328	Cut/pierce 366,926	Cut/pierce 286,432	Cut/pierce 157,098	Cut/pierce 118,967
6	Other bite/sting[a] 1,095,521	Other specified[b] 7,965	Cut/Pierce 79,713	Overexertion 78,518	Unknown/ unspecified 108,550	Other specified[b] 198,544	Other specified[b] 166,785	Other specified[b] 184,888	Other specified[b] 155,317	Other bite/sting[a] 66,296	Other bite/sting[a] 69,703
7	Other specified[b] 922,208	Overexertion 7,531	Other specified[b] 55,535	Motor-vehicle occupant 60,008	Motor-vehicle occupant 85,151	Other bite/sting[a] 190,130	Other bite/sting[a] 162,741	Other bite/sting[a] 154,357	Poisoning 137,855	Other specified[b] 61,633	Poisoning 65,292
8	Poisoning 703,702	Motor-vehicle occupant 6,885	Fire/burn 53,359	Foreign body 57,440	Other bite/sting[a] 66,784	Unknown/ unspecified 155,712	Poisoning 104,095	Poisoning 146,210	Other bite/sting[a] 119,980	Poisoning 60,990	Other transport[c] 58,823
9	Unknown/ unspecified 652,130	Poisoning 6,877	Poisoning 43,206	Other transport[c] 45,981	Other transport[c] 58,433	Other transport[c] 144,488	Other transport[c] 102,180	Other transport[c] 84,513	Other transport[c] 69,723	Other transport[c] 39,316	Unknown/ unspecified 47,405
10	Other transport[c] 635,018	Cut/pierce 6,479	Unknown/ unspecified 41,573	Dog bite 44,239	Other specified[b] 33,085	Poisoning 117,015	Foreign body 94,044	Foreign body 79,684	Foreign body 64,270	Foreign body 35,123	Other specified[b] 42,923
All Causes											
Number	27,671,499	239,984	2,029,808	1,751,906	2,231,963	5,398,111	4,185,393	3,829,453	3,187,684	1,847,407	2,969,790[d]
Per 1,000 population	92.8	58.1	124.6	88.9	108.2	127.2	103.6	87.7	73.7	58.5	79.7[d]

Source: NEISS All Injury Program, Office of Statistics and Programming, National Center for Injury Prevention and Control, CDC, and Consumer Product Safety Commission.
[a] Other than dog bite.
[b] Includes electric current, explosions, fireworks, radiation, animal scratch, etc. Excludes all causes listed in the table and bb/pellet gunshot, drowning and near drowning, firearm gunshot, suffocation, machinery, natural and environmental conditions, pedestrians, and motorcyclists.
[c] Includes occupant of any transport vehicle other than a motor vehicle or motor cycle (e.g., airplane, rail car, boat, ATV, animal rider).
[d] Includes 5,168 cases with age unknown.

LEADING CAUSES OF
UNINTENTIONAL-INJURY DEATH
BY AGE, 2005

UNINTENTIONAL-INJURY DEATHS BY AGE AND EVENT, UNITED STATES, 2005

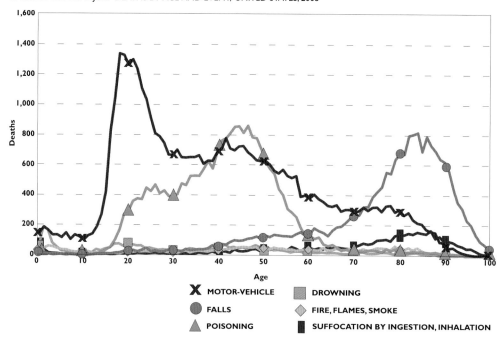

X	MOTOR-VEHICLE		DROWNING
●	FALLS	◆	FIRE, FLAMES, SMOKE
▲	POISONING	▮	SUFFOCATION BY INGESTION, INHALATION

Motor-vehicle crashes, poisonings, falls, choking (suffocation by inhalation or ingestion of food or other object), drownings, fires and flames, and mechanical suffocation were the seven leading causes of unintentional-injury death in the United States in 2005. The graph above depicts the number of deaths attributed to the top six causes by single years of age through age 99.

In 2005, motor-vehicle crashes were the leading cause of unintentional-injury death for all ages combined and the leading cause of unintentional-injury deaths for those one year of age, for each single year of age from 3 to 39, for age 42, and again for each single year of age from 52 to 72. Furthermore, with the lone exception of cancer deaths at age 7, motor-vehicle crashes caused more deaths than any other injury type or illness for those aged 3 through 34, combining to account for 24% of the total for that age range.

The distribution of 2005 motor-vehicle fatalities shows a sharp increase during adolescence, rising from 423 for 15-year-olds to 1,339 for 18-year-olds. The greatest number of motor-vehicle fatalities occurred to persons aged 18 in 2005.

The second leading cause of unintentional-injury death overall in 2005 was poisoning. Poisoning fatalities reached a high of 861 for 47-year-olds and **poisoning was the leading cause of unintentional-injury death for those aged 40–41 and 43–50.** Poisonings were the

second leading cause of unintentional-injury death for those aged 16 to 39, and again for each year from 50 to 60, at which point they were tied as the second leading cause with falls. Falls were the third leading cause of unintentional-injury death in the United States in 2005. **Falls were the leading cause of unintentional-injury death of persons aged 73 and older** and second leading cause from ages 60 through 72 for each year of age; deaths resulting from falls peaked at 817 for individuals age 85.

Choking[a] was the fourth leading cause of unintentional-injury death in 2005. Choking deaths peaked at age 88 with 165 deaths. It was the second leading cause of unintentional-injury death for those aged 88 and for each year of age 90 and over. **The fifth leading cause of unintentional-injury death was drowning, which peaked at 185 for 1-year-olds and was the leading cause for those aged 2.** Drownings were the second leading cause of injury death for children ages 3–4, 8, and 11–15.

Fires, flames, and smoke were the sixth leading cause of unintentional-injury death in 2005. Fatalities due to fires, flames, and smoke were the second leading cause of death for children aged 5–7 and 9–10 and for those aged 11. **Mechanical suffocation was the seventh leading cause overall and the leading cause for infants under 1 year old, with 700 deaths.**

Source: National Safety Council tabulations of National Center for Health Statistics data. See the Technical Appendix for ICD-10 codes for the leading causes and comparability with prior years.
[a] Inhalation or ingestion of food or other objects.

UNINTENTIONAL-INJURY DEATH RATES BY AGE, 2005

UNINTENTIONAL-INJURY DEATHS PER 100,000 POPULATION BY AGE AND EVENT, UNITED STATES, 2005

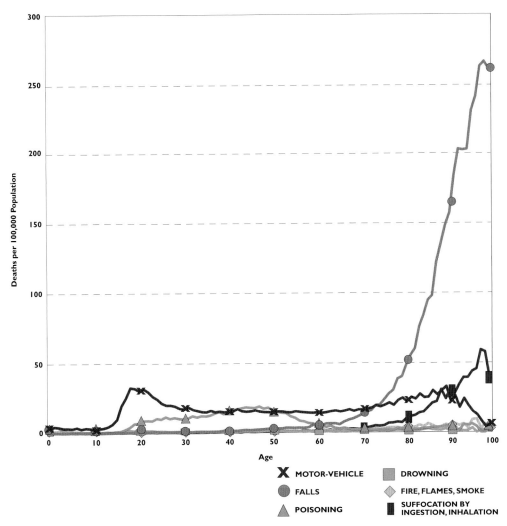

X MOTOR-VEHICLE   ■ DROWNING

● FALLS   ◆ FIRE, FLAMES, SMOKE

▲ POISONING   ▮ SUFFOCATION BY INGESTION, INHALATION

On the basis of deaths per 100,000 population at each age, motor-vehicle death rates in 2005 rose to an initial peak of 32.5 for persons 18 years of age. This rate declined to an average of about 15.0 for those aged 30 to 72, then increased to another peak at 32.9 for those 89 years of age.

While motor-vehicle crashes are a significant problem for all ages, deaths resulting from falls for certain older ages have even higher death rates. Beginning at about age 70, the death rate from falls increases dramatically. At age 73, the falls death rate surpasses that for motor-vehicle, with the death rate continuing to rise with increasing age.

The poisoning death rate remains low until about age 15 where it starts to increase up to its peak rate of 19.1 at 47 years of age and then falls again.

Death rates due to choking on inhaled or ingested food or other objects are quite low for most ages. Rates are slightly elevated for infants and toddlers and rise rapidly beginning at about age 70. The death rates for drownings show peaks at very young ages, in the late teens, and again at some very old ages. Similarly, the death rates for fire, flames, and smoke are slightly elevated at very young ages and begin to climb again at about age 75.

The graph above depicts death rates per 100,000 population for the six leading causes of unintentional-injury deaths in 2005 for single years of age through age 99.

Source: National Safety Council tabulations of National Center for Health Statistics data. See the Technical Appendix for ICD-10 codes for the leading causes and comparability with prior years.

UNINTENTIONAL-INJURY DEATHS
BY SEX AND AGE, 2005

UNINTENTIONAL-INJURY DEATHS BY SEX AND AGE, UNITED STATES, 2005

Males incur more deaths due to unintentional injuries than females at all ages from birth to age 83. The difference between the unintentional-injury death totals ranges from 6 at age 82 to 1,152 at age 21. The excess number of deaths for males compared to females is most evident from the late teenage years to the early fifties where the gap begins to narrow. Beginning at age 84, deaths of females exceed those of males by as little as 43 deaths to as much as 336 at age 92.

Unintentional-injury deaths are at their lowest level for both sexes from about age 4 to about age 13. For males the highest number of deaths (1,536) occurs at age 21,

with high totals—including another peak of 1,453 deaths for those aged 45—occurring from the late teens until the mid-fifties. For females, however, the highest totals occur among the elderly throughout the eighties and into the early nineties. The greatest number of female deaths (859) occurs at age 85.

The graph above shows the number of unintentional-injury deaths in 2005 for each sex by single years of age from under 1 year old to age 99. It is based on death certificate data from the National Center for Health Statistics.

UNINTENTIONAL-INJURY DEATH RATES BY SEX AND AGE, 2005

UNINTENTIONAL-INJURY DEATHS PER 100,000 POPULATION BY SEX AND AGE, UNITED STATES, 2005

Throughout the lifespan, males have greater unintentional-injury death rates for each year of age compared to females. The graph above shows the unintentional-injury death rates for males and females by single year of age from under 1 year old to age 99. It is based on National Center for Health Statistics mortality data and U.S. Census Bureau population data.

Death rates for both sexes are lowest from birth until the mid-teenage years where rates rise rapidly. Rates then remain fairly constant until the late sixties where they again rise steadily with increasing age. For comparison, the overall unintentional-injury death rate for all ages and both sexes was 39.7.

ALL DEATHS DUE TO INJURY

MORTALITY BY SELECTED EXTERNAL CAUSES, UNITED STATES, 2003–2005

Type of Accident or Manner of Injury	2005[a]	2004	2003
All External Causes of Mortality, V01–Y89, *U01, *U03[b]	176,406	170,067	166,857
Deaths Due to Unintentional (Accidental) Injuries, V01–X59, Y85–Y86	117,809	112,012	109,277
Transport Accidents, V01–V99, Y85	**48,441**	**47,385**	**48,071**
Motor-vehicle accidents, V02–V04, V09.0, V09.2, V12–V14, V19.0–V19.2, V19.4–V19.6, V20–V79, V80.3–V80.5, V81.0–V81.1, V82.0–V82.1, V83–V86, V87.0–V87.8, V88.0–V88.8, V89.0, V89.2	45,343	44,933	44,757
Pedestrian, V01–V09	6,074	5,976	5,991
Pedalcyclist, V10–V19	927	843	762
Motorcycle rider, V20–V29	4,387	4,018	3,676
Occupant of three-wheeled motor vehicle, V30–V39	5	13	13
Car occupant, V40–V49	14,584	15,282	15,797
Occupant of pick-up truck or van, V50–V59	3,797	3,908	4,163
Occupant of heavy transport vehicle, V60–V69	450	439	442
Bus occupant, V70–V79	59	40	36
Animal rider or occupant of animal-drawn vehicle, V80	120	91	101
Occupant of railway train or railway vehicle, V81	33	27	24
Occupant of streetcar, V82	0	1	2
Other and unspecified land transport accidents, V83–V89	16,148	15,494	15,107
Occupant of special industrial vehicle, V83	*19*	*12*	*12*
Occupant of special agricultural vehicle, V84	*154*	*105*	*175*
Occupant of special construction vehicle, V85	*33*	*27*	*20*
Occupant of all-terrain or other off-road motor vehicle, V86	*1,040*	*951*	*906*
Other and unspecified person, V87–V89	*14,902*	*14,399*	*13,994*
Water transport accidents, V90–V94	523	574	573
Drowning, V90, V92	*394*	*421*	*412*
Other and unspecified injuries, V91, V93–V94	*129*	*153*	*161*
Air and space transport accidents, V95–V97	590	679	742
Other and unspecified transport accidents and sequelae, V98–V99, Y85	744	668	642
Other specified transport accidents, V98	*2*	*0*	*2*
Unspecified transport accident, V99	*18*	*0*	*0*
Nontransport Unintentional (Accidental) Injuries, W00–X59, Y86	**69,368**	**63,959**	**61,206**
Falls, W00–W19	19,656	18,807	17,229
Fall on same level from slipping, tripping, and stumbling, W01	*698*	*584*	*597*
Other fall on same level, W00, W02–W03, W18	*5,224*	*4,458*	*3,896*
Fall involving bed, chair, other furniture, W06–W08	*899*	*774*	*838*
Fall on and from stairs and steps, W10	*1,690*	*1,638*	*1,588*
Fall on and from ladder or scaffolding, W11–W12	*477*	*392*	*417*
Fall from out of or through building or structure, W13	*533*	*587*	*600*
Other fall from one level to another, W09, W14–W17	*694*	*724*	*701*
Other and unspecified fall, W04–W05, W19	*9,441*	*9,650*	*8,592*
Exposure to inanimate mechanical forces, W20–W49	2,845	2,759	2,658
Struck by or striking against object, W20–W22	*854*	*833*	*809*
Caught between objects, W23	*103*	*134*	*136*
Contact with machinery, W24, W30–W31	*755*	*795*	*640*
Contact with sharp objects, W25–W29	*85*	*106*	*99*
Firearms discharge, W32–W34	*789*	*649*	*730*
Explosion and rupture of pressurized devices, W35–W38	*26*	*28*	*30*
Fireworks discharge, W39	*4*	*2*	*11*
Explosion of other materials, W40	*147*	*148*	*147*
Foreign body entering through skin or natural orifice, W44–W45	*37*	*32*	*22*
Other and unspecified inanimate mechanical forces, W41–W43, W49	*45*	*32*	*34*
Exposure to animate mechanical forces, W50–W64	161	139	171
Struck by or against another person, W50–W52	*26*	*13*	*39*
Bitten or struck by dog, W54	*33*	*27*	*32*
Bitten or struck by other mammals, W53, W55	*80*	*77*	*78*
Bitten or stung by nonvenomous insect and other arthropods, W57	*9*	*5*	*12*
Bitten or crushed by other reptiles, W59	*0*	*0*	*0*
Other and unspecified animate mechanical forces, W56, W58, W60, W64	*13*	*17*	*10*
Accidental drowning and submersion, W65–W74	3,582	3,308	3,306
Drowning and submersion while in or falling into bath-tub, W65–W66	*344*	*402*	*332*
Drowning and submersion while in or falling into swimming-pool, W67–W68	*607*	*625*	*515*
Drowning and submersion while in or falling into natural water, W69–W70	*1,603*	*1,333*	*1,225*
Other and unspecified drowning and submersion, W73–W74	*1,028*	*948*	*1,234*
Other accidental threats to breathing, W75–W84	5,900	5,891	5,579
Accidental suffocation and strangulation in bed, W75	*573*	*596*	*497*
Other accidental hanging and strangulation, W76	*274*	*252*	*277*
Threat to breathing due to cave-in, falling earth and other substances, W77	*50*	*48*	*46*
Inhalation of gastric contents, W78	*333*	*377*	*393*
Inhalation and ingestion of food causing obstruction of respiratory tract, W79	*864*	*878*	*875*
Inhalation and ingestion of other objects causing obstruction of respiratory tract, W80	*3,189*	*3,215*	*3,004*
Confined to or trapped in a low-oxygen environment, W81	*14*	*16*	*16*
Other and unspecified threats to breathing, W83–W84	*603*	*509*	*471*

See source and footnotes on page 19.

MORTALITY BY SELECTED EXTERNAL CAUSES, UNITED STATES, 2003–2005, Cont.

Type of Accident or Manner of Injury	2005[a]	2004	2003
Exposure to electric current, radiation, temperature, and pressure, W85–W99	420	405	396
Electric transmission lines, W85	105	94	96
Other and unspecified electric current, W86–W87	293	288	280
Radiation, W88–W91	0	0	0
Excessive heat or cold of man-made origin, W92–W93	13	14	10
High and low air pressure and changes in air pressure, W94	9	9	10
Other and unspecified man-made environmental factors, W99	0	0	0
Exposure to smoke, fire and flames, X00–X09	3,197	3,229	3,369
Uncontrolled fire in building or structure, X00	2,617	2,635	2,761
Uncontrolled fire not in building or structure, X01	52	37	57
Controlled fire in building or structure, X02	28	28	35
Controlled fire not in building or structure, X03	33	48	39
Ignition of highly flammable material, X04	63	55	55
Ignition or melting of nightwear, X05	6	7	3
Ignition or melting of other clothing and apparel, X06	97	119	104
Other and unspecified smoke fire and flames, X08–X09	301	300	315
Contact with heat and hot substances, X10–X19	102	93	88
Contact with hot tap-water, X11	43	30	26
Other and unspecified heat and hot substances, X10, X12–X19	59	63	62
Contact with venomous animals and plants, X20–X29	105	81	94
Contact with venomous snakes and lizards, X20	7	6	2
Contact with venomous spiders, X21	10	14	8
Contact with hornets, wasps and bees, X23	82	52	66
Contact with other and unspecified venomous animal or plant, X22, X24–X29	6	9	18
Exposure to forces of nature, X30–X39	2,179	1,102	1,140
Exposure to excessive natural heat, X30	466	226	273
Exposure to excessive natural cold, X31	700	676	620
Lightning, X33	48	46	47
Earthquake and other earth movements, X34–X36	37	30	32
Cataclysmic storm, X37	874	63	75
Flood, X38	12	22	26
Exposure to other and unspecified forces of nature, X32, X39	42	39	67
Accidental poisoning by and exposure to noxious substances, X40–X49	23,618	20,950	19,457
Nonopioid analgesics, antipyretics, and antirheumatics, X40	226	212	210
Antiepileptic, sedative-hypnotic, antiparkinsonism, and psychotropic drugs n.e.c., X41	1,496	1,300	1,205
Narcotics and psychodysleptics [hallucinogens] n.e.c., X42	11,050	9,798	9,231
Other and unspecified drugs, medicaments, and biologicals, X43–X44	9,676	8,528	7,648
Alcohol, X45	346	358	373
Gases and vapors, X46–X47	703	629	690
Other and unspecified chemicals and noxious substances, X48–X49	121	125	100
Overexertion, travel and privation, X50–X57	32	39	48
Accidental exposure to other and unspecified factors and sequelae, X58–X59, Y86	7,571	7,156	7,671
Intentional self-harm, X60–X84, Y87.0, *U03	**32,637**	**32,439**	**31,484**
Intentional self-poisoning, X60–X69	5,744	5,800	5,462
Intentional self-harm by hanging, strangulation, and suffocation, X70	7,248	7,336	6,635
Intentional self-harm by firearm, X72–X74	17,002	16,750	16,907
Other and unspecified means and sequelae, X71, X75–X84, Y87.0	2,643	2,553	2,480
Terrorism, *U03	0	0	0
Assault, X85–Y09, Y87.1, *U01	**18,124**	**17,357**	**17,732**
Assault by firearm, X93–X95	12,352	11,624	11,920
Assault by sharp object, X99	2,097	2,079	2,049
Other and unspecified means and sequelae, X85–X92, X96–X98, Y00–Y09, Y87.1	3,675	3,654	3,763
Terrorism, *U01	0	0	0
Event of undetermined intent, Y10–Y34, Y87.2, Y89.9	**4,742**	**4,976**	**5,072**
Poisoning, Y10–Y19	3,240	3,455	3,700
Hanging, strangulation, and suffocation, Y20	139	152	108
Drowning and submersion, Y21	242	223	215
Firearm discharge, Y22–Y24	221	235	232
Exposure to smoke, fire, and flames, Y26	120	83	100
Falling, jumping, or pushed from a high place, Y30	69	71	77
Other and unspecified means and sequelae, Y25, Y27–Y29, Y31–Y34, Y87.2, Y89.9	711	757	640
Legal intervention, Y35, Y89.0	**414**	**372**	**423**
Legal intervention involving firearm discharge, Y35.0	330	311	347
Legal execution, Y35.5	54	52	60
Other and unspecified means and sequelae, Y35.1–Y35.4, Y35.6–Y35.7, Y89.0	30	9	16
Operations of war and sequelae, Y36, Y89.1	**27**	**28**	**14**
Complications of medical and surgical care and sequelae, Y40–Y84, Y88.0–Y88.3	**2,653**	**2,883**	**2,855**

Source: National Center for Health Statistics. Deaths are classified on the basis of the Tenth Revision of "The International Classification of Diseases" (ICD-10), which became effective in 1999.

Note: "n.e.c." means not elsewhere classified.

[a] Latest official figures.

[b] Numbers following titles refer to external cause of injury and poisoning classifications in ICD-10.

DEATHS BY AGE, SEX, AND TYPE

UNINTENTIONAL-INJURY DEATHS BY AGE, SEX, AND TYPE, UNITED STATES, 2005[a]

Age & Sex	Total[b]	Motor-vehicle	Poisoning	Falls	Choking[c]	Fires/Flames	Drowning[d]	Mechanical Suffocation	Natural Heat/Cold	All Types Males	All Types Females
Total	117,809	45,343	23,618	19,656	4,386	3,582	3,197	1,514	1,166	76,375	41,434
0–4	2,747	763	41	50	110	557	238	764	33	1,605	1,142
5–14	2,415	1,447	51	32	34	253	222	69	6	1,493	922
15–24	15,753	10,908	2,484	236	72	649	168	103	45	11,827	3,926
25–44	30,916	13,987	11,115	902	272	882	558	230	203	22,691	8,225
45–64	29,192	10,851	8,990	2,632	751	758	895	224	432	20,509	8,683
65–74	8,632	3,110	435	566	193	390	47	128	5,343	3,289
75+	28,154	4,277	502	13,485	2,581	290	726	77	319	12,907	15,247
Males	76,375	31,631	15,884	10,154	2,209	2,818	1,886	1,030	830		
Females	41,434	13,712	7,734	9,502	2,177	764	1,311	484	336		

Source: National Safety Council analysis of National Center for Health Statistics mortality data.
[a]Latest official figures.
[b]Includes types not shown separately.
[c]Inhalation or ingestion of food or other object obstructing breathing.
[d]Excludes transport drownings.

Of the 117,809 unintentional-injury deaths in 2005, men accounted for 65% of all deaths. Women had the greatest share of deaths in the 75 and over age group (54% women). By type of accident, men accounted for 79% of all drownings and 71% of natural heat/cold deaths. Males and females equally split, 50% each for deaths due to choking (inhalation or ingestion of food or other object obstructing breathing).

UNINTENTIONAL-INJURY DEATH RATES BY TYPE AND SEX, UNITED STATES, 2005[a]

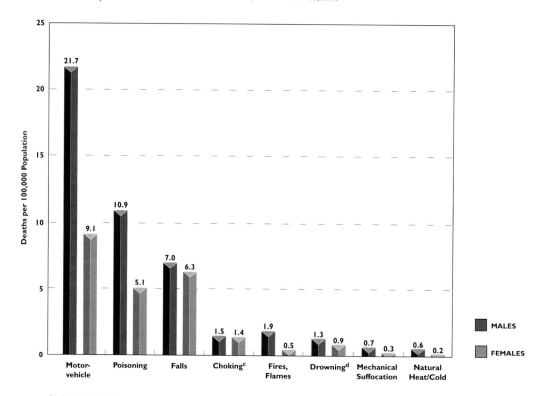

See footnotes in table above.

UNINTENTIONAL-INJURY DEATHS BY MONTH AND TYPE, UNITED STATES, 2005[a]

Month	All Types	Motor-vehicle	Poisoning	Falls	Choking[b]	Fires/Flames	Drowning[c]	Mechanical Suffocation	Natural Heat/Cold	Struck By/Against	All Other Types
Total	**117,809**	**45,343**	**23,618**	**19,656**	**4,386**	**3,582**	**3,197**	**1,514**	**1,166**	**854**	**14,493**
January	9,461	3,305	1,994	1,704	448	154	408	116	180	65	1,087
February	8,530	3,042	1,884	1,562	379	132	292	105	94	57	983
March	9,376	3,334	2,029	1,707	424	187	338	120	68	68	1,101
April	9,459	3,686	1,960	1,536	372	245	295	112	31	64	1,158
May	9,865	3,874	1,965	1,602	354	347	227	140	36	95	1,225
June	9,788	3,865	1,885	1,525	360	574	182	115	77	64	1,141
July	10,952	4,391	2,008	1,654	332	701	148	162	223	75	1,258
August	10,840	4,039	1,899	1,648	329	483	173	142	108	84	1,935
September	9,677	3,920	1,922	1,566	357	301	169	133	47	74	1,188
October	10,043	4,209	1,999	1,713	324	193	240	120	35	75	1,135
November	9,738	3,922	1,959	1,650	342	139	300	123	87	67	1,149
December	10,080	3,756	2,114	1,789	365	126	425	126	180	66	1,133
Average	**9,817**	**3,779**	**1,968**	**1,638**	**366**	**299**	**266**	**126**	**97**	**71**	**1,208**

Source: National Safety Council tabulations of National Center for Health Statistics mortality data.
[a]Latest official figures.
[b]Inhalation or ingestion of food or other object obstructing breathing.
[c]Excludes water transport drownings.

UNINTENTIONAL-INJURY DEATHS BY MONTH AND TYPE, UNITED STATES, 2005[a]

ALL UNINTENTIONAL-INJURY DEATHS

UNINTENTIONAL DROWNING DEATHS

UNINTENTIONAL FIRES AND FLAMES DEATHS

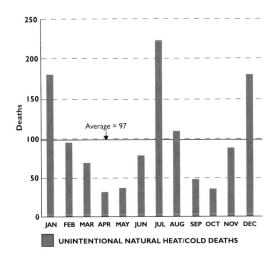

UNINTENTIONAL NATURAL HEAT/COLD DEATHS

See page 107 for motor-vehicle deaths by month and page 145 for pedalcycle deaths by month.

THE NATIONAL HEALTH INTERVIEW SURVEY, 2006

The National Health Interview Survey, conducted by the National Center for Health Statistics, is a continuous, personal-interview sampling of households to obtain information about the health status of household members, including injuries experienced during the 5 weeks prior to the interview. Responsible family members residing in the household supplied the information found in the survey. In 2006, interviews were completed for 75,716 persons living in 29,204 households throughout the United States. See page 23 for definitions.

NUMBER OF LEADING EXTERNAL CAUSES OF INJURY AND POISONING EPISODES BY AGE, UNITED STATES, 2006

	Population[a] (000)	External Cause of Injury and Poisoning (number in thousands)						
		Fall	Transportation[b]	Overexertion	Struck by or Against Person or Object	Cutting-Piercing Instruments	Poisoning[b]	Other Injury Causes[b]
All Ages	**293,423**	**13,071**	**3,396**	**4,572**	**3,935**	**2,628**	**636[c]**	**5,018**
Under 12 years	48,167	2,223	336[c]	(d)	976	278[c]	(d)	449[c]
12–17 years	25,343	1,473	426[c]	515	694	286[c]	0	433[c]
18–44 years	110,049	2,822	1,371	2,035	1,284	1,408	(d)	2,602
45–64 years	74,254	2,603	999	1,377	835	532[c]	(d)	1,184
65–74 years	18,666	1,230	(d)	(d)	(d)	(d)	(d)	159[c]
75 years and over	16,944	2,720	(d)	(d)	(d)	0	(d)	(d)

[a]Civilian noninstitutionalized population.
[b]"Transportation" includes motor vehicle, bicycle, motorcycle, pedestrian, train, boat, or airplane. "Poisoning" does not include food poisoning or allergic reaction. "Other Injury Causes" includes fire/burn/scald related, animal or insect bites, machinery, and unknown causes.
[c]Figure does not meet standard of reliability or precision and should be used with caution.
[d]Estimate is not shown because it does not meet standard of reliability or precision.

LEADING EXTERNAL CAUSES OF INJURY AND POISONING EPISODES BY SEX, UNITED STATES, 2006

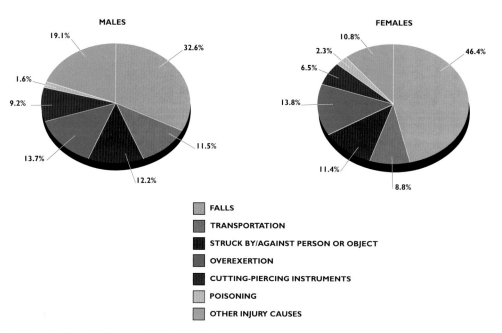

- FALLS
- TRANSPORTATION
- STRUCK BY/AGAINST PERSON OR OBJECT
- OVEREXERTION
- CUTTING-PIERCING INSTRUMENTS
- POISONING
- OTHER INJURY CAUSES

Source: Adams, P.F., & Barnes P.M. (2008, January). Summary health statistics for the U.S. population: National Health Interview Survey, 2006. National Center for Health Statistics. Vital and Health Statistics, Series 10 (No. 236).

In 2006, an estimated 33.3 million medically consulted injury and poisoning episodes were recorded, of which 51.4% were among males and 48.6% among females. The overall injury rate was 113 episodes per 1,000 population, with men (119 per 1,000 men) experiencing higher rates than women (108 per 1,000 women). Most injuries occurred in or around the home (50.4%) followed by injuries at recreational and sport facilities (12.3%) and injuries on streets, highways and parking lots (11.5%).

For the 17.1 million injuries reported by men, the single most common place of injury occurrence was outside the home (24.4%), with injuries inside the home contributing an additional 18.7%. Injuries in public areas, such as schools, hospitals, streets, recreational facilities, industrial and trade areas, and public buildings, together accounted for 48.3% of the total.

More than half of injuries among women occurred either inside or outside the home environment. However, three times as many women were injured inside than outside the home. Streets, parking lots and highways along with sport facilities and recreational areas were the next most common locations for injuries among women, accounting for 10% each. The comparison of women and men reveals that women are more likely to be injured inside the home (43.6%) than men (30.8%), while men are more likely to be injured outside the home (19.6%) than women (14.5%).

The 2006 NHIS injury definitions are listed below for comparability with prior years and other injury figures published in *Injury Facts*.

NUMBER AND PERCENT OF INJURY EPISODES BY PLACE OF OCCURRENCE AND SEX, UNITED STATES, 2006

Place of Occurrence of Injury Episode	Both Sexes		Male		Female	
	Number of Episodes (000)	Percent	Number of Episodes (000)	Percent	Number of Episodes (000)	Percent
Total episodes[a]	**33,256**	**100%**	**17,107**	**100%**	**16,149**	**100%**
Home (inside)	10,248	30.8	3,204	18.7	7,045	43.6
Home (outside)	6,521	19.6	4,177	24.4	2,344	14.5
School/child care center/preschool	1,771	5.3	1,006	5.9	765	4.7
Hospital/residential institution	854[b]	2.6	(c)	—	618[b]	3.8
Street/highway/parking lot	3,818	11.5	2,201	12.9	1,617	10.0
Sport facility/recreation area/lake/river/pool	4,105	12.3	2,494	14.6	1,611	10.0
Industrial/construction/farm/mine/quarry	1,769	5.3	1,769	10.3	(c)	—
Trade/service area	1,538	4.6	785	4.6	752	4.7
Other public building	509[b]	1.5	(c)	—	434[b]	2.7
Other (unspecified)	1,955	5.9	1,221	7.1	734	4.5

Source: Adams, P.F., & Barnes P.M. (2008, January). Summary health statistics for the U.S. population: National Health Interview Survey, 2006. National Center for Health Statistics. Vital and Health Statistics, Series 10 (No. 236).
[a]Numbers and percents may not sum to respective totals due to rounding and unknowns.
[b]Figure does not meet standard of reliability or precision and should be used with caution.
[c]Estimate is not shown because it does not meet standard of reliability or precision.

Injury definitions

National Health Interview Survey definitions. The 2006 National Health Interview Survey (NHIS) figures include medically consulted injury and poisoning *episodes* (e.g., call to a poison control center; use of an emergency vehicle or emergency room; visit to a doctor's office or other health clinic; phone call to a doctor, nurse, or other health care professional) that reportedly occurred during the three months prior to the date of the interview and resulted in one or more *conditions*. Beginning in 2004, injury and poisoning estimates were calculated using only those episodes that occurred five weeks or less before the interview date. This reflects a change from 1997–2003, when the NHIS data contained injury and poisoning episodes that were reported to occur within four months of the interview, and estimates were calculated using a three-month recall period. Also, an imputation procedure was performed for injury and poisoning episodes to assign a date of occurrence if it was not reported. Therefore, figures for 2004 and subsequent years are not comparable to estimates from prior years.

In the 2006 NHIS Injury and Poisoning file, an *injury episode* refers to the traumatic event in which the person was injured one or more times from an external cause (e.g., a fall, a motor vehicle traffic accident). An *injury condition* is the acute condition or the physical harm caused by the traumatic event. Likewise, a *poisoning episode* refers to the event resulting from ingestion of or contact with harmful substances, as well as overdoses or wrong use of any drug or medication, while a *poisoning condition* is the acute condition or the physical harm caused by the event. Each episode must have at least one injury condition or poisoning classified according to the nature-of-injury codes 800–909.2, 909.4, 909.9, 910–994.9, 995.5–995.59, and 995.80–995.85 in the Ninth Revision of the International Classification of Diseases (ICD-9-CM). Poisoning episodes exclude food poisoning, sun poisoning, or poison ivy rashes.

National Safety Council definition of injury. A disabling injury is defined as one that results in death, some degree of permanent impairment, or renders the injured person unable to effectively perform their regular duties or activities for a full day beyond the day of the injury. This definition applies to all unintentional injuries. All injury totals labeled "disabling injuries" in *Injury Facts* are based on this definition. Some *rates* in the Work section are based on OSHA definitions of recordable cases (see Glossary).

THE NATIONAL HEALTH INTERVIEW SURVEY, 2006 (CONT.)

Of the 33,256 medically consulted injuries in 2006, nearly 40% were related to leisure or sports activities. Leisure and sports injuries accounted for 70% of all injury episodes among children under the age of 12 and about 75% of injury episodes among teenagers between the ages of 12 and 17 years.

The rate of injuries occurring during leisure activities was higher for men (33.9 cases per 1,000 population) than for women (23.2 per 1,000 pop.). The rate of sports injuries among men (21.1 per 1,000) was also substantially higher than among women (12.2 per 1,000 pop.). The charts on this page illustrate these gender differences in terms of percentages and rates.

NUMBER OF INJURY EPISODES BY AGE AND ACTIVITY AT TIME OF INJURY, UNITED STATES, 2006

| | Total[a] | Activity at Time of Injury[b] (number in thousands) | | | | | | |
		Leisure Activities	Sports	Working Around House or Yard	Working at Paid Job	Driving[c]	Attending School	Other[d]
All Ages	**33,256**	**8,287**	**4,824**	**5,170**	**4,661**	**1,813**	**586**	**7,908**
Under 12 years	4,642	2,151	1,119[f]	(e)	0	0	182[f]	1,193
12–17 years	3,825	1,085	1,801	(e)	(e)	196[f]	337[f]	214[f]
18–44 years	11,772	2,654	1,253	1,623	2,549	997	(e)	2,763
45–64 years	7,642	1,466	461[f]	1,891	1,806	511[f]	0	1,592
65–74 years	1,727	211[f]	(e)	736	(e)	(e)	0	363[f]
75 years and over	3,648	720	(e)	881	0	(e)	0	1,784

[a]Numbers and percents may not sum to respective totals due to rounding and unknowns.
[b]Activity at time of injury and poisoning episodes is based on the question, "What was [person] doing when the injury/poisoning happened?" Respondents could indicate up to two activities.
[c]Driving includes both drivers and passengers.
[d]"Other" includes unpaid work such as housework, shopping, volunteer work, sleeping, resting, eating, drinking, cooking, hands-on care from another person, and other unspecified activities.
[e]Estimate is not shown because it does not meet standard of reliability or precision.
[f]Figure does not meet standard of reliability or precision and should be used with caution.

PERCENT AND RATES OF INJURY EPISODES BY SEX AND ACTIVITY AT TIME OF INJURY, UNITED STATES, 2005

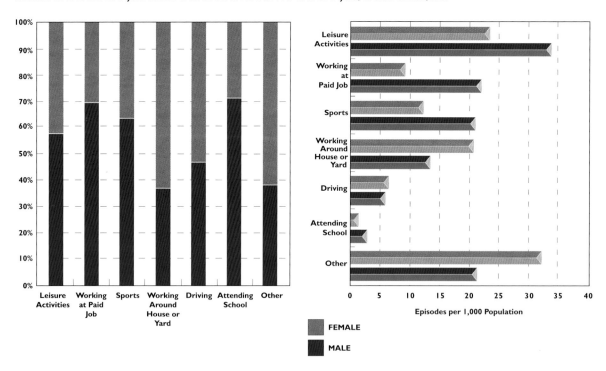

Source: Adams, P.F., & Barnes P.M. (2008, January). Summary health statistics for the U.S. population: National Health Interview Survey, 2006. National Center for Health Statistics. Vital and Health Statistics, Series 10 (No. 236).

There is a wealth of research demonstrating the role of socioeconomic status (SES) in the etiology of heart disease, lung disease, stroke, cancer, hypertension, and diabetes. In general, persons with the highest levels of income and education are healthier than those with median income and education, who, in turn, tend to be in better health than the poor and less educated.[a]

Lower SES is known to contribute to increased rates of fatal injuries among children and adults. Although research provides some evidence of links between SES and nonfatal injuries, the results at present are inconsistent and depend in part on the study design, population, and context.

The National Health Interview Survey provides an opportunity to look at the occurrence of unintentional injuries in the U.S. population as a function of socioeconomic position using two SES measures — family income and education.[b]

Although NHIS data indicate that all people are affected by injuries regardless of income or educational attainment, high school or GED graduates followed by college graduates had the lowest medically consulted injury rate in 2006. Persons with an incomplete college degree had the highest injury rate. The relationship between injury rates and family income followed a U-shaped curve with peaks among the very poor (less than $20,000) as well as persons with annual family incomes of at least $75,000.

[a]Banks, J., Marmot, M., Oldfield, Z., & Smith, J.P. (2006). Disease and disadvantage in the United States and in England. Journal of American Medical Association, 295 (17), 2037–2045.
[b]Education data are shown for persons aged 25 years and older.

PERCENTAGES AND RATES OF MEDICALLY CONSULTED INJURIES BY LEVEL OF EDUCATION, UNITED STATES, 2006

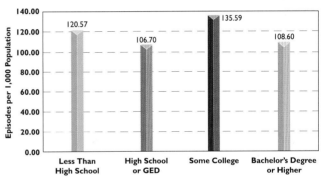

PERCENTAGES AND RATES OF MEDICALLY CONSULTED INJURIES BY FAMILY INCOME, UNITED STATES, 2006

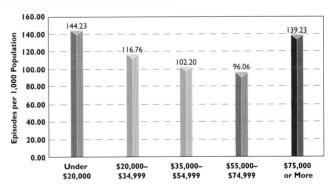

Source: Adams, P.F., Dey, A.N., & Vickerie, J.L. (2007, January). Summary health statistics for the U.S. population: National Health Interview Survey, 2005. Vital and Health Statistics, Series 10 (No. 233). Hyattsville, MD: National Center for Health Statistics.

INJURY-RELATED HOSPITAL EMERGENCY DEPARTMENT VISITS, 2006
About 42.4 million visits to hospital emergency departments in 2006 were due to injuries.

About 36% of all hospital emergency department visits in the United States were injury related, according to information from the 2006 National Hospital Ambulatory Medical Care Survey conducted for the National Center for Health Statistics. There were approximately 119.2 million visits made to emergency departments, of which about 42.4 million were injury related. This resulted in an annual rate of about 40.5 emergency department visits per 100 persons, of which about 14.4 visits per 100 persons were injury related.

Males had a higher overall rate of injury-related visits than females. For males, about 15.5 visits per 100 persons were recorded; for females the rate was 13.4 per 100 persons. Males also had higher rates of injury-related visits than females for age groups from under 15 years of age through age 64, while females had higher rates for age groups beginning at age 65. Those aged 15 to 24 had the highest rate of injury-related visits for males, while those aged 75 and over had the highest rate for females.

Falls and motor-vehicle accidents were the leading causes of injury-related emergency department visits, accounting for 20% and 10% of the total, respectively. In total, about 8.6 million visits to emergency departments were made in 2005 due to accidental falls, and about 4.3 million were made due to motor-vehicle accidents. The next leading types were struck against or struck accidentally by objects or persons with 2.9 million visits (7% of the total), and accidents caused by cutting or piercing instruments, which accounted for about 2.3 million visits (6% of the total).

Black or African American persons had higher rates of injury-related visits to emergency departments than did whites for every age group. The difference varied from a high of 11.8 injuries per 100 population in the 25- to 44-year-old age group to a low of 5.1 injuries per 100 population for those in the 75-years-and-over age group.

NUMBER AND PERCENT DISTRIBUTION OF EMERGENCY DEPARTMENT VISITS BY CAUSE OF INJURY, UNITED STATES, 2006

Cause of Injury and E-code[a]	Number of Visits (000)	Percent
All Injury-Related Visits	42,386	100.0
Unintentional Injuries, E800–E869, E880–E929	27,653	65.2
Accidental Falls, E880.0–E886.9, E888	8,614	20.3
Total Motor Vehicle Accidents, E810–E825 (.0-.5, .7-.9)	4,329	10.2
Motor vehicle traffic, E810–E819	4,043	9.5
Motor vehicle, nontraffic, E820–E825 (.0-.5, .7-.9)	286	0.7
Striking Against or Struck Accidentally by Objects or Persons, E916–E917	2,921	6.9
Accidents Caused by Cutting or Piercing Instruments, E920	2,323	5.5
Accidents Due to Natural and Environmental Factors, E900–E909, E928.0–E928.2	2,036	4.8
Overexertion and Strenuous Movements, E927	1,969	4.6
Foreign Body, E914–E915	930	2.2
Accidental Poisoning by Drugs, Medicinal Substances, Biologicals, Other Solid and Liquid Substances, Gases and Vapors, E850–E869	794	1.9
Caught Accidentally In or Between Objects, E918	511	1.2
Accidents Caused by Fire and Flames, Hot Substances or Object, Caustic or Corrosive Material, and Steam, E890–E899, E924	501	1.2
Pedalcycle, Nontraffic and Other, E800–E807(.3), E820–E825(.6), E826.1, E826.9	394	0.9
Machinery, E919	315	0.7
Other Transportation, E800-807(.0–.2, .8–.9), E826(.0, .2–.8), E827–E829, E831, E833–E845	152	0.4

Cause of Injury and E-code[a]	Number of Visits (000)	Percent
Suffocation, E911–E913	108	0.3
Other Mechanism[b], E830, E832, E846-E848, E910, E921-E923, E925-E926, E928.3, E928.8, E929.0-E929.5	1,693	4.0
Mechanism Unspecified, E887, E928.9, E929.8, E929.9	(c)	(c)
Intentional Injuries, E950–E959, E960–E969, E970–E978, E990–E999	2,485	5.9
Assault, E960–E969	1,821	4.3
Unarmed Fight or Brawl and Striking by Blunt or Thrown Object, E960.0, E968.2	974	2.3
Assault by Cutting and Piercing Instrument, E966	129	0.3
Assault by Other and Unspecified Mechanism,[d] E960.1, E961–E964, E965.0–E965.9, E967–E968.1, E968.3–E969	718	1.7
Self-inflicted Injury, E950–E959	594	1.4
Poisoning by Solid or Liquid Substances, Gases or Vapors, E950–E952	401	0.9
Other and Unspecified Mechanism,[e] E954–E959	193	0.5
Injuries of Undetermined Intent, E980–E989	497	1.2
Adverse Effects of Medical Treatment, E870–E879, E930–E949	1,860	4.4
Medical and Surgical Complications, E870–E879	1,076	2.5
Adverse Drug Effects, E930–E949	783	1.8
Alcohol and/or Drug Abuse[f]	2,166	5.1
Other and Unknown[g]	7,725	18.2

Source: Pits, S. R.., Niska, R. W., Jianmin, X., & Burt, C. W. (2008). National Hospital Ambulatory Medical Care Survey: 2006 Emergency Department Summary (National Health Statistics Reports, Number 7, August 6, 2008). Hyattsville, MD: National Center for Health Statistics

Note: Sum of parts may not add to total due to rounding.

[a] Based on the International Classification of Diseases, 9th Revision, Clinical Modification (ICD-9-CM).
[b] Includes drowning, firearms, and other & not elsewhere classified mechanism.
[c] Figure did not meet standard of reliability or precision.
[d] Includes assault by firearms and explosives, and other mechanism.
[e] Includes injury by cutting and piercing instrument, and other and unspecified mechanism.
[f] Alcohol and drug abuse are not contained in the "Supplementary Classification of External Causes of Injury and Poisoning," but are frequently recorded as a cause of injury or poisoning.
[g] Includes illegible and blank E-codes.

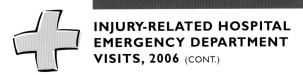

RATEª OF INJURY-RELATED VISITS TO EMERGENCY DEPARTMENTS BY PATIENT AGE AND SEX, 2006

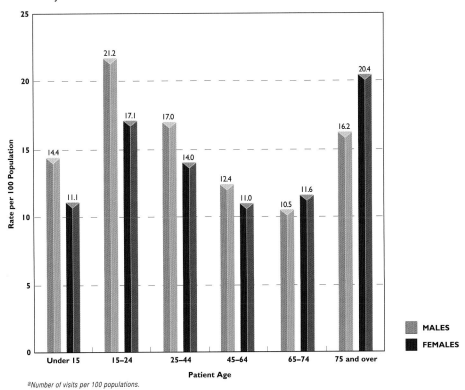

ªNumber of visits per 100 populations.

RATEª OF INJURY-RELATED VISITS TO EMERGENCY DEPARTMENTS BY PATIENT AGE AND RACE, 2006

ªNumber of visits per 100 populations.

The states listed below participate in the Injury Mortality Tabulations reporting system. Reports from these states are used to make current year estimates. See the Technical Appendix for more information.

The estimated Total number of unintentional-injury deaths for All Classes decreased less than 0.5% in 2007 from the revised 2006 estimate. The number of unintentional-injury deaths in the Home class was down 11%, while the number in the Work and Motor-Vehicle classes declined by 8% and 3%, respectively. The Public Nonmotor-vehicle class showed an increase of 26%. Similarly, the population death rate for the Home class decreased 12%, the rate for the Work class declined 6%, the rate for the Motor-Vehicle class was reduced by 4%, and the rate for the Total decreased 1%. The rate for the Public Nonmotor-Vehicle class showed an increase of 25% from 2006 to 2007.

PRINCIPAL CLASSES OF UNINTENTIONAL-INJURY DEATHS BY STATE, 2007

State	Total[a]		Motor-Vehicle[b]		Work[c]		Home		Public Nonmotor-Vehicle	
	Deaths	Rate[d]	Deaths	Rate[d]	Deaths	Rate[d]	Deaths	Rate[d]	Deaths	Rate[d]
Total U.S.	120,000	39.8	43,100	14.3	4,689	1.6	43,500	14.4	30,500	10.1
Arizona	2,799	44.2	958	15.1	59	0.9	1,032	16.3	1,799	28.4
Arkansas	1,300	54.5	603	25.3	65	2.7	225	9.4	436	18.3
Florida	9,001	49.3	3,338	18.3	225	1.2	1,539	8.4	3,764	20.6
Idaho	643	42.9	265	17.7	27	1.8	211	14.1	148	9.9
Kansas	1,100	39.6	434	15.6	62	2.2	358	12.9	261	9.4
Missouri	2,770	47.1	1,003	17.1	89	1.5	1,132	19.3	569	9.7
Ohio	4,717	41.1	1,316	11.5	—	—	—	—	—	—
South Dakota	372	46.7	159	20.0	21	2.6	100	12.6	97	12.2
Virginia	2,595	33.6	912	11.8	86	1.1	828	10.7	307	4.0

Source: Provisional reports of vital statistics registrars; deaths are by place of occurrence. U.S. totals are National Safety Council estimates.
[a] The all-class total may not equal the sum of the separate class totals because Motor-Vehicle and other transportation deaths occurring to persons in the course of their employment are included in the Work death totals as well as the Motor-Vehicle and Public Nonmotor-Vehicle totals and also because unclassified deaths are included in the total.
[b] Differences between the figures given above and those on pages 172 and 173 are due in most cases to the inclusion of nontraffic deaths in this table.
[c] Work death totals may be too low where incomplete information on death certificates results in the deaths being included in the Public class. The Work totals may include some cases that are not compensable. For compensable cases only, see page 53.
[d] Deaths per 100,000 population.

The rank of unintentional-injuries as a cause of death varies with race and Hispanic origin. While ranking fifth overall (following heart disease, cancer, stroke, and chronic lower respiratory diseases), unintentional injuries rank third for Hispanics after heart disease and cancer.

By race, unintentional injuries rank fifth for whites (after heart disease, cancer, stroke, and chronic lower respiratory diseases), and fourth for blacks, Asians, Pacific Islanders, American Indians, and Alaskan Natives.

UNINTENTIONAL-INJURY DEATH RATES BY RACE, HISPANIC ORIGIN, AND SEX, UNITED STATES, 2005

| | Total | | | Hispanic Origin | | | | | |
| | | | | Non-Hispanic | | | Hispanic | | |
Race and Sex	Rank	Number	Rate	Rank	Number	Rate	Rank	Number	Rate
All Races	5	117,809	39.7	5	105,967	41.8	3	11,464	26.7
Males	3	76,375	52.3	3	67,494	54.5	3	8,612	38.9
Females	6	41,434	27.5	6	38,473	29.6	5	2,852	13.8
White	5	100,406	41.8	5	88,970	44.4	3	11,161	(b)
Males	3	64,600	54.3	3	56,021	57.0	3	8,389	(b)
Females	6	35,806	29.5	6	32,949	32.3	5	2,772	(b)
Black	4	13,652	34.9	4	13,393	35.9	3	169	(b)
Males	3	9,329	50.1	3	9,130	51.4	3	129	(b)
Females	6	4,323	21.2	6	4,263	21.8	5	40	(b)
Not White or Black[a]	4	3,751	21.7	4	3,604	22.4	3	134	(b)
Males	3	2,446	29.0	3	2,343	29.9	3	94	(b)
Females	4	1,305	14.8	4	1,261	15.3	3	40	(b)

Source: National Safety Council analysis of National Center for Health Statistics mortality data and Census Bureau population data.
Note: Rates are deaths per 100,000 population in each race/sex/Hispanic origin group. Total column includes 369 deaths for which Hispanic origin was not determined.
[a]Includes American Indian, Alaskan Native, Asian, Native Hawaiian and Pacific Islander.
[b]Race is not well reported for persons of Hispanic origin. Population death rates are unreliable.

LEADING CAUSES OF UNINTENTIONAL-INJURY DEATH BY RACE, HISPANIC ORIGIN, AND SEX, UNITED STATES, 2005

| | All Races | | | White | | | Black | | | Not White or Black[a] | | |
Cause of Death	Both	Male	Female	Both	Male	Female	Both	Male	Female	Both	Male	Female
Total	117,809	76,375	41,434	100,406	64,600	35,806	13,652	9,329	4,323	3,751	2,446	1,305
Motor Vehicle	45,343	31,631	13,712	38,041	26,508	11,533	5,491	3,957	1,534	1,811	1,166	645
Poisoning	23,618	15,884	7,734	20,163	13,561	6,602	2,986	2,015	971	469	308	161
Fall	19,656	10,154	9,502	18,113	9,246	8,867	1,027	602	425	516	306	210
Suffocation by inhalation or ingestion	4,386	2,209	2,177	3,739	1,882	1,857	558	282	276	89	45	44
Drowning	3,582	2,818	764	2,819	2,191	628	556	471	85	207	156	51
Fires, flames, smoke	3,197	1,886	1,311	2,351	1,392	959	746	442	304	100	52	48
Population (thousands)	296,507	145,974	150,534	240,175	118,898	121,277	39,067	18,639	20,429	17,265	8,437	8,828

| | Non-Hispanic | | | Hispanic | | | Unknown | | |
Cause of Death	Both	Male	Female	Both	Male	Female	Both	Male	Female
Total	105,967	67,494	38,473	11,464	8,612	2,852	378	269	109
Motor Vehicle	39,125	26,982	12,143	6,103	4,570	1,533	115	79	36
Poisoning	21,488	14,198	7,290	2,018	1,603	415	112	83	29
Fall	18,551	9,442	9,109	1,064	689	375	41	23	18
Suffocation by inhalation or ingestion	4,171	2,088	2,083	203	117	86	12	4	8
Drowning	3,047	2,375	672	518	430	88	17	13	4
Fires, flames, smoke	2,971	1,751	1,220	211	125	86	15	10	5
Population (thousands)	253,635	123,813	129,822	42,872	22,161	20,711	—	—	—

Source: National Safety Council analysis of National Center for Health Statistics mortality data.
Note: Dashes (—) indicate not applicable.
[a]Includes American Indian, Alaskan Native, Asian, Native Hawaiian and Pacific Islander.

DISASTER DEATHS, 2007

Disasters are front page news even though the lives lost in the United States are relatively few when compared to the day-to-day life losses from unintentional injuries (see "While You Speak! page 31). Listed below are the United States disasters, of which the National Safety Council is aware, that occurred in 2007 and took five or more lives.

In addition to the disasters listed in the table, there were 11 residential fires that claimed five or six lives each. There were also 40 motor-vehicle traffic crashes in 2007 that resulted in five or six deaths each.

DISASTER DEATHS, UNITED STATES, 2007

Type and Location	No. of Deaths	Date of Disaster
Major Disasters (25 or more deaths)		
Winter storm, Texas, Oklahoma, Missouri, Michigan, Indiana, Iowa, New York, New Hampshire, Maine	65	January 12–16
Heat wave, Southeastern states	50	August
Other Disasters (5–24 deaths)		
Tornadoes and thunderstorms, Florida	20	February 2
Tornadoes, Alabama, Minnesota, Mississippi, Georgia	20	March 1
Storms, Midwest and Plains states	20	mid–August
Bridge collapse, Minnesota	12	August 1
Residential fire, Kentucky	10	February
Residential fire, New York	10	March
Tornado, Kansas	10	May 7
Wildfire, California	10	October
Residential fire, West Virginia	9	January
Furniture store and warehouse fire, South Carolina	9	June 18
Crandall Canyon Mine collapse, Utah	9	August 6
Motor-vehicle traffic crash, Utah	8	April 16
Motor-vehicle traffic crash, Indiana	8	April 26
Residential fire, Maryland	8	May
Motor-vehicle traffic crash, Oklahoma	7	January 14
Residential fire, Pennsylvania	7	February
Motor-vehicle traffic crash, Georgia	7	March 2
Motor-vehicle traffic crash, Oklahoma	7	May 18
Motor-vehicle traffic crash, Texas	7	June 1
Residential fire, North Carolina	7	October
Motor-vehicle traffic crash, Texas	7	October 22
Motor-vehicle traffic crash, California	7	November 17
Race car stunt, Tennessee	6	June 17
Airplane crash into two homes, fire, Florida	5	July
Hydroelectric plant fire, Colorado	5	October

Source: National Climatic Data Center, infoplease.com, National Fire Protection Association, and National Highway Traffic Safety Administration.
Note: Some death totals are estimates and may differ among sources.

While you make a 10-minute safety speech, 2 persons will be killed and about 500 will suffer a disabling injury. Costs will amount to $13,020,000. On the average, there are 14 unintentional-injury deaths and about 3,000 disabling injuries every hour during the year.

Deaths and disabling injuries by class occurred in the nation at the following rates in 2007:

DEATHS AND DISABLING INJURIES BY CLASS, 2007

| Class | Severity | One Every— | Number per ... | | | 2007 Total |
			Hour	Day	Week	
All	**Deaths**	**4 minutes**	**14**	**329**	**2,310**	**120,000**
	Injuries	**1 second**	**3,000**	**72,100**	**505,800**	**26,300,000**
Motor-Vehicle	Deaths	12 minutes	5	118	830	43,100
	Injuries	14 seconds	260	6,300	44,200	2,300,000
Work	Deaths	112 minutes	1	13	90	4,689
	Injuries	9 seconds	400	9,600	67,300	3,500,000
Workers Off-the-Job	Deaths	10 minutes	6	144	1,010	52,500
	Injuries	3 seconds	1,070	25,800	180,800	9,400,000
Home	Deaths	12 minutes	5	119	840	43,500
	Injuries	3 seconds	1,190	28,500	200,000	10,400,000
Public Nonmotor-Vehicle	Deaths	17 minutes	3	84	590	30,500
	Injuries	3 seconds	1,160	27,900	196,200	10,200,000

Source: National Safety Council estimates.

DEATHS EVERY HOUR ...

▨	MOTOR-VEHICLE
▧	WORK
▩	HOME
▦	PUBLIC

AN UNINTENTIONAL-INJURY DEATH EVERY FOUR MINUTES ...

Four Minutes

CHILDREN AND YOUTHS

Motor-vehicle crashes are the leading cause of injury deaths among children.

Unintentional injuries are a major public health concern affecting children and adolescents in the United States. They are the underlying cause of death in two out of every five childhood mortality cases for persons aged 1–19 years, and 15 to 19 year olds account for more than 60% of the total.

Fatal injuries in the first year of life numbered 1,083 in 2005, or approximately 26 deaths per 100,000 population. Mechanical suffocation constituted the majority (65%) of all injury-related mortality cases for infants. Motor-vehicle crashes were the second leading cause of injury mortality. In addition, over 300 infant deaths that year were attributed to homicide (for more information on intentional injuries, see pages 152–157).

In the second year of life, the risk of fatal injury is reduced by nearly half. In 2005, 555 fatal injury cases, or about 14 deaths per 100,000 population, were recorded among one-year-old children. Motor-vehicle crashes were the leading cause of injury death in this age group, followed closely by drowning.

In the following three-year period (ages 2–4), the injury mortality rate drops even lower, averaging about 9

deaths per 100,000 population in 2005. Motor-vehicle crashes were the number one cause of injury mortality followed by drowning and fires/burns/flames.

From the age of 5 to early adolescence (ages 12–14), the injury mortality rate shows a general U-shaped pattern, reaching its lowest level at around the age of 10. Motor-vehicle crashes, unintentional drowning, and incidents related to fire, burns, and smoke were the leading causes of injury mortality for children aged 5–14 years in 2005.

Teenagers (15–19 years) make up 27% of the U.S. population between the ages of 1 and 19 and 62% of all injury mortality cases in that age group. Most importantly, three out of four teenage injury deaths are attributed to motor-vehicle crashes. Of the 6,600 injury deaths among teens in 2005, nearly 5,000 occurred in crashes. That same year, the injury mortality rate for 19 year olds exceeded 44 deaths per 100,000 population.

For all children and adolescents under 19 years old, the injury mortality rate by age can be described as a J-shaped relationship, peaking during infancy and again in the late teenage years.

UNINTENTIONAL-INJURY DEATHS BY EVENT, AGE 0–19, UNITED STATES, 2005

Age	Population (000)	Unintentional-Injury Deaths										
		Total	Rates[a]	Motor-vehicle	Falls	Poisoning	Drowning	Fires/Flames	Choking[b]	Mechanical Suffocation	Firearms	All Other
<1 year	4,104	1,083	26.4	146	16	20	64	34	48	700	1	54
1–19 years	77,710	10,695	13.8	7,031	143	709	1,056	488	119	180	172	797
1 year	4,095	555	13.6	186	13	9	185	45	33	36	2	46
2 years	4,043	470	11.6	164	7	7	169	60	12	9	4	38
3 years	4,008	343	8.6	133	7	1	83	55	9	14	6	35
4 years	4,064	296	7.3	134	7	4	56	44	8	5	10	28
5 years	3,911	228	5.8	116	4	7	30	36	2	6	2	25
6 years	3,869	245	6.3	147	0	4	28	35	5	4	4	18
7 years	3,880	182	4.7	104	4	3	21	25	3	1	0	21
8 years	3,907	211	5.4	134	2	1	24	21	5	3	4	17
9 years	3,991	206	5.2	122	4	2	18	20	2	13	5	20
10 years	4,055	175	4.3	100	3	2	16	18	6	8	2	20
11 years	4,090	230	5.6	128	2	0	25	24	1	12	7	31
12 years	4,174	228	5.5	141	2	3	19	15	4	9	12	23
13 years	4,245	301	7.1	188	5	11	40	14	3	6	6	28
14 years	4,313	409	9.5	267	6	18	32	14	3	7	10	52
15 years	4,390	602	13.7	423	10	35	44	11	5	9	13	52
16 years	4,227	1,054	24.9	826	9	56	50	10	2	13	15	73
17 years	4,165	1,367	32.8	1,050	15	103	75	12	3	10	24	75
18 years	4,124	1,754	42.5	1,339	17	170	78	10	7	3	27	103
19 years	4,156	1,839	44.2	1,329	26	273	63	19	6	12	19	92
0–4 years	20,314	2,747	13.5	763	50	41	557	238	110	764	23	201
5–9 years	19,558	1,072	5.5	623	14	17	121	137	17	27	15	101
10–14 years	20,877	1,343	6.4	824	18	34	132	85	17	42	37	154
15–19 years	21,062	6,616	31.4	4,967	77	637	310	62	23	47	98	395

Source: National Safety Council tabulations of National Center for Health Statistics mortality data.
Note: Data does not include "age unknown" cases, which totaled 57 in 2005.
[a] Deaths per 100,000 population in each age group.
[b] Suffocation by inhalation or ingestion of food or other object.

Unintentional injuries cause significant mortality among adults in the United States. In 2005 alone, injuries were responsible for nearly 106,000 deaths among Americans age 20 and older.

The leading causes of injury mortality include motor-vehicle crashes, poisoning, falls, choking, fires and burns, and drowning. Motor-vehicle crashes (36.0%), poisoning (21.6%), and falls (18.4%), the three leading causes of injury mortality, combined to account for over three-fourths of all fatal injuries sustained by adults over the age of 20 in 2005.

Age plays an important role in the occurrence of injuries. Motor-vehicle crashes are the leading cause of injury mortality up to the fourth decade of life, when the incidence of poisoning cases reaches its peak. Beginning at age 50, motor-vehicle crashes once again take over as the leading cause of injury mortality until superseded by falls beginning in the mid-seventies.

The highest fall mortality rates occur among adults age 75 and older, who are particularly prone to falls and fall-related injuries because of a high prevalence of

chronic illness and age-related physiologic changes that may adversely affect injury severity and, furthermore, increase the risk of complications and re-injury following an injury episode. Clinical studies demonstrate that after a serious trauma, elderly patients have higher in-hospital and long-term mortality than their younger counterparts even when other factors (e.g., injury severity, number of injuries, presence of other medical conditions, complications) are taken into consideration. At the same time, injury severity, number of injuries, and complications each independently correlates with increased injury mortality among the elderly.[a]

The increase in the incidence of fatal falls appears to be the driving force behind a surge in the overall injury mortality rate in later life. As the table below illustrates, the number of injury-related deaths per 100,000 population in 2005 increased from 54 for 70–74 year olds to 340 for 90–94 year olds—an over six-fold increase.

[a] Jacoby, S.F., Ackerson, T.H., & Richmond, T.S. (2006). Outcome from serious injury in older adults. Journal of Nursing Scholarship, 38 (2), 133–140.

UNINTENTIONAL-INJURY DEATHS BY EVENT, AGES 20 AND OLDER, UNITED STATES, 2005

| Age | Population (000) | Unintentional-Injury Deaths | | | | | | | | | | | |
		Total	Rates[a]	Motor-vehicle	Falls	Poisoning	Drowning	Fires/ Flames	Choking[b]	Mechanical Suffocation	Natural Heat/Cold	Firearms	All Other
20–24	21,053	9,137	43.4	5,941	159	1,847	339	106	49	56	31	105	504
25–29	20,054	7,215	36.0	3,926	139	2,124	206	116	52	41	30	68	513
30–34	20,090	6,782	33.8	3,313	156	2,262	179	108	44	59	33	62	566
35–39	21,006	7,419	35.3	3,175	227	2,830	208	138	66	53	53	60	609
40–44	22,860	9,500	41.6	3,573	380	3,899	289	196	110	77	87	54	835
45–49	22,486	10,019	44.6	3,430	544	4,096	279	269	156	61	120	55	1,009
50–54	20,001	8,320	41.6	2,967	637	2,887	213	228	178	71	131	53	955
55–59	17,353	6,168	35.5	2,533	679	1,435	150	193	194	53	97	42	792
60–64	13,002	4,685	36.0	1,921	772	572	116	205	223	39	84	25	728
65–69	10,134	4,060	40.1	1,596	894	265	90	194	247	22	63	21	668
70–74	8,516	4,572	53.7	1,514	1,425	170	103	196	319	25	65	23	732
75–79	7,419	6,126	82.6	1,601	2,366	173	102	229	482	29	78	16	1,050
80–84	5,641	7,728	137.0	1,390	3,591	144	78	239	690	25	82	17	1,472
85–89	3,206	7,303	227.8	915	3,720	117	66	153	720	11	92	10	1,499
90–94	1,408	4,791	340.3	313	2,624	48	18	71	466	10	43	3	1,195
95–99	396	1,778	449.0	42	981	13	7	27	192	2	13	2	499
100 and older	67	371	553.7	10	201	1	1	3	31	0	3	0	121
20 and older	214,692	105,974	49.4	38,160	19,495	22,883	2,444	2,671	4,219	634	1,105	616	13,747
25 and older	193,639	96,837	50.0	32,219	19,336	21,036	2,105	2,565	4,170	578	1,074	511	13,243
35 and older	153,495	82,840	54.0	24,980	19,041	16,650	1,720	2,341	4,074	478	1,011	381	12,164
45 and older	109,629	65,921	60.1	18,232	18,434	9,921	1,223	2,007	3,898	348	871	267	10,720
55 and older	67,142	47,582	70.9	11,835	17,253	2,938	731	1,510	3,564	216	620	159	8,756
65 and older	36,787	36,729	99.8	7,381	15,802	931	465	1,112	3,147	124	439	92	7,236
75 and older	18,137	28,097	154.9	4,271	13,483	496	272	722	2,581	77	311	48	5,836

Source: National Safety Council tabulations of National Center for Health Statistics mortality data.
Note: Data does not include "age unknown" cases, which totaled 57 in 2005.
[a] Deaths per 100,000 population in each age group.
[b] Suffocation by inhalation or ingestion of food or other object.

TRENDS IN UNINTENTIONAL-INJURY DEATH RATES

Age-adjusted rates, which eliminate the effect of shifts in the age distribution of the population, have decreased 61% from 1912 to 2007—from 100.4 to 39.3. The adjusted rates, which are shown in the graph on the opposite page, are standardized to the year 2000 standard U.S. population. The break in the lines at 1948 shows the estimated effect of changes in the International Classification of Diseases (ICD). The break in the lines at 1992 resulted from the adoption of the Bureau of Labor Statistics Census of Fatal Occupational Injuries for work-related deaths. Another change in the ICD in 1999 also affects the trends. See the Technical Appendix for comparability.

The table below shows the change in the age distribution of the population since 1910.

The age-adjusted death rate for all unintentional-injuries increased and decreased significantly several times during the period from 1910 to 1940. Since 1940, there were some setbacks, such as in the early 1960s, but the overall trend through the early 1990s was positive. The age-adjusted death rates for unintentional-injury deaths in the work and home classes declined fairly steadily since they became available in the late 1920s, although the home class rates have increased since the early 1990s they have shown improvement this latest year. The rates in the public class declined for three decades, rose in the 1960s and then continued declining until leveling in the 1990s and rising in recent years. The age-adjusted motor-vehicle death rate rose steadily from 1910 to the late 1930s as the automobile became more widely used. A sharp drop in use occurred during World War II and a sharp rise in rates occurred in the 1960s, with death rates reflecting economic cycles and a long-term downward trend since then.

UNITED STATES POPULATION, SELECTED YEARS

Year	All Ages	0–14	15–24	25–44	45–64	65 & Older
Number (in thousands)						
1910	91,973[a]	29,499	18,121	26,810	13,424	3,950
2000[b]	274,634	58,964	38,077	81,892	60,991	34,710
2007	301,621	60,888	42,506	83,752	76,587	37,888
Percent						
1910	100.0%	32.1%	19.7%	29.2%	14.6%	4.3%
2000[b]	100.0%	21.5%	13.9%	29.8%	22.2%	12.6%
2007	100.0%	20.2%	14.1%	27.8%	25.4%	12.5

Source: For 1910: U. S. Bureau of the Census. (1960). Historical Statistics of the United States, Colonial Times to 1957. Series A 71-85. Washington, DC: U.S. Government Printing Office. For 2000: Anderson, R.N., & Rosenberg, H.M. (1998). Age standardization of death rates: Implementation of the year 2000 standard. National Vital Statistics Reports, 47(3), 13. For 2007: U.S. Census Bureau, Monthly Postcensal Resident Population, by Single Year of Age, Sex, Race, and Hispanic Origin. Retrieved June 2008 from: www.census.gov/popest/national/asrh/2007_nat_res.html.
[a] Includes 169,000 persons with age unknown.
[b] This is the population used for standardization (age-adjustment) and differs slightly from the actual 2000 population which totaled 275,306,000.

AGE-ADJUSTED DEATH RATES BY CLASS OF INJURY, UNITED STATES, 1910–2007

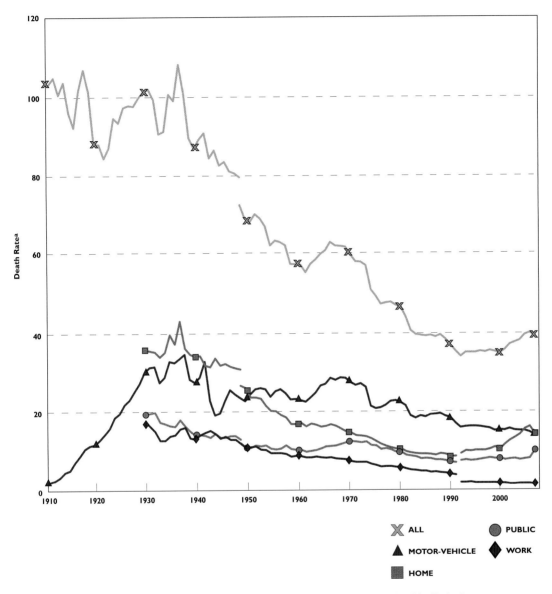

ⁿDeaths per 100,000 population, adjusted to 2000 standard population. The break at 1948 shows the estimated effect of classification changes.
The break at 1992 is due to the adoption of the Bureau of Labor Statistics' Census of Fatal Occupational Injuries for work-related deaths.

PRINCIPAL CLASSES OF UNINTENTIONAL-INJURY DEATHS

PRINCIPAL CLASSES OF UNINTENTIONAL-INJURY DEATHS, UNITED STATES, 1903–2007

Year	Total[a] Deaths	Rate[b]	Motor-Vehicle Deaths	Rate[b]	Work Deaths	Rate[b]	Home Deaths	Rate[b]	Public Nonmotor-Vehicle Deaths	Rate[b]
1903	70,600	87.2	(c)	—	(c)	—	(c)	—	(c)	—
1904	71,500	86.6	(c)	—	(c)	—	(c)	—	(c)	—
1905	70,900	84.2	(c)	—	(c)	—	(c)	—	(c)	—
1906	80,000	93.2	400	0.5	(c)	—	(c)	—	(c)	—
1907	81,900	93.6	700	0.8	(c)	—	(c)	—	(c)	—
1908	72,300	81.2	800	0.9	(c)	—	(c)	—	(c)	—
1909	72,700	80.1	1,300	1.4	(c)	—	(c)	—	(c)	—
1910	77,900	84.4	1,900	2.0	(c)	—	(c)	—	(c)	—
1911	79,300	84.7	2,300	2.5	(c)	—	(c)	—	(c)	—
1912	78,400	82.5	3,100	3.3	(c)	—	(c)	—	(c)	—
1913	82,500	85.5	4,200	4.4	(c)	—	(c)	—	(c)	—
1914	77,000	78.6	4,700	4.8	(c)	—	(c)	—	(c)	—
1915	76,200	76.7	6,600	6.6	(c)	—	(c)	—	(c)	—
1916	84,800	84.1	8,200	8.1	(c)	—	(c)	—	(c)	—
1917	90,100	88.2	10,200	10.0	(c)	—	(c)	—	(c)	—
1918	85,100	82.1	10,700	10.3	(c)	—	(c)	—	(c)	—
1919	75,500	71.9	11,200	10.7	(c)	—	(c)	—	(c)	—
1920	75,900	71.2	12,500	11.7	(c)	—	(c)	—	(c)	—
1921	74,000	68.4	13,900	12.9	(c)	—	(c)	—	(c)	—
1922	76,300	69.4	15,300	13.9	(c)	—	(c)	—	(c)	—
1923	84,400	75.7	18,400	16.5	(c)	—	(c)	—	(c)	—
1924	85,600	75.6	19,400	17.1	(c)	—	(c)	—	(c)	—
1925	90,000	78.4	21,900	19.1	(c)	—	(c)	—	(c)	—
1926	91,700	78.7	23,400	20.1	(c)	—	(c)	—	(c)	—
1927	92,700	78.4	25,800	21.8	(c)	—	(c)	—	(c)	—
1928	95,000	79.3	28,000	23.4	19,000	15.8	30,000	24.9	21,000	17.4
1929	98,200	80.8	31,200	25.7	20,000	16.4	30,000	24.6	20,000	16.4
1930	99,100	80.5	32,900	26.7	19,000	15.4	30,000	24.4	20,000	16.3
1931	97,300	78.5	33,700	27.2	17,500	14.1	29,000	23.4	20,000	16.1
1932	89,000	71.3	29,500	23.6	15,000	12.0	29,000	23.2	18,000	14.4
1933	90,932	72.4	31,363	25.0	14,500	11.6	29,500	23.6	18,500	14.7
1934	100,977	79.9	36,101	28.6	16,000	12.7	34,000	26.9	18,000	14.2
1935	99,773	78.4	36,369	28.6	16,500	13.0	32,000	25.2	18,000	14.2
1936	110,052	85.9	38,089	29.7	18,500	14.5	37,000	28.9	19,500	15.2
1937	105,205	81.7	39,643	30.8	19,000	14.8	32,000	24.8	18,000	14.0
1938	93,805	72.3	32,582	25.1	16,000	12.3	31,000	23.9	17,000	13.1
1939	92,623	70.8	32,386	24.7	15,500	11.8	31,000	23.7	16,000	12.2
1940	96,885	73.4	34,501	26.1	17,000	12.9	31,500	23.9	16,500	12.5
1941	101,513	76.3	39,969	30.0	18,000	13.5	30,000	22.5	16,500	12.4
1942	95,889	71.6	28,309	21.1	18,000	13.4	30,500	22.8	16,000	12.0
1943	99,038	73.8	23,823	17.8	17,500	13.0	33,500	25.0	17,000	12.7
1944	95,237	71.7	24,282	18.3	16,000	12.0	32,500	24.5	16,000	12.0
1945	95,918	72.4	28,076	21.2	16,500	12.5	33,500	25.3	16,000	12.1
1946	98,033	70.0	33,411	23.9	16,500	11.8	33,000	23.6	17,500	12.5
1947	99,579	69.4	32,697	22.8	17,000	11.9	34,500	24.1	18,000	12.6
1948 (5th Rev.)[d]	98,001	67.1	32,259	22.1	16,000	11.0	35,000	24.0	17,000	11.6
1948 (6th Rev.)[d]	93,000	63.7	32,259	22.1	16,000	11.0	31,000	21.2	16,000	11.0
1949	90,106	60.6	31,701	21.3	15,000	10.1	31,000	20.9	15,000	10.1
1950	91,249	60.3	34,763	23.0	15,500	10.2	29,000	19.2	15,000	9.9
1951	95,871	62.5	36,996	24.1	16,000	10.4	30,000	19.6	16,000	10.4
1952	96,172	61.8	37,794	24.3	15,000	9.6	30,500	19.6	16,000	10.3
1953	95,032	60.1	37,955	24.0	15,000	9.5	29,000	18.3	16,500	10.4
1954	90,032	55.9	35,586	22.1	14,000	8.7	28,000	17.4	15,500	9.6
1955	93,443	56.9	38,426	23.4	14,200	8.6	28,500	17.3	15,500	9.4
1956	94,780	56.6	39,628	23.7	14,300	8.5	28,000	16.7	16,000	9.6
1957	95,307	55.9	38,702	22.7	14,200	8.3	28,000	16.4	17,500	10.3
1958	90,604	52.3	36,981	21.3	13,300	7.7	26,500	15.3	16,500	9.5
1959	92,080	52.2	37,910	21.5	13,800	7.8	27,000	15.3	16,500	9.3
1960	93,806	52.1	38,137	21.2	13,800	7.7	28,000	15.6	17,000	9.4
1961	92,249	50.4	38,091	20.8	13,500	7.4	27,000	14.8	16,500	9.0
1962	97,139	52.3	40,804	22.0	13,700	7.4	28,500	15.3	17,000	9.2
1963	100,669	53.4	43,564	23.1	14,200	7.5	28,500	15.1	17,500	9.3
1964	105,000	54.9	47,700	25.0	14,200	7.4	28,000	14.6	18,500	9.7
1965	108,004	55.8	49,163	25.4	14,100	7.3	28,500	14.7	19,500	10.1
1966	113,563	58.1	53,041	27.1	14,500	7.4	29,500	15.1	20,000	10.2
1967	113,169	57.3	52,924	26.8	14,200	7.2	29,000	14.7	20,500	10.4
1968	114,864	57.6	54,862	27.5	14,300	7.2	28,000	14.0	21,500	10.8
1969	116,385	57.8	55,791	27.7	14,300	7.1	27,500	13.7	22,500	11.2
1970	114,638	56.2	54,633	26.8	13,800	6.8	27,000	13.2	23,500	11.5
1971	113,439	54.8	54,381	26.3	13,700	6.6	26,500	12.8	23,500	11.4
1972	115,448	55.2	56,278	26.9	14,000	6.7	26,500	12.7	23,500	11.2
1973	115,821	54.8	55,511	26.3	14,300	6.8	26,500	12.5	24,500	11.6

See source and footnotes on page 37.

PRINCIPAL CLASSES OF UNINTENTIONAL-INJURY DEATHS, UNITED STATES, 1903–2007, Cont.

Year	Total[a] Deaths	Total[a] Rate[b]	Motor-Vehicle Deaths	Motor-Vehicle Rate[b]	Work Deaths	Work Rate[b]	Home Deaths	Home Rate[b]	Public Nonmotor-Vehicle Deaths	Public Nonmotor-Vehicle Rate[b]
1974	104,622	49.0	46,402	21.8	13,500	6.3	26,000	12.2	23,000	10.8
1975	103,030	47.8	45,853	21.3	13,000	6.0	25,000	11.6	23,000	10.6
1976	100,761	46.3	47,038	21.6	12,500	5.7	24,000	11.0	21,500	10.0
1977	103,202	47.0	49,510	22.5	12,900	5.9	23,200	10.6	22,200	10.1
1978	105,561	47.5	52,411	23.6	13,100	5.9	22,800	10.3	22,000	9.9
1979	105,312	46.9	53,524	23.8	13,000	5.8	22,500	10.0	21,000	9.4
1980	105,718	46.5	53,172	23.4	13,200	5.8	22,800	10.0	21,300	9.4
1981	100,704	43.9	51,385	22.4	12,500	5.4	21,700	9.5	19,800	8.6
1982	94,082	40.6	45,779	19.8	11,900	5.1	21,200	9.2	19,500	8.4
1983	92,488	39.6	44,452	19.0	11,700	5.0	21,200	9.1	19,400	8.3
1984	92,911	39.4	46,263	19.6	11,500	4.9	21,200	9.0	18,300	7.8
1985	93,457	39.3	45,901	19.3	11,500	4.8	21,600	9.1	18,800	7.9
1986	95,277	39.7	47,865	19.9	11,100	4.6	21,700	9.0	18,700	7.8
1987	95,020	39.2	48,290	19.9	11,300	4.7	21,400	8.8	18,400	7.6
1988	97,100	39.7	49,078	20.1	11,000	4.5	22,700	9.3	18,400	7.5
1989	95,028	38.5	47,575	19.3	10,900	4.4	22,500	9.1	18,200	7.4
1990	91,983	36.9	46,814	18.8	10,100	4.0	21,500	8.6	17,400	7.0
1991	89,347	35.4	43,536	17.3	9,800	3.9	22,100	8.8	17,600	7.0
1992	86,777	34.0	40,982	16.1	4,968[e]	1.9[e]	24,000[e]	9.4[e]	19,000[e]	7.4[e]
1993	90,523	35.1	41,893	16.3	5,035	2.0	26,100	10.1	19,700	7.6
1994	91,437	35.1	42,524	16.3	5,338	2.1	26,300	10.1	19,600	7.5
1995	93,320	35.5	43,363	16.5	5,018	1.9	27,200	10.3	20,100	7.6
1996	94,948	35.8	43,649	16.5	5,058	1.9	27,500	10.4	21,000	7.9
1997	95,644	35.7	43,458	16.2	5,162	1.9	27,700	10.3	21,700	8.1
1998	97,835	36.2	43,501	16.1	5,120	1.9	29,000	10.7	22,600	8.4
1999[f]	97,860	35.9	42,401	15.5	5,185	1.9	30,500	11.2	22,200	8.1
2000	97,900	35.6	43,354	15.7	5,022	1.8	29,200	10.6	22,700	8.2
2001	101,537	35.6	43,788	15.4	5,042	1.8	33,200	11.6	21,800	7.6
2002	106,742	37.1	45,380	15.8	4,726	1.6	36,400	12.6	22,500	7.8
2003	109,277	37.6	44,757	15.4	4,725	1.6	38,800	13.3	23,200	8.0
2004	112,012	38.1	44,933	15.3	5,000	1.7	41,700	14.2	22,700	7.7
2005[g]	117,809	39.7	45,343	15.3	4,987	1.7	46,400	15.6	23,400	7.9
2006[g]	120,500	40.3	44,600	14.9	5,092	1.7	48,800	16.3	24,300	8.1
2007[h]	120,000	39.8	43,100	14.3	4,689	1.6	43,500	14.4	30,500	10.1

Changes										
1997 to 2007	+25%	+11%	−1%	−12%	−9%	−16%	+57%	+40%	+41%	+25%
2006 to 2007	(i)	−1%	−3%	−4%	−8%	−6%	−11%	−12%	+26%	+25%

Source: Total and motor-vehicle deaths, 1903-1932 based on National Center for Health Statistics death registration states; 1933–1948 (5th Rev.), 1949–1963, 1965–2005 are NCHS totals for the U.S. Work deaths for 1992–2007 are from the Bureau of Labor Statistics, Census of Fatal Occupational Injuries. All other figures are National Safety Council estimates.
[a] Duplications between Motor-Vehicle, Work, and Home are eliminated in the Total column.
[b] Rates are deaths per 100,000 population.
[c] Data insufficient to estimate yearly totals.
[d] In 1948 a revision was made in the International Classification of Diseases. The first figures for 1948 are comparable with those for earlier years, the second with those for later years.
[e] Adoption of the Census of Fatal Occupational Injuries figure for the Work class necessitated adjustments to the Home and Public classes. See the Technical Appendix for details.
[f] In 1999 a revision was made in the International Classification of Diseases. See the Technical Appendix for comparability with earlier years.
[g] Revised.
[h] Preliminary.
[i] Change less than 0.5%.

UNINTENTIONAL-INJURY DEATHS BY AGE

UNINTENTIONAL-INJURY DEATHS BY AGE, UNITED STATES, 1903–2007

Year	All Ages	Under 5 Years	5–14 Years	15–24 Years	25–44 Years	45–64 Years	65–74 Years	75 Years & Over[a]
1903	70,600	9,400	8,200	10,300	20,100	12,600	10,000	
1904	71,500	9,700	9,000	10,500	19,900	12,500	9,900	
1905	70,900	9,800	8,400	10,600	19,600	12,600	9,900	
1906	80,000	10,000	8,400	13,000	24,000	13,600	11,000	
1907	81,900	10,500	8,300	13,400	24,900	14,700	10,100	
1908	72,300	10,100	7,600	11,300	20,500	13,100	9,700	
1909	72,700	9,900	7,400	10,700	21,000	13,300	10,400	
1910	77,900	9,900	7,400	11,900	23,600	14,100	11,000	
1911	79,300	11,000	7,500	11,400	22,400	15,100	11,900	
1912	78,400	10,600	7,900	11,500	22,200	14,700	11,500	
1913	82,500	9,800	7,400	12,200	24,500	16,500	12,100	
1914	77,000	10,600	7,900	11,000	21,400	14,300	11,800	
1915	76,200	10,300	8,200	10,800	20,500	14,300	12,100	
1916	84,800	11,600	9,100	7,700	24,900	17,800	13,700	
1917	90,100	11,600	9,700	11,700	24,400	18,500	14,200	
1918	85,100	10,600	10,100	10,600	21,900	17,700	14,200	
1919	75,500	10,100	10,000	10,200	18,600	13,800	12,800	
1920	75,900	10,200	9,900	10,400	18,100	13,900	13,400	
1921	74,000	9,600	9,500	9,800	18,000	13,900	13,200	
1922	76,300	9,700	9,500	10,000	18,700	14,500	13,900	
1923	84,400	9,900	9,800	11,000	21,500	16,900	15,300	
1924	85,600	10,200	9,900	11,900	20,900	16,800	15,900	
1925	90,000	9,700	10,000	12,400	22,200	18,700	17,000	
1926	91,700	9,500	9,900	12,600	22,700	19,200	17,800	
1927	92,700	9,200	9,900	12,900	22,900	19,700	18,100	
1928	95,000	8,900	9,800	13,100	23,300	20,600	19,300	
1929	98,200	8,600	9,800	14,000	24,300	21,500	20,000	
1930	99,100	8,200	9,100	14,000	24,300	22,200	21,300	
1931	97,300	7,800	8,700	13,500	23,100	22,500	21,700	
1932	89,000	7,100	8,100	12,000	20,500	20,100	21,200	
1933	90,932	6,948	8,195	12,225	21,005	20,819	21,740	
1934	100,977	7,034	8,272	13,274	23,288	24,197	24,912	
1935	99,773	6,971	7,808	13,168	23,411	23,457	24,958	
1936	110,052	7,471	7,866	13,701	24,990	26,535	29,489	
1937	105,205	6,969	7,704	14,302	23,955	24,743	27,532	
1938	93,805	6,646	6,593	12,129	20,464	21,689	26,284	
1939	92,628	6,668	6,378	12,066	20,164	20,842	26,505	
1940	96,885	6,851	6,466	12,763	21,166	21,840	27,799	
1941	101,513	7,052	6,702	14,346	22,983	22,509	27,921	
1942	95,889	7,220	6,340	13,732	21,141	20,764	26,692	
1943	99,038	8,039	6,636	15,278	20,212	20,109	28,764	
1944	95,237	7,912	6,704	14,750	19,115	19,097	27,659	
1945	95,918	7,741	6,836	12,446	19,393	20,097	29,405	
1946	98,033	7,949	6,545	13,366	20,705	20,249	29,219	
1947	99,579	8,219	6,069	13,166	21,155	20,513	30,457	
1948 (5th Rev.)[b]	98,001	8,387	5,859	12,595	20,274	19,809	31,077	
1948 (6th Rev.)[b]	93,000	8,350	5,850	12,600	20,300	19,300	9,800	16,800
1949	90,106	8,469	5,539	11,522	19,432	18,302	9,924	16,918
1950	91,249	8,389	5,519	12,119	20,663	18,665	9,750	16,144
1951	95,871	8,769	5,892	12,366	22,363	19,610	10,218	16,653
1952	96,172	8,871	5,980	12,787	21,950	19,892	10,026	16,667
1953	95,032	8,678	6,136	12,837	21,422	19,479	9,927	16,553
1954	90,032	8,380	5,939	11,801	20,023	18,299	9,652	15,938
1955	93,443	8,099	6,099	12,742	29,911	19,199	9,929	16,464
1956	94,780	8,173	6,319	13,545	20,986	19,207	10,160	16,393
1957	95,307	8,423	6,454	12,973	20,949	19,495	10,076	16,937
1958	90,604	8,789	6,514	12,744	19,658	18,095	9,431	15,373
1959	92,080	8,748	6,511	13,269	19,666	18,937	9,475	15,474
1960	93,806	8,950	6,836	13,457	19,600	19,385	9,689	15,829
1961	92,249	8,622	6,717	13,431	19,273	19,134	9,452	15,620
1962	97,139	8,705	6,751	14,557	19,955	20,335	10,149	16,687
1963	100,669	8,688	6,962	15,889	20,529	21,262	10,194	17,145
1964	100,500	8,670	7,400	17,420	22,080	22,100	10,400	16,930
1965	108,004	8,586	7,391	18,688	22,228	22,900	10,430	17,781
1966	113,563	8,507	7,958	21,030	23,134	24,022	10,706	18,206
1967	113,169	7,825	7,874	21,645	23,255	23,826	10,645	18,099
1968	114,864	7,263	8,369	23,012	23,684	23,896	10,961	17,679
1969	116,385	6,973	8,186	24,668	24,410	24,192	10,643	17,313
1970	114,638	6,594	8,203	24,336	23,979	24,164	10,644	16,718
1971	113,439	6,496	8,143	24,733	23,535	23,240	10,494	16,798
1972	115,448	6,142	8,242	25,762	23,852	23,658	10,446	17,346
1973	115,821	6,037	8,102	26,550	24,750	23,059	10,243	17,080

See source and footnotes on page 39.

UNINTENTIONAL-INJURY DEATHS BY AGE, UNITED STATES, 1903–2007, Cont.

Year	All Ages	Under 5 Years	5–14 Years	15–24 Years	25–44 Years	45–64 Years	65–74 Years	75 Years & Over[a]
1974	104,622	5,335	7,037	24,200	22,547	20,334	9,323	15,846
1975	103,030	4,948	6,818	24,121	22,877	19,643	9,220	15,403
1976	100,761	4,692	6,308	24,316	22,399	19,000	8,823	15,223
1977	103,202	4,470	6,305	25,619	23,460	19,167	9,006	15,175
1978	105,561	4,766	6,118	26,622	25,024	18,774	9,072	15,185
1979	105,312	4,429	5,689	26,574	26,097	18,346	9,013	15,164
1980	105,718	4,479	5,224	26,206	26,722	18,140	8,997	15,950
1981	100,704	4,130	4,866	23,582	26,928	17,339	8,639	15,220
1982	94,082	4,108	4,504	21,306	25,135	15,907	8,224	14,898
1983	92,488	3,999	4,321	19,756	24,996	15,444	8,336	15,636
1984	92,911	3,652	4,198	19,801	25,498	15,273	8,424	16,065
1985	93,457	3,746	4,252	19,161	25,940	15,251	8,583	16,524
1986	95,277	3,843	4,226	19,975	27,201	14,733	8,499	16,800
1987	95,020	3,871	4,198	18,695	27,484	14,807	8,686	17,279
1988	97,100	3,794	4,215	18,507	28,279	15,177	8,971	18,157
1989	95,028	3,770	4,090	16,738	28,429	15,046	8,812	18,143
1990	91,983	3,496	3,650	16,241	27,663	14,607	8,405	17,921
1991	89,347	3,626	3,660	15,278	26,526	13,693	8,137	18,427
1992	86,777	3,286	3,388	13,662	25,808	13,882	8,165	18,586
1993	90,523	3,488	3,466	13,966	27,277	14,434	8,125	19,767
1994	91,437	3,406	3,508	13,898	27,012	15,200	8,279	20,134
1995	93,320	3,067	3,544	13,842	27,660	16,004	8,400	20,803
1996	94,948	2,951	3,433	13,809	27,092	16,717	8,780	22,166
1997	95,644	2,770	3,371	13,367	27,129	17,521	8,578	22,908
1998	97,835	2,689	3,254	13,349	27,172	18,286	8,892	24,193
1999[c]	97,860	2,743	3,091	13,656	27,121	18,924	8,208	24,117
2000	97,900	2,707	2,979	14,113	27,182	19,783	7,698	23,438
2001	101,537	2,690	2,836	14,411	27,784	21,002	7,835	24,979
2002	106,742	2,587	2,718	15,412	29,279	23,020	8,086	25,640
2003	109,277	2,662	2,618	15,272	29,307	25,007	8,081	26,330
2004	112,012	2,693	2,666	15,449	29,503	26,593	8,116	26,992
2005[d]	117,809	2,747	2,415	15,753	30,916	29,192	8,632	28,154
2006[d]	120,500	2,600	2,300	16,200	31,400	30,500	8,900	28,600
2007[e]	120,000	2,500	2,300	15,800	30,300	30,300	9,000	29,800
Changes								
1997 to 2007	+25%	−10%	−32%	+18%	+12%	+73%	+5%	+30%
2006 to 2007	([f])	−4%	0%	−2%	−4%	−1%	+1%	+4%

Source: 1903 to 1932 based on National Center for Health Statistics data for registration states; 1933–1948 (5th Rev.), 1949–1963, 1965–2005 are NCHS totals. All other figures are National Safety Council estimates. See Technical Appendix for comparability.
[a] *Includes age unknown. In 2005, these deaths numbered 57.*
[b] *In 1948, a revision was made in the International Classification of Diseases. The first figures for 1948 are comparable with those for earlier years, the second with those for later years.*
[c] *In 1999, a revision was made in the International Classification of Diseases. See the Technical Appendix for comparability with earlier years.*
[d] *Revised.*
[e] *Preliminary.*
[f] *Change less than 0.5%.*

UNINTENTIONAL-INJURY DEATH RATES[a] BY AGE, UNITED STATES, 1903–2007

Year	Standardized Rate[b]	All Ages	Under 5 Years	5–14 Years	15–24 Years	25–44 Years	45–64 Years	65–74 Years	75 Years & Over[c]
1903	99.4	87.2	98.7	46.8	65.0	87.4	111.7	299.8	
1904	103.4	86.6	99.1	50.9	64.9	84.6	108.1	290.0	
1905	98.4	84.2	98.6	47.0	64.1	81.4	106.2	282.5	
1906	114.2	93.2	99.1	46.5	77.1	97.3	111.7	306.0	
1907	112.4	93.6	102.7	45.5	78.0	98.8	117.8	274.2	
1908	99.7	81.2	97.5	41.2	64.4	79.5	102.2	256.7	
1909	97.4	80.1	94.2	39.6	59.9	79.6	101.0	268.2	
1910	103.0	84.4	92.8	39.1	65.3	87.3	104.0	276.0	
1911	104.7	84.7	101.9	39.3	62.1	81.4	108.7	292.1	
1912	100.4	82.5	97.1	40.5	62.3	79.2	103.2	275.8	
1913	103.5	85.5	88.4	37.4	65.2	85.6	112.5	281.7	
1914	95.9	78.6	94.3	38.9	58.5	73.2	94.6	268.1	
1915	92.1	76.7	90.8	39.7	57.3	69.0	92.1	268.8	
1916	101.4	84.1	101.4	43.3	40.8	82.5	112.1	297.6	
1917	106.7	88.2	108.4	45.3	62.1	79.8	113.8	301.2	
1918	101.2	82.1	91.0	46.5	58.7	72.2	106.3	294.2	
1919	87.7	71.9	87.2	45.9	55.3	60.1	81.8	262.0	
1920	87.8	71.2	87.4	44.9	55.5	56.9	85.6	289.5	
1921	84.3	68.4	80.8	42.4	51.4	55.5	79.4	259.8	
1922	86.9	69.4	80.6	41.5	51.4	57.1	81.4	265.1	
1923	94.5	75.7	82.0	42.4	55.6	64.5	92.6	282.8	
1924	93.3	75.6	82.9	42.4	58.6	61.7	90.2	283.5	
1925	97.2	78.4	78.6	42.3	59.7	64.7	97.8	293.9	
1926	97.7	78.7	77.9	41.4	59.9	65.4	98.2	298.7	
1927	97.5	78.4	75.9	41.0	60.2	65.2	98.0	295.4	
1928	99.6	79.3	74.4	40.4	59.9	65.6	99.9	306.2	
1929	101.2	80.8	73.3	40.0	63.1	67.7	102.1	308.9	
1930	101.8	80.5	71.8	36.9	62.3	67.0	102.9	317.9	
1931	99.2	78.5	69.9	35.2	59.7	63.0	102.1	313.3	
1932	90.5	71.3	65.1	32.8	52.7	55.6	89.3	296.9	
1933	91.1	72.4	65.5	33.4	53.6	56.3	90.8	295.3	
1934	100.5	79.9	68.1	33.9	57.8	61.8	103.3	328.5	
1935	97.9	78.4	68.5	32.2	56.9	61.6	98.0	319.8	
1936	108.1	85.9	74.4	32.9	58.8	65.3	108.6	367.4	
1937	100.7	81.7	69.6	32.7	60.9	62.1	99.3	333.4	
1938	89.4	72.3	65.3	28.5	51.3	52.5	85.4	308.9	
1939	86.7	70.8	62.9	28.2	50.7	51.2	81.0	300.0	
1940	89.1	73.4	64.8	28.8	53.5	53.2	83.4	305.7	
1941	90.7	76.3	65.0	29.7	60.9	57.2	84.8	297.4	
1942	84.3	71.6	63.9	27.9	59.8	52.4	77.1	275.5	
1943	86.3	73.8	66.9	29.0	69.7	50.3	73.6	287.8	
1944	82.5	71.7	63.2	29.1	72.9	48.9	68.9	268.6	
1945	83.4	72.4	59.8	29.5	64.5	50.5	71.6	277.6	
1946	81.0	70.0	60.2	28.1	61.7	48.8	70.9	267.9	
1947	80.5	69.4	57.4	25.8	59.6	49.0	70.6	270.7	
1948 (5th Rev.)[d]	79.5	67.1	56.3	24.6	56.8	46.2	66.8	267.4	
1948 (6th Rev.)[d]	72.5	63.7	56.0	24.5	56.8	46.2	65.1	122.4	464.3
1949	69.0	60.6	54.4	23.0	52.2	43.5	60.6	120.4	450.7
1950	68.1	60.3	51.4	22.6	55.0	45.6	60.5	115.8	414.7
1951	70.1	62.5	50.8	23.6	57.7	49.0	62.7	117.1	413.6
1952	69.0	61.8	51.5	22.5	60.9	47.7	62.7	111.1	399.8
1953	67.0	60.1	49.5	22.1	61.4	46.4	60.5	106.7	383.6
1954	62.2	55.9	46.7	20.5	56.4	43.0	55.9	100.7	354.4
1955	63.4	56.9	43.9	20.7	60.1	44.7	57.7	100.8	350.2
1956	63.0	56.6	43.3	20.2	63.3	44.7	56.7	100.6	335.6
1957	62.2	55.9	43.5	19.9	59.5	44.6	56.6	97.5	333.3
1958	57.5	52.3	44.5	19.6	56.2	42.0	51.7	89.3	292.6
1959	57.4	52.2	43.6	18.9	56.5	42.1	53.2	87.7	284.7
1960	57.3	52.1	44.0	19.1	55.6	42.0	53.6	87.6	281.4
1961	55.4	50.4	42.0	18.1	54.0	41.2	52.1	83.8	267.9
1962	57.5	52.3	42.6	18.0	55.0	42.7	54.6	88.5	277.7
1963	58.6	53.4	42.8	18.2	57.2	44.0	56.3	87.9	277.0
1964	60.0	54.9	43.1	19.1	59.9	47.3	57.6	88.9	263.9
1965	61.9	55.8	43.4	18.7	61.6	47.7	58.8	88.5	268.7
1966	63.0	58.1	44.4	19.9	66.9	49.6	60.7	89.8	267.4
1967	62.1	57.3	42.2	19.4	66.9	49.7	59.2	88.5	257.4
1968	62.0	57.6	40.6	20.5	69.2	50.1	58.5	90.2	244.0
1969	61.8	57.8	40.2	20.0	71.8	51.2	58.4	86.6	232.0
1970	59.8	56.2	38.4	20.1	68.0	49.8	57.6	85.2	219.6
1971	58.1	54.8	37.7	20.1	66.1	48.4	54.7	82.7	213.2
1972	58.0	55.2	35.9	20.6	67.6	47.5	55.2	80.8	214.2
1973	57.1	54.8	35.8	20.6	68.2	48.0	53.3	77.3	206.3

See source and footnotes on page 41.

UNINTENTIONAL-INJURY DEATHS BY AGE, UNITED STATES, 1903–2007, Cont.

Year	Standardized Rate[b]	All Ages	Under 5 Years	5–14 Years	15–24 Years	25–44 Years	45–64 Years	65–74 Years	75 Years & Over[c]
1974	50.9	49.0	32.4	18.2	60.9	42.7	46.7	68.7	186.7
1975	49.3	47.8	30.7	17.8	59.5	42.3	44.9	66.2	175.5
1976	47.3	46.3	30.0	16.7	58.9	40.3	43.2	62.0	168.4
1977	47.6	47.0	28.7	17.0	61.3	40.9	43.4	61.5	164.0
1978	47.8	47.5	30.3	16.9	63.1	42.3	42.4	60.5	159.7
1979	47.0	46.9	27.6	16.1	62.6	42.7	41.3	58.8	154.8
1980	46.5	46.5	27.2	15.0	61.7	42.3	40.8	57.5	158.6
1981	44.0	43.9	24.4	14.2	55.9	41.2	39.0	54.4	147.4
1982	40.6	40.6	23.8	13.2	51.2	37.3	35.8	50.9	140.0
1983	39.6	39.6	22.8	12.7	48.2	36.0	34.7	50.8	142.8
1984	39.4	39.4	20.6	12.4	48.9	35.7	34.3	50.7	142.8
1985	39.2	39.3	21.0	12.6	47.9	35.3	34.2	50.9	143.0
1986	39.4	39.7	21.4	12.6	50.5	36.1	33.0	49.6	141.5
1987	39.0	39.2	21.4	12.4	48.1	35.7	33.0	49.8	141.6
1988	39.5	39.7	20.9	12.3	48.5	36.1	33.4	50.9	145.3
1989	38.4	38.5	20.4	11.8	44.8	35.7	32.8	49.3	141.5
1990	36.8	36.9	18.5	10.4	44.0	34.2	31.6	46.4	136.5
1991	35.3	35.4	18.9	10.2	42.0	32.3	29.3	44.5	136.7
1992	34.0	34.0	16.8	9.3	37.8	31.3	28.7	44.2	134.5
1993	35.0	35.1	17.7	9.4	38.8	33.0	29.1	43.6	139.9
1994	35.0	35.1	17.3	9.4	38.4	32.5	29.9	44.3	139.2
1995	35.0	35.5	15.7	9.3	38.2	33.2	30.6	44.8	140.6
1996	35.3	35.8	15.3	8.9	38.1	32.3	31.1	47.0	145.9
1997	35.1	35.7	14.5	8.7	36.5	32.5	31.6	46.3	146.2
1998	35.5	36.2	14.2	8.3	35.9	32.6	31.9	48.3	151.1
1999[e]	35.2	35.9	14.5	7.8	36.1	32.7	32.0	45.0	147.7
2000	34.8	35.6	14.3	7.5	36.7	33.0	32.3	42.3	140.8
2001	35.7	35.6	13.9	6.9	36.1	32.7	32.6	42.8	146.8
2002	37.1	37.1	13.2	6.6	37.9	34.7	34.6	44.2	148.2
2003	37.6	37.6	13.5	6.4	37.0	34.8	36.4	44.0	149.6
2004	38.1	38.1	13.4	6.5	37.1	35.1	37.6	43.9	151.4
2005[f]	39.5	39.7	13.5	6.0	37.4	36.8	40.1	46.3	155.2
2006[f]	40.0	40.3	12.7	5.7	38.3	37.5	40.8	47.7	155.9
2007[g]	39.3	39.8	12.1	5.7	37.2	36.2	39.6	46.5	160.8

Changes									
1997 to 2007		+11%	−17%	−34%	+2%	+11%	+25%	([i])	+10%
2006 to 2007		−1%	−5%	0%	−3%	−3%	−3%	−2%	+3%

2007 Population (Millions)									
Total[h]		301,621	20,724	40,164	42,506	83,752	76,587	19,352	18,536
Male		148,659	10,603	20,549	21,860	42,301	37,370	8,887	7,089
Female		152,962	10,121	19,615	20,646	41,451	39,217	10,465	11,446

Source: All figures are National Safety Council estimates. See Technical Appendix for comparability.
[a] Rates are deaths per 100,000 resident population in each age group.
[b] Adjusted to the year 2000 standard population to remove the influence of changes in age distribution between 1903 and 2007.
[c] Includes age unknown.
[d] In 1948, a revision was made in the International Classification of Diseases. The first figures for 1948 are comparable with those for earlier years, the second with those for later years.
[e] In 1999, a revision was made in the International Classification of Diseases. See the Technical Appendix for comparability.
[f] Revised.
[g] Preliminary.
[h] Sum of parts may not equal total due to rounding.
[i] Change less than 0.5%.

PRINCIPAL TYPES OF UNINTENTIONAL-INJURY DEATHS

PRINCIPAL TYPES OF UNINTENTIONAL-INJURY DEATHS, UNITED STATES, 1903–1998

Year	Total	Motor-Vehicle	Falls	Drowning[a]	Fires/Burns[b]	Ingest. of Food/Object	Firearms	Poison (Solid, Liquid)	Poison (Gas, Vapor)	All Other
1903	70,600	(c)	(c)	9,200	(c)	(c)	2,500	(c)	(c)	58,900
1904	71,500	(c)	(c)	9,300	(c)	(c)	2,800	(c)	(c)	59,400
1905	70,900	(c)	(c)	9,300	(c)	(c)	2,000	(c)	(c)	59,600
1906	80,000	400	(c)	9,400	(c)	(c)	2,100	(c)	(c)	68,100
1907	81,900	700	(c)	9,000	(c)	(c)	1,700	(c)	(c)	70,500
1908	72,300	800	(c)	9,300	(c)	(c)	1,900	(c)	(c)	60,300
1909	72,700	1,300	(c)	8,500	(c)	(c)	1,600	(c)	(c)	61,300
1910	77,900	1,900	(c)	8,700	(c)	(c)	1,900	(c)	(c)	65,400
1911	79,300	2,300	(c)	9,000	(c)	(c)	2,100	(c)	(c)	65,900
1912	78,400	3,100	(c)	8,600	(c)	(c)	2,100	(c)	(c)	64,600
1913	82,500	4,200	15,100	10,300	8,900	(c)	2,400	3,200	(c)	38,400
1914	77,000	4,700	15,000	8,700	9,100	(c)	2,300	3,300	(c)	33,900
1915	76,200	6,600	15,000	8,600	8,400	(c)	2,100	2,800	(c)	32,700
1916	84,800	8,200	15,200	8,900	9,500	(c)	2,200	2,900	(c)	37,900
1917	90,100	10,200	15,200	7,600	10,800	(c)	2,300	2,800	(c)	41,200
1918	85,100	10,700	13,200	7,000	10,200	(c)	2,500	2,700	(c)	38,800
1919	75,500	11,200	11,900	9,100	9,100	(c)	2,800	3,100	(c)	28,300
1920	75,900	12,500	12,600	6,100	9,300	(c)	2,700	3,300	(c)	29,400
1921	74,000	13,900	12,300	7,800	7,500	(c)	2,800	2,900	(c)	26,800
1922	76,300	15,300	13,200	7,000	8,300	(c)	2,900	2,800	(c)	26,800
1923	84,400	18,400	14,100	6,800	9,100	(c)	2,900	2,800	2,700	27,600
1924	85,600	19,400	14,700	7,400	7,400	(c)	2,900	2,700	2,900	28,200
1925	90,000	21,900	15,500	7,300	8,600	(c)	2,800	2,700	2,800	28,400
1926	91,700	23,400	16,300	7,500	8,800	(c)	2,800	2,600	3,200	27,100
1927	92,700	25,800	16,500	8,100	8,200	(c)	3,000	2,600	2,700	25,800
1928	95,000	28,000	17,000	8,600	8,400	(c)	2,900	2,800	2,800	24,500
1929	98,200	31,200	17,700	7,600	8,200	(c)	3,200	2,600	2,800	24,900
1930	99,100	32,900	18,100	7,500	8,100	(c)	3,200	2,600	2,500	24,200
1931	97,300	33,700	18,100	7,600	7,100	(c)	3,100	2,600	2,100	23,000
1932	89,000	29,500	18,600	7,500	7,100	(c)	3,000	2,200	2,100	19,000
1933	90,932	31,363	18,962	7,158	6,781	(c)	3,014	2,135	1,633	19,886
1934	100,977	36,101	20,725	7,077	7,456	(c)	3,033	2,148	1,643	22,794
1935	99,773	36,369	21,378	6,744	7,253	(c)	2,799	2,163	1,654	21,413
1936	110,052	38,089	23,562	6,659	7,939	(c)	2,817	2,177	1,665	27,144
1937	105,205	39,643	22,544	7,085	7,214	(c)	2,576	2,190	1,675	22,278
1938	93,805	32,582	23,239	6,881	6,491	(c)	2,726	2,077	1,428	18,381
1939	92,623	32,386	23,427	6,413	6,675	(c)	2,618	1,963	1,440	17,701
1940	96,885	34,501	23,356	6,202	7,521	(c)	2,375	1,847	1,583	19,500
1941	101,513	39,969	22,764	6,389	6,922	(c)	2,396	1,731	1,464	19,878
1942	95,889	28,309	22,632	6,696	7,901	(c)	2,678	1,607	1,741	24,325
1943	99,038	23,823	24,701	7,115	8,726	921	2,282	1,745	2,014	27,711
1944	95,237	24,282	22,989	6,511	8,372	896	2,392	1,993	1,860	25,942
1945	95,918	28,076	23,847	6,624	7,949	897	2,385	1,987	2,120	22,033
1946	98,033	33,411	23,109	6,442	7,843	1,076	2,801	1,961	1,821	19,569
1947	99,579	32,697	24,529	6,885	8,033	1,206	2,439	1,865	1,865	14,060
1948 (5th Rev.)[d]	98,001	32,259	24,836	6,428	7,743	1,315	2,191	1,753	2,045	19,611
1948 (6th Rev.)[d]	93,000	32,259	22,000	6,500	6,800	1,299	2,330	1,600	2,020	17,192
1949	90,106	31,701	22,308	6,684	5,982	1,341	2,326	1,634	1,617	16,513
1950	91,249	34,763	20,783	6,131	6,405	1,350	2,174	1,584	1,769	16,290
1951	95,871	36,996	21,376	6,489	6,788	1,456	2,247	1,497	1,627	17,395
1952	96,172	37,794	20,945	6,601	6,922	1,434	2,210	1,440	1,397	17,429
1953	95,032	37,955	20,631	6,770	6,579	1,603	2,277	1,391	1,223	16,603
1954	90,032	35,586	19,771	6,334	6,083	1,627	2,271	1,339	1,223	15,798
1955	93,443	38,426	20,192	6,344	6,352	1,608	2,120	1,431	1,163	15,807
1956	94,780	39,628	20,282	6,263	6,405	1,760	2,202	1,422	1,213	15,605
1957	95,307	38,702	20,545	6,613	6,269	2,043	2,369	1,390	1,143	16,233
1958	90,604	36,981	18,248	6,582e	7,291e	2,191e	2,172	1,429	1,187	14,523
1959	92,080	37,910	18,774	6,434	6,898	2,189	2,258	1,661	1,141	14,815
1960	93,806	38,137	19,023	6,529	7,645	2,397	2,334	1,679	1,253	14,809
1961	92,249	38,091	18,691	6,525	7,102	2,499	2,204	1,804	1,192	14,141
1962	97,139	40,804	19,589	6,439	7,534	1,813	2,092	1,833	1,376	15,659
1963	100,669	43,564	19,335	6,347	8,172	1,949	2,263	2,061	1,489	15,489
1964	105,000	47,700	18,941	6,709	7,379	1,865	2,275	2,100	1,360	16,571
1965	108,004	49,163	19,984	6,799	7,347	1,836	2,344	2,110	1,526	16,895
1966	113,563	53,041	20,066	7,084	8,084	1,831	2,558	2,283	1,648	16,968
1967	113,169	52,924	20,120	7,076	7,423	1,980	2,896	2,506	1,574	16,670
1968	114,864	54,862	18,651	7,372e	7,335	3,100e	2,394e	2,583	1,526	17,041
1969	116,385	55,791	17,827	7,699	7,163	3,712	2,309	2,967	1,549	16,368
1970	114,638	54,633	16,926	7,860	6,718	2,753	2,406	3,679	1,620	18,043
1971	113,439	54,381	16,755	7,396	6,776	2,877	2,360	3,710	1,646	17,538
1972	115,448	56,278	16,744	7,586	6,714	2,830	2,442	3,728	1,690	17,436
1973	115,821	55,511	16,506	8,725	6,503	3,013	2,618	3,683	1,652	17,610

See source and footnotes on page 43.

PRINCIPAL TYPES OF UNINTENTIONAL-INJURY DEATHS, UNITED STATES, 1903–1998, Cont.

Year	Total	Motor-Vehicle	Falls	Drowning[a]	Fires/Burns[b]	Ingest. of Food/Object	Firearms	Poison (Solid, Liquid)	Poison (Gas, Vapor)	All Other
1974	104,622	46,402	16,339	7,876	6,236	2,991	2,513	4,016	1,518	16,731
1975	103,030	45,853	14,896	8,000	6,071	3,106	2,380	4,694	1,577	16,453
1976	100,761	47,038	14,136	6,827	6,338	3,033	2,059	4,161	1,569	15,600
1977	103,202	49,510	13,773	7,126	6,357	3,037	1,982	3,374	1,596	16,447
1978	105,561	52,411	13,690	7,026	6,163	3,063	1,806	3,035	1,737	16,630
1979	105,312	53,524	13,216	6,872	5,991	3,243	2,004	3,165	1,472	15,825
1980	105,718	53,172	13,294	7,257	5,822	3,249	1,955	3,089	1,242	16,638
1981	100,704	51,385	12,628	6,277	5,697	3,331	1,871	3,243	1,280	14,992
1982	94,082	45,779	12,077	6,351	5,210	3,254	1,756	3,474	1,259	14,922
1983	92,488	44,452	12,024	6,353	5,028	3,387	1,695	3,382	1,251	14,916
1984	92,911	46,263	11,937	5,388	5,010	3,541	1,668	3,808	1,103	14,193
1985	93,457	45,901	12,001	5,316	4,938	3,551	1,649	4,091	1,079	14,931
1986	95,277	47,865	11,444	5,700	4,835	3,692	1,452	4,731	1,009	14,549
1987	95,020	48,290	11,733	5,100	4,710	3,688	1,440	4,415	900	14,744
1988	97,100	49,078	12,096	4,966	4,965	3,805	1,501	5,353	873	14,463
1989	95,028	47,575	12,151	4,015	4,716	3,578	1,489	5,603	921	14,980
1990	91,983	46,814	12,313	4,685	4,175	3,303	1,416	5,055	748	13,474
1991	89,347	43,536	12,662	4,818	4,120	3,240	1,441	5,698	736	13,096
1992	86,777	40,982	12,646	3,542	3,958	3,182	1,409	6,449	633	13,976
1993	90,523	41,893	13,141	3,807	3,900	3,160	1,521	7,877	660	14,564
1994	91,437	42,524	13,450	3,942	3,986	3,065	1,356	8,309	685	14,120
1995	93,320	43,363	13,986	4,350	3,761	3,185	1,225	8,461	611	14,378
1996	94,948	43,649	14,986	3,959	3,741	3,206	1,134	8,872	638	14,763
1997	95,644	43,458	15,447	4,051	3,490	3,275	981	9,587	576	14,779
1998	97,835	43,501	16,274	4,406	3,255	3,515	866	10,255	546	15,217

PRINCIPAL TYPES OF UNINTENTIONAL-INJURY DEATHS, UNITED STATES, 1999–2007

Year	Total	Motor-Vehicle	Falls	Poisoning	Ingest. of Food/Object	Drowning[f]	Fires, Flames, Smoke[b]	Mechanical Suffocation	Firearms	All Other
1999[g]	97,860	42,401	13,162	12,186	3,885	3,529	3,348	1,618	824	16,907
2000	97,900	43,354	13,322	12,757	4,313	3,482	3,377	1,335	776	15,184
2001	101,537	43,788	15,019	14,078	4,185	3,281	3,309	1,370	802	15,705
2002	106,742	45,380	16,257	17,550	4,128	3,447	3,159	1,389	762	13,670
2003	109,277	44,757	17,229	19,457	4,272	3,306	3,369	1,309	730	14,850
2004	112,012	44,933	18,807	20,950	4,470	3,308	3,229	1,421	649	14,245
2005[h]	117,809	45,343	19,656	23,617	4,386	3,582	3,197	1,514	789	15,725
2006[h]	120,500	44,600	19,700	25,300	3,500	3,500	3,300	1,200	850	18,550
2007[i]	120,000	43,100	21,600	22,700	3,700	4,700	2,700	1,200	830	19,370

Changes										
1997 to 2007	+25%	−1%	(i)	(i)	+13%	(i)	−23%	(i)	−15%	(i)
2006 to 2007	(k)	−3%	+10%	−10%	+6%	+34%	−18%	0%	−2%	+4%

Source: National Center for Health Statistics and National Safety Council. See Technical Appendix for comparability.
[a] Includes drowning in water transport accidents.
[b] Includes burns by fire, and deaths resulting from conflagration regardless of nature of injury.
[c] Comparable data not available.
[d] In 1948, a revision was made in the International Classification of Diseases. The first figures for 1948 are comparable with those for earlier years, the second with those for later years.
[e] Data are not comparable to previous years shown due to classification changes in 1958 and 1968.
[f] Excludes water transport drownings.
[g] In 1999, a revision was made in the International Classification of Diseases. See the Technical Appendix for comparability.
[h] Revised.
[i] Preliminary.
[j] Comparison not valid because of change in classifications (see footnote "g").
[k] Change less than 0.5%.

UNINTENTIONAL-INJURY DEATH RATES[a] FOR PRINCIPAL TYPES, UNITED STATES, 1903–1998

Year	Total	Motor-Vehicle	Falls	Drowning[b]	Fires/Burns[c]	Ingest. of Food/Object	Firearms	Poison (Solid, Liquid)	Poison (Gas, Vapor)	All Other
1903	87.2	(d)	(d)	11.4	(d)	(d)	3.1	(d)	(d)	72.7
1904	86.6	(d)	(d)	11.3	(d)	(d)	3.4	(d)	(d)	71.9
1905	84.2	(d)	(d)	11.1	(d)	(d)	2.4	(d)	(d)	70.7
1906	93.2	0.5	(d)	11.0	(d)	(d)	2.4	(d)	(d)	79.3
1907	93.6	0.8	(d)	10.4	(d)	(d)	2.0	(d)	(d)	80.4
1908	81.2	0.9	(d)	10.5	(d)	(d)	2.1	(d)	(d)	67.7
1909	80.1	1.4	(d)	9.4	(d)	(d)	1.8	(d)	(d)	67.5
1910	84.4	2.0	(d)	9.4	(d)	(d)	2.1	(d)	(d)	70.9
1911	84.7	2.5	(d)	9.6	(d)	(d)	2.2	(d)	(d)	70.4
1912	82.5	3.3	(d)	9.0	(d)	(d)	2.2	(d)	(d)	68.0
1913	85.5	4.4	15.5	10.6	9.1	(d)	2.5	3.3	(d)	40.1
1914	78.6	4.8	15.1	8.8	9.1	(d)	2.3	3.3	(d)	35.2
1915	76.7	6.6	14.9	8.6	8.4	(d)	2.1	2.8	(d)	33.3
1916	84.1	8.1	14.9	8.7	9.3	(d)	2.2	2.8	(d)	38.1
1917	88.2	10.0	14.7	7.4	10.5	(d)	2.2	2.7	(d)	40.7
1918	82.1	10.3	12.8	6.8	9.9	(d)	2.4	2.6	(d)	37.3
1919	71.9	10.7	11.4	6.9	8.7	(d)	2.7	3.0	(d)	28.5
1920	71.2	11.7	11.8	5.7	8.7	(d)	2.5	3.1	(d)	27.7
1921	68.4	12.9	11.3	7.2	6.9	(d)	2.6	2.7	(d)	24.8
1922	69.4	13.9	12.0	6.4	7.5	(d)	2.6	2.5	(d)	24.5
1923	75.7	16.5	12.6	6.1	8.1	(d)	2.6	2.5	2.4	24.9
1924	75.6	17.1	12.9	6.5	8.4	(d)	2.5	2.4	2.5	23.3
1925	78.4	19.1	13.4	6.3	7.4	(d)	2.4	2.3	2.4	25.1
1926	78.7	20.1	13.9	6.4	7.5	(d)	2.4	2.2	2.7	23.5
1927	78.4	21.8	13.9	6.8	6.9	(d)	2.5	2.2	2.3	22.0
1928	79.3	23.4	14.1	7.1	7.0	(d)	2.4	2.3	2.3	20.7
1929	80.8	25.7	14.5	6.2	6.7	(d)	2.6	2.1	2.3	20.7
1930	80.5	26.7	14.7	6.1	6.6	(d)	2.6	2.1	2.0	19.7
1931	78.5	27.2	14.6	6.1	5.7	(d)	2.5	2.1	1.7	18.6
1932	71.3	23.6	14.9	6.0	5.7	(d)	2.4	1.8	1.7	15.2
1933	72.4	25.0	15.1	5.7	5.4	(d)	2.4	1.7	1.3	15.8
1934	79.9	28.6	16.4	5.6	5.9	(d)	2.4	1.7	1.3	18.0
1935	78.4	28.6	16.8	5.3	5.7	(d)	2.2	1.7	1.3	16.8
1936	85.9	29.7	18.4	5.2	6.2	(d)	2.2	1.7	1.3	21.2
1937	81.7	30.8	17.5	5.5	5.6	(d)	2.0	1.7	1.3	17.3
1938	72.3	25.1	17.9	5.3	5.0	(d)	2.1	1.6	1.1	14.2
1939	70.8	24.7	17.9	4.9	5.1	(d)	2.0	1.5	1.1	13.6
1940	73.4	26.1	17.7	4.7	5.7	(d)	1.8	1.4	1.2	14.8
1941	76.3	30.0	17.1	4.8	5.2	(d)	1.8	1.3	1.1	15.0
1942	71.6	21.1	16.9	5.0	5.9	(d)	2.0	1.2	1.3	18.2
1943	73.8	17.8	18.4	5.3	6.5	0.7	1.7	1.3	1.5	20.6
1944	71.7	18.3	17.3	4.9	6.3	0.7	1.8	1.5	1.4	19.5
1945	72.4	21.2	18.0	5.0	6.0	0.7	1.8	1.5	1.6	16.6
1946	70.0	23.9	16.5	4.6	5.6	0.8	2.0	1.4	1.3	13.9
1947	69.4	22.8	17.1	4.8	5.6	0.8	1.7	1.3	1.3	14.0
1948 (5th Rev.)[e]	67.1	22.1	17.0	4.4	5.3	0.9	1.5	1.2	1.4	13.3
1948 (6th Rev.)[e]	63.7	22.1	15.1	4.5	4.7	0.9	1.6	1.1	1.4	12.3
1949	60.6	21.3	15.0	4.5	4.0	0.9	1.6	1.1	1.1	11.1
1950	60.3	23.0	13.7	4.1	4.2	0.9	1.4	1.1	1.2	10.7
1951	62.5	24.1	13.9	4.2	4.4	1.0	1.5	1.0	1.1	11.3
1952	61.8	24.3	13.5	4.2	4.5	0.9	1.4	0.9	0.9	11.2
1953	60.1	24.0	13.0	4.3	4.2	1.0	1.4	0.9	0.8	10.2
1954	55.9	22.1	12.3	3.9	3.8	1.0	1.4	0.8	0.8	9.8
1955	56.9	23.4	12.3	3.9	3.9	1.0	1.3	0.9	0.7	9.5
1956	56.6	23.7	12.1	3.7	3.8	1.1	1.3	0.8	0.7	9.4
1957	55.9	22.7	12.1	3.9	3.7	1.2	1.4	0.8	0.7	9.4
1958	52.3	21.3	10.5	3.8[f]	4.2[f]	1.3[f]	1.3	0.8	0.7	8.4
1959	52.2	21.5	10.6	3.7	3.9	1.2	1.3	0.9	0.7	8.4
1960	52.1	21.2	10.6	3.6	4.3	1.3	1.3	0.9	0.7	8.2
1961	50.4	20.8	10.2	3.6	3.9	1.4	1.2	1.0	0.7	7.6
1962	52.3	22.0	10.5	3.5	4.1	1.0	1.1	1.0	0.7	8.4
1963	53.4	23.1	10.3	3.4	4.3	1.0	1.2	1.1	0.8	8.2
1964	54.9	25.0	9.9	3.5	3.9	1.0	1.2	1.1	0.7	8.4
1965	55.8	25.4	10.3	3.5	3.8	1.0	1.2	1.1	0.8	8.7
1966	58.1	27.1	10.3	3.6	4.8	0.9	1.3	1.2	0.8	8.1
1967	57.3	26.8	10.2	3.6	3.8	1.0	1.5	1.3	0.8	8.3
1968	57.6	27.5	9.4	3.7[f]	3.7[f]	1.6[f]	1.2[f]	1.3	0.8	8.4
1969	57.8	27.7	8.9	3.8	3.6	1.8	1.2	1.5	0.8	8.5
1970	56.2	26.8	8.3	3.9	3.3	1.4	1.2	1.8	0.8	8.7
1971	54.8	26.3	8.1	3.6	3.3	1.4	1.1	1.8	0.8	8.4
1972	55.2	26.9	8.0	3.6	3.2	1.4	1.2	1.8	0.8	8.3
1973	54.8	26.3	7.8	4.1	3.1	1.4	1.2	1.7	0.8	8.4

See source and footnotes on page 45.

UNINTENTIONAL-INJURY DEATH RATES[a] FOR PRINCIPAL TYPES, UNITED STATES, 1903–1998, Cont.

Year	Total	Motor-Vehicle	Falls	Drowning[b]	Fires/Burns[c]	Ingest. of Food/Object	Firearms	Poison (Solid, Liquid)	Poison (Gas, Vapor)	All Other
1974	49.0	21.8	7.7	3.7	2.9	1.4	1.2	1.8	0.7	7.8
1975	47.8	21.3	6.9	3.7	2.8	1.4	1.1	2.2	0.7	7.7
1976	46.3	21.6	6.5	3.1	2.9	1.4	0.9	1.9	0.7	7.3
1977	47.0	22.5	6.3	3.2	2.9	1.4	0.9	1.5	0.7	7.6
1978	47.5	23.6	6.2	3.2	2.8	1.4	0.8	1.4	0.8	7.3
1979	46.9	23.8	5.9	3.1	2.7	1.4	0.9	1.4	0.7	7.0
1980	46.5	23.4	5.9	3.2	2.6	1.4	0.9	1.4	0.5	7.2
1981	43.9	22.4	5.5	2.7	2.5	1.5	0.8	1.4	0.6	6.5
1982	40.6	19.8	5.2	2.7	2.2	1.4	0.8	1.5	0.5	6.5
1983	39.6	19.0	5.1	2.7	2.2	1.4	0.7	1.4	0.5	6.6
1984	39.4	19.6	5.1	2.3	2.1	1.5	0.7	1.6	0.5	6.0
1985	39.3	19.3	5.0	2.2	2.1	1.5	0.7	1.7	0.5	6.3
1986	39.7	19.9	4.8	2.4	2.0	1.5	0.6	2.0	0.4	6.1
1987	39.2	19.9	4.8	2.1	1.9	1.5	0.6	1.8	0.4	6.2
1988	39.7	20.1	4.9	2.0	2.0	1.6	0.6	2.2	0.4	5.9
1989	38.5	19.3	4.9	1.9	1.9	1.4	0.6	2.3	0.4	5.8
1990	36.9	18.8	4.9	1.9	1.7	1.3	0.6	2.0	0.3	5.4
1991	35.4	17.3	5.0	1.8	1.6	1.3	0.6	2.3	0.3	5.2
1992	34.0	16.1	5.0	1.4	1.6	1.2	0.6	2.5	0.2	5.4
1993	35.1	16.3	5.1	1.5	1.5	1.2	0.6	3.1	0.3	5.5
1994	35.1	16.3	5.2	1.5	1.5	1.2	0.5	3.2	0.3	5.4
1995	35.5	16.5	5.3	1.7	1.4	1.2	0.5	3.2	0.2	5.5
1996	35.8	16.5	5.6	1.5	1.4	1.2	0.4	3.3	0.2	5.7
1997	35.7	16.2	5.8	1.5	1.3	1.2	0.4	3.6	0.2	5.5
1998	36.2	16.1	6.0	1.6	1.2	1.3	0.3	3.8	0.2	5.7

UNINTENTIONAL-INJURY DEATH RATES[a] FOR PRINCIPAL TYPES, UNITED STATES, 1999–2007

Year	Total	Motor-Vehicle	Falls	Poisoning	Ingest. of Food/Object	Drowning[g]	Fires, Flames Smoke[c]	Mechanical Suffocation	Firearms	All Other
1999[h]	35.9	15.5	4.8	4.5	1.4	1.3	1.2	0.6	0.3	6.3
2000	35.6	15.7	4.8	4.6	1.6	1.3	1.2	0.5	0.3	5.5
2001	35.6	15.4	5.3	4.9	1.5	1.2	1.2	0.5	0.3	5.5
2002	37.1	15.8	5.6	6.4	1.4	1.2	1.1	0.5	0.3	4.7
2003	37.6	15.4	5.9	6.7	1.5	1.1	1.2	0.4	0.2	5.1
2004	38.1	15.3	6.4	7.1	1.5	1.1	1.1	0.5	0.2	4.9
2005[i]	39.7	15.3	6.6	8.0	1.5	1.2	1.1	0.5	0.3	5.3
2006[i]	40.3	14.9	6.6	8.5	1.2	1.2	1.1	0.4	0.3	6.2
2007[i]	39.8	14.3	7.2	7.5	1.2	1.6	0.9	0.4	0.3	6.4

Changes										
1997 to 2007	+11%	−12%	(k)	(k)	0%	(k)	−31%	(k)	−25%	(k)
2006 to 2007	−1%	−4%	+9%	−12%	0%	+33%	−18%	0%	0%	+3%

Source: National Safety Council estimates. See Technical Appendix for comparability.
[a] *Deaths per 100,000 population.*
[b] *Includes drowning in water transport accidents.*
[c] *Includes burns by fire, and deaths resulting from conflagration regardless of nature of injury.*
[d] *Comparable data not available.*
[e] *In 1948, a revision was made in the International Classification of Diseases. The first figures for 1948 are comparable with those for earlier years, the second with those for later years.*
[f] *Data are not comparable to previous years shown due to classification changes in 1958 and 1968.*
[g] *Excludes water transport drownings.*
[h] *In 1999, a revision was made in the International Classification of Diseases. See the Technical Appendix for comparability.*
[i] *Revised.*
[j] *Preliminary.*
[k] *Comparison not valid because of change in classifications (see footnote "h").*

NATIONAL SAFETY COUNCIL

INJURY FACTS®

WORK, 2007

Between 1912 and 2007, unintentional work deaths per 100,000 population were reduced 92% , from 21 to 1.6. In 1912, an estimated 18,000 to 21,000 workers' lives were lost. In 2007, in a work force nearly quadrupled in size and producing ten times the goods and services, there were only 4,685 accidental work deaths.

In addition to unintentional (accidental) fatal work injuries, 799 homicides and suicides occurred in the workplace in 2007. These intentional injuries are not included in the unintentional-injury data shown here.

The State Data section, which begins on page 160, shows fatal occupational injuries and nonfatal injury and illness incidence rates by state.

Unintentional-Injury Deaths **4,689**
Unintentional-Injury Deaths per 100,000 workers **3.2**
Disabling Unintentional Injuries **3,500,000**
Workers **147,203,000**
Costs . . . . **$175.3 billion**

UNINTENTIONAL INJURIES AT WORK BY INDUSTRY, UNITED STATES, 2007

| Industry Division | Workers[a] (000) | Deaths[a] | | Deaths per 100,000 Workers[a] | | Disabling Injuries |
		2007	Change from 2006	2007	Change from 2006	
All Industries[b]	**147,203**	**4,689**	**–8%**	**3.2**	**–9%**	**3,500,000**
Agriculture[c]	2,045	552	–13%	26.3	–9%	70,000
Mining[c]	730	178	–6%	24.4	–12%	20,000
Construction	11,416	1,140	–5%	10.0	–6%	420,000
Manufacturing	16,204	358	–15%	2.2	–15%	410,000
Wholesale trade	4,357	183	–13%	4.2	–9%	110,000
Retail trade	16,478	156	–18%	0.9	–17%	450,000
Transportation & warehousing	5,265	766	–5%	14.5	–7%	280,000
Utilities	851	32	–38%	3.8	–39%	20,000
Information	3,372	70	+15%	2.1	+15%	50,000
Financial activities	10,249	69	–16%	0.7	–16%	100,000
Professional & business services	15,219	407	0%	2.7	–5%	180,000
Educational & health services	19,904	121	–15%	0.6	–16%	500,000
Leisure & hospitality	11,972	130	–4%	1.1	–6%	250,000
Other services[c]	6,934	113	–20%	1.6	–19%	130,000
Government	22,207	412	1%	1.8	–2%	510,000

Source: Deaths from Bureau of Labor Statistics, Census of Fatal Occupational Injuries. All other figures are National Safety Council estimates based on data from the Bureau of Labor Statistics.
Note: The National Safety Council adopted the Bureau of Labor Statistics' Census of Fatal Occupational Injuries (CFOI), beginning with the 1992 data year, as the authoritative count of work-related deaths. See the Technical Appendix for additional information.
[a] Deaths include persons of all ages. Workers and death rates include persons 16 years and older.
[b] All Industries includes 2 deaths for which industry could not be determined.
[c] Agriculture includes forestry, fishing, and hunting. Mining includes oil and gas extraction. Other services excludes public administration.

OCCUPATIONAL UNINTENTIONAL-INJURY DEATHS AND DEATH RATES BY INDUSTRY, UNITED STATES, 2007

See footnotes above.

UNINTENTIONAL WORK-INJURY DEATHS AND DEATH RATES, UNITED STATES, 1992–2007

Year	Deaths	Workers (in thousands)	Death per 100,000 workers
1992	4,965	119,168	4.2
1993	5,034	120,778	4.2
1994	5,338	124,470	4.3
1995	5,015	126,248	4.0
1996	5,069	127,997	4.0
1997	5,160	130,810	3.9
1998	5,117	132,772	3.9
1999	5,184	134,688	3.8
2000	5,022	136,402	3.7
2001	5,042	136,246	3.7
2002	4,726	137,731	3.4
2003	4,725	138,988	3.4
2004	4,995	140,504	3.6
2005[a]	4,984	142,946	3.5
2006[a]	5,088	145,607	3.5
2007[b]	4,689	147,203	3.2

Source: Deaths are from the Bureau of Labor Statistics, Census of Fatal Occupational Injuries. Employment is from the Bureau of Labor Statistics and is based on the Current Population Survey. All other data are National Safety Council estimates.
Note: Deaths include persons of all ages. Workers and death rates include persons 16 years and older. Workers are persons ages 16 and older gainfully employed, including owners, managers, other paid employees, the self-employed, unpaid family workers, and active duty resident military personnel. Because of adoption of the Census of Fatal Occupational Injuries, deaths and rates from 1992 to the present are not comparable to prior years. See the Technical Appendix for additional information.
[a] Revised.
[b] Preliminary.

WORKERS, UNINTENTIONAL-INJURY DEATHS, AND DEATH RATES, UNITED STATES, 1992–2007

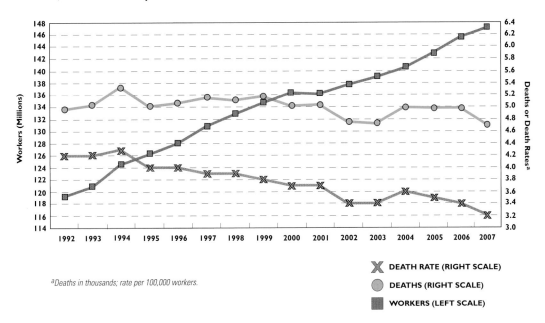

[a]Deaths in thousands; rate per 100,000 workers.

X DEATH RATE (RIGHT SCALE)

● DEATHS (RIGHT SCALE)

■ WORKERS (LEFT SCALE)

WORK, 2007 (CONT.)

OCCUPATIONAL-INJURY DEATHS AND DEATH RATES, UNITED STATES, 1992–2002

Year	Total	Homicide & Suicide	Unintentional All Industries[a]	Agriculture[b]	Mining, Quarrying[c]	Construction	Manufacturing	Transportation & Public Utilities	Trade[d]	Services[e]	Government
Deaths											
1992	6,217	1,252	4,965	779	175	889	707	767	415	601	586
1993	6,331	1,297	5,034	842	169	895	698	753	450	631	527
1994	6,632	1,294	5,338	814	177	1,000	734	819	492	676	534
1995	6,275	1,260	5,015	769	155	1,021	640	784	461	608	528
1996	6,202	1,133	5,069	762	151	1,025	660	883	451	615	321
1997	6,238	1,078	5,160	799	156	1,075	678	882	451	593	504
1998	6,055	938	5,117	808	143	1,136	631	830	443	634	465
1999	6,054	870	5,184	776	122	1,168	671	918	425	623	451
2000	5,920	898	5,022	693	153	1,114	624	872	447	643	460
2001	5,915	873[f]	5,042	714	169	1,183	546	844	431	636	507
2002	5,534	808	4,726	758	120	1,092	523	843	381	569	437
Deaths per 100,000 Workers											
1992	5.2	1.0	4.2	23.1	26.4	13.7	3.6	11.5	1.7	1.6	3.0
1993	5.2	1.0	4.2	26.0	25.3	13.3	3.6	11.0	1.8	1.6	2.6
1994	5.3	1.0	4.3	22.8	26.5	14.4	3.7	11.6	1.9	1.7	2.7
1995	4.9	1.0	4.0	21.4	24.8	14.3	3.1	11.0	1.8	1.5	2.7
1996	4.8	0.9	4.0	21.2	26.6	13.7	3.2	12.2	1.7	1.4	1.6
1997	4.8	0.8	3.9	22.5	24.7	13.7	3.3	11.6	1.7	1.3	2.6
1998	4.5	0.7	3.9	22.7	23.1	14.1	3.1	10.8	1.6	1.4	2.4
1999	4.5	0.6	3.8	22.6	21.7	13.8	3.4	11.5	1.5	1.3	2.2
2000	4.3	0.7	3.7	20.1	29.4	12.4	3.1	10.8	1.6	1.4	2.3
2001	4.3	0.6[f]	3.7	22.0	29.9	13.0	2.9	10.4	1.6	1.3	2.5
2002	4.0	0.6	3.4	21.8	23.3	11.9	2.9	10.5	1.4	1.1	2.1

Source: Deaths are from Bureau of Labor Statistics, Census of Fatal Occupational Injuries. Rates are National Safety Council estimates based on Bureau of Labor Statistics employment data. Deaths include persons of all ages. Death rates include persons 16 years and older. Industry divisions based on the Standard Industrial Classification Manual.
[a] *Includes deaths with industry unknown.*
[b] *Agriculture includes forestry, fishing, and agricultural services.*
[c] *Mining includes oil and gas extraction.*
[d] *Trade includes wholesale and retail trade.*
[e] *Services includes finance, insurance, and real estate.*
[f] *Excludes 2,886 homicides of workers on September 11, 2001.*

OCCUPATIONAL-INJURY DEATHS AND DEATH RATES, UNITED STATES, 2003–2007

Year	Total	Homicide & Suicide	Unintentional All Industries[a]	Agriculture, Forestry, Fishing & Hunting	Mining	Construction	Manufacturing	Wholesale Trade	Retail Trade	Transportation & Warehousing	Utilities	Information	Financial Activities	Professional & Business Services	Educational & Health Services	Leisure & Hospitality	Other Services	Government
Deaths																		
2003	5,575	850	4,725	676	141	1,094	379	169	148	735	29	57	82	396	116	142	123	434
2004	5,764	769	4,995	651	151	1,203	421	187	189	779	49	49	68	401	123	144	144	432
2005	5,734	750	4,984	697	154	1,161	357	197	198	831	28	56	66	442	122	114	149	404
2006[b]	5,840	752	5,088	635	190	1,199	423	210	190	803	52	61	82	407	142	136	142	409
2007[c]	5,488	799	4,689	552	178	1,139	358	183	156	766	32	70	69	407	121	130	113	409
Deaths per 100,000 Workers																		
2003	4.0	0.6	3.4	30.0	26.9	11.4	2.3	3.8	0.9	16.0	3.3	1.6	0.9	2.9	0.6	1.3	1.8	2.1
2004	4.1	0.5	3.6	29.7	28.1	11.7	2.6	4.1	1.2	16.7	5.9	1.5	0.7	2.9	0.7	1.3	2.1	2.0
2005	4.0	0.5	3.5	31.7	24.8	10.8	2.2	4.3	1.2	16.7	3.4	1.7	0.7	3.2	0.6	1.0	2.1	1.9
2006[b]	3.8	0.5	3.5	29.1	27.8	10.6	2.6	4.6	1.1	15.7	6.2	1.8	0.8	2.8	0.7	1.2	2.0	1.9
2007[c]	3.7	0.5	3.2	26.3	24.4	10.0	2.2	4.2	0.9	14.5	3.8	2.1	0.7	2.7	0.6	1.1	1.6	1.8

Source: Deaths are from Bureau of Labor Statistics, Census of Fatal Occupational Injuries. Rates are National Safety Council estimates based on Bureau of Labor Statistics employment data. Deaths include persons of all ages. Death rates include persons 16 years and older. Industry divisions based on the North American Industry Classification System.
[a] *Includes deaths with industry unknown.*
[b] *Revised.*
[c] *Preliminary.*

WORK INJURY COSTS

The true cost to the nation, to employers, and to individuals of work-related deaths and injuries is much greater than the cost of workers' compensation insurance alone. The figures presented below show the National Safety Council's estimates of the total economic costs of occupational deaths and injuries. Cost estimating procedures were revised for the 1993 edition of *Accident Facts*® and additional revisions were made for the 2005–2006 edition. For this reason, **costs should not be compared to prior years.**

TOTAL COST IN 2007 . . . . **$175.3 billion**

Includes wage and productivity losses of $84.1 billion, medical costs of $35.3 billion, and administrative expenses of $40.4 billion. Includes employers' uninsured costs of $10.4 billion such as the money value of time lost by workers other than those with disabling injuries, who are directly or indirectly involved in injuries, and the cost of time required to investigate injuries, write up injury reports, etc. Also includes damage to motor vehicles in work injuries of $1.7 billion and fire losses of $3.4 billion.

Cost per Worker **$1,200**
This figure indicates the value of goods or services each worker must produce to offset the cost of work injuries. It is *not* the average cost of a work injury.

Cost per Death **$1,270,000**
Cost per Disabling Injury **$43,000**

These figures include estimates of wage losses, medical expenses, administrative expenses, and employer costs, and exclude property damage costs except to motor-vehicles.

TIME LOST BECAUSE OF WORK INJURIES

DAYS LOST

TOTAL TIME LOST IN 2007 . . . . **114,000,000**

Due to Injuries in 2007 . . . . **75,000,000**
Includes primarily the actual time lost during the year from disabling injuries, except that it does not include time lost on the day of the injury or time required for further medical treatment or check-up following the injured person's return to work.

Fatalities are included at an average loss of 150 days per case, and permanent impairments are included at actual days lost plus an allowance for lost efficiency resulting from the impairment.

Not included is time lost by persons with nondisabling injuries or other persons directly or indirectly involved in the incidents.

DAYS LOST

Due to Injuries in Prior Years **39,000,000**
This is an indicator of the productive time lost in 2007 due to permanently disabling injuries that occurred in prior years.

DAYS LOST

TIME LOSS IN FUTURE YEARS
FROM 2007 INJURIES **60,000,000**
Includes time lost in future years due to on-the-job deaths and permanently disabling injuries that occurred in 2007.

WORKER DEATHS AND INJURIES ON AND OFF THE JOB

Nine out of 10 deaths and more than two thirds of the disabling injuries suffered by workers in 2007 occurred off the job. The ratios of off-the-job deaths and injuries to on-the-job were 11.2 to 1 and 2.7 to 1, respectively.

Production time lost due to off-the-job injuries totaled about 225,000,000 days in 2007, compared with 75,000,000 days lost by workers injured on the job.

Production time lost in future years due to off-the-job injuries in 2007 will total an estimated 505,000,000 days, over eight times the 60,000,000 days lost in future years from 2007's on-the-job injuries.

Off-the-job injuries to workers cost the nation at least $246.8 billion in 2007 compared to $175.3 billion for on-the-job injuries.

WORKERS' ON- AND OFF-THE-JOB INJURIES, UNITED STATES, 2007

Place	Deaths		Disabling Injuries	
	Number	Rate[a]	Number	Rate[a]
On- and off-the-job	57,189	0.013	12,900,000	3.0
On-the-job	4,689	0.003	3,500,000	2.2
Off-the-job	52,500	0.019	9,400,000	3.3
Motor-vehicle	23,200	0.079	1,200,000	4.1
Public nonmotor-vehicle	12,300	0.027	4,100,000	9.0
Home	17,000	0.008	4,100,000	2.0

Source: National Safety Council estimates. Procedures for allocating time spent on and off the job were revised for the 1990 edition. Rate basis changed to 200,000 hours for the 1998 edition. Death and injury rates are not comparable to rate estimates prior to the 1998 edition.
[a] Per 200,000 hours exposure by place.

WORKERS' ON- AND OFF-THE-JOB INJURIES, 2007

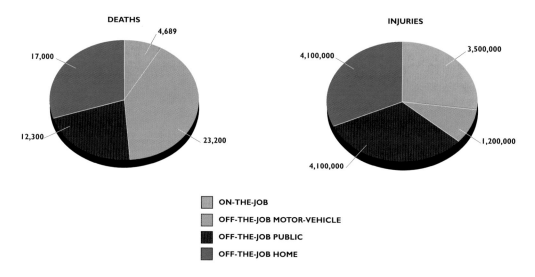

DEATHS

INJURIES

- ON-THE-JOB
- OFF-THE-JOB MOTOR-VEHICLE
- OFF-THE-JOB PUBLIC
- OFF-THE-JOB HOME

WORKERS' COMPENSATION CASES

According to the National Academy of Social Insurance, an estimated $54.7 billion, including benefits under deductible provisions, was paid out under workers' compensation in 2006 (the latest year for which data were available), a decrease of about 1.5% from 2005. Of this total, $28.2 billion was for income benefits and $26.5 billion was for medical and hospitalization costs. Private carriers paid about $27.6 billion of the total workers' compensation benefits in 2006. In 2006, approximately 130.3 million workers were covered by workers' compensation—an increase of 1.7% from the 128.1 million in 2005.

The table below shows the trend in the number of compensated or reported cases in each reporting state. Due to the differences in population, industries, and coverage of compensation laws, comparison among states should not be made.

WORKERS' COMPENSATION CASES, 2005–2007

State	Deaths[a] 2007	2006	2005	Cases[a] 2007	2006	2005	2006 Compensation Paid ($000)
Alabama[b]	70	86	86	16,537	19,439	18,848	609,167
Arizona	69	69	79	—	127,156	124,353	608,258
California	516	638	635	670,401	722,445	748,900	10,149,271
Colorado	---	120	108	—	30,715	29,282	870,908
Delaware	10	15	11	16,169	17,524	17,256	206,623
Florida	178	197	240	61,843	74,636	79,188	2,532,864
Hawaii	27	32	21	26,105	27,440	28,018	242,685
Indiana[b]	97	104	129	65,826	61,898	67,537	615,323
Iowa[b]	69	62	54	19,242	20,105	19,688	492,346
Kansas	56	52	54	72,464	68,882	65,723	397,713
Kentucky	45	29	—	31,780	33,633	—	709,628
Louisiana	59	62	66	16,159	18,568	13,447	578,804
Maryland	85	73	71	24,924	26,143	27,122	815,351
Massachusetts[c]	58	110	106	40,292	41,894	45,833	934,660
Minnesota[d]	37	53	60	116,500	121,300	125,900	921,232
Mississippi[c]	81	88	83	12,450	12,686	12,619	341,078
Montana	—	23	22	30,970	32,903	32,356	248,299
Nebraska	51	24	43	49,396	49,868	52,798	263,435
Nevada[c]	86	47	71	65,842	78,625	82,864	393,555
New Hampshire	23	18	23	46,171	46,349	46,797	213,719
New Mexico[c]	37	47	31	24,072[e]	21,570[e]	22,488[e]	237,551
New York	339	349	353	139,250	140,109	142,611	3,323,634
North Dakota	23	19	13	21,309	21,588	19,887	81,197
Ohio	176	196	227	171,692	185,232	197,704	2,383,544
Oregon[b]	35	37	31	23,434	23,373	22,114	613,288
Pennsylvania	148	133	122	115,845	110,657	102,259	2,684,611
Rhode Island	2	6	4	25,544	26,209	27,438	155,707
South Dakota	14	17	14	24,769	24,675	24,547	90,937
Tennessee	94	112	114	123,572	129,822	132,202	793,559
Vermont	12	19	10	21,771	22,276	20,950	124,323
Wyoming[d]	45	32	34	16,363	16,292	16,301	117,311

Source: Deaths and Cases—State workers' compensation authorities for calendar or fiscal year. States not listed did not respond to the survey. Compensation Paid—Sengupta, I., Reno, V., P., & Burton, J. F., Jr. (August, 2008). Workers' compensation: benefits, coverage, and costs, 2006. Washington DC: National Academy of Social Insurance.

Note: Dash (—) indicates data not available.

Definitions:
Reported case — a reported case may or may not be work-related and may not receive compensation.
Compensated case — a case determined to be work-related and for which compensation was paid.

[a]Reported cases involving medical and indemnity benefits, unless otherwise noted.
[b]Reported cases involving indemnity benefits only.
[c]Reported and closed or compensated cases.
[d]Closed or compensated cases only.
[e]Total includes only compensable workers' compensation fatalities.

WORKERS' COMPENSATION CLAIMS COSTS, 2005–2006

Head injuries are the most costly workers' compensation claims.

The data in the graphs on this and the next page are from the National Council on Compensation Insurance's (NCCI) Detailed Claim Information (DCI) file, a stratified random sample of lost-time claims in 42 states. Total incurred costs consist of medical and indemnity payments plus case reserves on open claims, and are calculated as of the second report (18 months after the initial report of injury). Injuries that result in medical payments only, without lost time, are not included. For open claims, costs include all payments as of the second report plus case reserves for future payments. Because the estimates are based on a sample, they can be volatile from year to year due to the influence of a small but variable number of large claims.

The average cost for all claims combined in 2005–2006 was $21,452, up 2.4% from the 2004–2005 average of $20,953.

Cause of Injury. The most costly lost-time workers' compensation claims by cause of injury, according to the NCCI data, are for those resulting from motor-vehicle crashes. These injuries averaged $44,853 per workers' compensation claim filed in 2005 and 2006. The only other cause with above average costs was fall or slip ($25,228).

Nature of Injury. The most costly lost-time workers' compensation claims by the nature of the injury are for those resulting from amputation. These injuries averaged $41,307 per workers' compensation claim filed in 2005 and 2006. The next highest costs were for injuries resulting in fracture ($31,698), and other trauma ($24,660).

Part of Body. The most costly lost-time workers' compensation claims are for those involving the head or central nervous system. These injuries averaged $57,865 per workers' compensation claim filed in 2005 and 2006. The next highest costs were for injuries involving the neck ($33,117) and leg ($29,731). Injuries to the arm/shoulder; hip, thigh, and pelvis; lower back; and multiple body parts also had above average costs.

AVERAGE TOTAL INCURRED COSTS PER CLAIM BY CAUSE OF INJURY, 2005–2006

AVERAGE TOTAL INCURRED COSTS PER CLAIM BY NATURE OF INJURY, 2005–2006

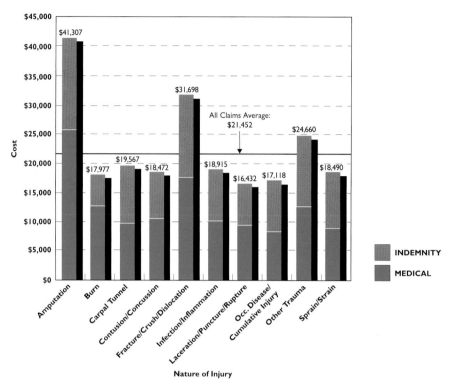

AVERAGE TOTAL INCURRED COSTS PER CLAIM BY PART OF BODY, 2005–2006

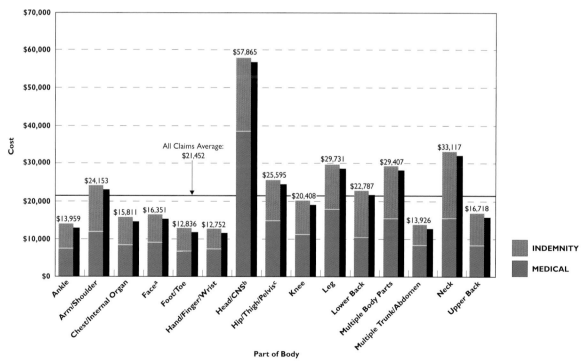

[a] Includes teeth, mouth, and eyes.
[b] Central nervous system.
[c] Includes sacrum and coccyx.

Please note that these are estimates based on a sample of claims reported to NCCI and can be volatile from year to year due to the influence of a small but variable number of large claims.

CAUSES OF WORK-RELATED DEATHS AND INJURIES

Incidents involving motor-vehicles are the leading cause of work-related deaths followed by contacts with objects or equipment and falls. For nonfatal cases with days away from work, contacts with objects or equipment are the leading cause followed by overexertion and falls.

WORK-RELATED DEATHS AND INJURIES BY EVENT OR EXPOSURE, UNITED STATES, 2006

Event or Exposure	Deaths[a]
Total, all events or exposures	5,840
Contact with object or equipment	993
Struck against object	10
Struck by object	589
Caught in objects or equipment	283
Caught in collapsing materials	108
Fall	827
Fall to lower level	738
Fall on same level	67
Bodily reaction and exertion	14
Exposure to harmful substance	547
Contact with electric current	250
Contact with temperature extremes	56
Exposure to caustic or noxious substances	165
Oxygen deficiency	68
Drowning	53
Choking on object or substance	11
Transportation accidents	2,459
Motor-vehicle accidents	2,080
Highway accident	1,356
Nonhighway accident except rail, air, water	345
Pedestrian struck by vehicle, mobile equipment	379
Railway accident	65
Water vehicle accident	96
Aircraft accident	217
Fires, explosions	202
Fires	102
Explosions	99
Assaults and violent acts	788
By person	540
Self-inflicted	208
By animals	36
Other and nonclassifiable	10

Event or Exposure	Cases With Days Away From Work[b]
Total, all events or exposures	1,183,500
Contact with object or equipment	335,460
Struck against object	85,710
Struck by object	164,670
Caught in object or equipment	58,760
Caught in collapsing material	510
Fall	234,450
Fall to lower level	74,280
Fall on same level	151,750
Bodily reaction and exertion	461,530
Bodily reaction	128,770
Bending, climbing, crawling, reaching, twisting	53,170
Slips, trips, loss of balance—without fall	35,440
Overexertion	284,910
Overexertion in lifting	150,990
Repetitive motion	38,310
Exposure to harmful substance	56,510
Contact with electric current	2,620
Contact with temperature extremes	20,000
Exposure to caustic or noxious substances	28,940
Transportation accidents	56,170
Highway accident	36,330
Nonhighway accident except rail, air, water	8,560
Pedestrian struck by vehicle, mobile equipment	8,400
Railway accident	220
Water vehicle accident	220
Aircraft accident	610
Fires, explosions	2,270
Fires	1,300
Explosions	960
Assaults and violent acts	22,430
By person	15,970
By animals	6,220
Other and nonclassifiable	14,670

Source: Bureau of Labor Statistics.
[a]Includes deaths among all workers.
[b]Includes cases with days away from work among private sector wage and salary workers. Excludes government employees, the self employed, and unpaid family workers.

DEATHS[a] BY EVENT OR EXPOSURE, UNITED STATES, 2006

0.2% 9.4% 14.2% 17.0% 0.2% 13.5% 3.5% 42.1%

CASES WITH DAYS AWAY FROM WORK[b] BY EVENT OR EXPOSURE, UNITED STATES, 2006

4.8% 4.7% 0.2% 1.9% 1.2% 39.0% 28.3% 19.8%

- ☐ BODILY REACTION AND EXERTION
- ☐ FALL
- ☐ CONTACT WITH OBJECT OR EQUIPMENT
- ☐ OTHER AND NONCLASSIFIABLE
- ☐ ASSAULTS AND VIOLENT ACTS
- ☐ FIRES, EXPLOSIONS
- ☐ TRANSPORTATION ACCIDENTS
- ☐ EXPOSURE TO HARMFUL SUBSTANCE

[a]Includes deaths among all workers.
[b]Includes cases with days away from work among private sector wage and salary workers. Excludes government employees, the self employed, and unpaid family workers.

According to the Bureau of Labor Statistics, sprains and strains were the most common type of injury involving days away from work in 2006, accounting for 40% of the total 1,183,500 injuries in private industry. Cuts, lacerations, and punctures were the second most

common type of injury, followed by soreness, pain. Overall, the manufacturing, education and health services, and retail trade industry sectors had the highest number of injuries, combining to make up over 46% of the total.

NUMBER OF NONFATAL OCCUPATIONAL INJURIES AND ILLNESSES INVOLVING DAYS AWAY FROM WORK[a] BY NATURE OF INJURY AND INDUSTRY SECTOR, PRIVATE INDUSTRY, UNITED STATES, 2006

Nature of Injury	Private Sector[b,c,d]	Industry Sector								
		Manufac-turing	Education and Health Services	Retail Trade	Construc-tion	Trans. & Ware-housing[d]	Leisure and Hospitality	Prof. and Business Services	Wholesale Trade	All Other Sectors[b,d,e]
Total[c]	1,183,500	200,970	182,210	162,800	153,180	109,800	96,910	89,940	75,700	112,010
Sprains, strains	472,740	67,810	89,950	71,040	52,880	52,030	31,850	32,910	31,290	42,980
Fractures	94,110	16,760	10,590	11,370	17,670	8,750	6,540	6,350	6,230	9,840
Cuts, lacerations, punctures	115,210	24,240	5,900	16,590	23,930	4,860	15,900	8,900	6,450	8,440
Bruises, contusions	101,260	16,810	15,710	15,340	9,460	11,310	8,370	7,540	6,790	9,920
Heat burns	17,440	3,440	2,130	1,310	1,490	300	6,130	690	670	1,260
Chemical burns	7,490	1,840	780	740	1,070	400	860	690	760	360
Amputations	7,990	3,800	90	610	1,220	260	450	440	370	750
Carpal tunnel syndrome	13,010	5,050	1,210	1,340	890	400	650	790	900	1,780
Tendonitis	4,750	1,680	680	630	220	230	270	440	170	440
Multiple injuries	45,890	7,130	7,860	5,710	5,690	4,520	3,010	3,820	2,930	5,240
With fractures	10,600	2,070	1,050	1,160	1,750	740	650	1,390	550	1,240
With sprains	18,020	1,920	4,090	2,070	1,990	1,680	1,470	1,390	1,340	2,060
Soreness, Pain	105,050	14,360	21,370	13,470	12,030	10,150	8,820	8,550	7,140	9,160
Back pain	35,330	4,610	7,950	4,350	4,050	3,820	2,750	2,290	2,830	2,670
All other natures	198,550	38,050	25,950	24,650	26,620	16,580	14,060	18,820	12,030	21,790

Source: Bureau of Labor Statistics Occupational Injuries and Illnesses Profiles Data, accessed July 25, 2008 from http://data.bls.gov/GQT/servlet/InitialPage.

[a]Days-away-from-work cases include those that result in days away from work with or without job transfer or restriction.
[b]Excludes farms with less than 11 employees.
[c]Data may not sum to row and column totals because of rounding and exclusion of nonclassifiable responses.
[d]Data for transportation and mining do not reflect the changes OSHA made to its recordkeeping requirements effective January 1, 2002; therefore, estimates for these industries are not comparable with estimates for other industries.
[e]Includes Agriculture, Forestry, Fishing and Hunting; Financial Activities; Information; Mining (including oil and gas extraction); Other Services (except Public Administration); and Utilities.

BENCHMARKING INCIDENCE RATES

Safety professionals in business and industry often want to compare, or benchmark, the occupational injury and illness incidence rates of their establishments with the national average rates compiled by the U.S. Bureau of Labor Statistics (BLS) through its annual Survey of Occupational Injuries and Illnesses.[a] The incidence rates published on the following pages are for 2007 and were compiled under the revised OSHA record-keeping requirements that became effective in 2002.

Step 1.

The first step in benchmarking is to calculate the incidence rates for the establishment. The basic formula for computing incidence rates is $(N \times 200,000)/EH$, or, the number of cases (N) multiplied by $200,000$ then divided by the number of hours worked (EH) by all employees during the time period, where $200,000$ is the base for 100 full-time workers (working 40 hours per week, 50 weeks per year). Because the BLS rates are based on reports from entire establishments, both the OSHA 300 Log and the number of hours worked should cover the whole establishment being benchmarked. The hours worked and the log also should cover the same time period, (e.g., a month, quarter, or full year). The following rates may be calculated.

Total Cases — the incidence rate of total OSHA-recordable cases per 200,000 hours worked. For this rate, N is the total number of cases on the OSHA 300 Log.

Cases With Days Away From Work or Job Transfer or Restriction — the incidence rate of cases with days away from work, or job transfer, or restriction. N is the count of cases with a check in column H or column I of the OSHA 300 Log.

Cases With Days Away From Work — the incidence rate of cases with days away from work. N is the count of cases with a check in column H of the OSHA 300 Log.

Cases With Job Transfer or Restriction — the incidence rate of cases with job transfer or restriction, but no days away from work. N is the count of cases with a check in column I of the OSHA 300 Log.

Other Recordable Cases — the incidence rate of recordable cases without days away from work or job transfer or restriction. N is the count of cases with a check in column J of the OSHA 300 Log.

In the flow chart on the opposite page, post the number of cases to each box in the top row and the number of employee hours worked in its box. Then use the formula to calculate the rates and write them in the last row of boxes in Step 1.

Step 2.

After computing one or more of the rates, the next step is to determine the North American Industry Classification System (NAICS) code for the establishment.[b] (NAICS replaced the Standard Industrial Classification [SIC] code beginning in 2003.) This code is used to find the appropriate BLS rate for comparison. NAICS codes may be found on the Internet at www.census.gov/naics. The site also contains a crosswalk between NAICS and SIC codes. Otherwise, call a regional BLS office for assistance.

Write the establishment's NAICS code in the box in Step 2 of the flow chart.

Step 3.

Once the NAICS code is known, the national average incidence rates may be found by (a) consulting the table of rates on pages 62–64, (b) visiting the BLS Internet site (www.bls.gov/iif), or (c) by calling a regional BLS office. Note that some tables on the Internet site provide incidence rates by size of establishment and rate quartiles within each NAICS code. These rates may be useful for a more precise comparison. Note that the incidence rates for 2001 and earlier years were compiled under the old OSHA record-keeping requirements in effect at that time. Caution must be used in comparing rates computed for 2002 and later years with earlier years—keeping in mind the differences in record-keeping requirements.

In the flow chart on the opposite page, post the rates from the BLS survey to the boxes in Step 3. Now compare these with the rates calculated in Step 1.

An alternative way of benchmarking is to compare the current incidence rates for an establishment to its own prior historical rates to determine if the rates are improving and if progress is satisfactory (using criteria set by the organization).

[a]Bureau of Labor Statistics. (1997). BLS Handbook of Methods. Washington, DC: U.S. Government Printing Office (or on the Internet at http://www.bls.gov/opub/hom/home.htm).
[b]Executive Office of the President, Office of Management and Budget. (2002). North American Industry Classification System, United States 2002. Springfield, VA: National Technical Information Service.

STEP 1: COMPUTE ESTABLISHMENT INCIDENCE RATES

| Total Cases | DAFW, Transfer, or Restriction Cases | DAFW Cases | Transfer or Restriction Cases | Other Cases |

Cases (N)   X 200,000

Incidence Rate =

EH

Employee-Hours Worked

| Total Cases Incidence Rate | DAFW, Transfer, or Restriction Cases Incidence Rate | DAFW Cases Incidence Rate | Transfer or Restriction Cases Incidence Rate | Other Cases Incidence Rate |

STEP 2: DETERMINE NORTH AMERICAN INDUSTRY CLASSIFICATION SYSTEM (NAICS) CODE

NAICS Code = ____ ____ ____ ____

STEP 3: COMPARE TO BLS INCIDENCE RATE AVERAGES FOR THE INDUSTRY (NAICS Code)

| Total Cases Incidence Rate | DAFW, Transfer, or Restriction Cases Incidence Rate | DAFW Cases Incidence Rate | Transfer or Restriction Cases Incidence Rate | Other Cases Incidence Rate |

See page 58 for detailed instructions.
DAFW = Days Away From Work

TRENDS IN OCCUPATIONAL INCIDENCE RATES

Incidence rates continue downward trend.

Four of the five occupational injury and illness incidence rates published by the Bureau of Labor Statistics for 2007 decreased from 2006. The incidence rate for total recordable cases was 4.2 per 100 full-time workers in 2007, down over 4% from the 2006 rate of 4.4. The incidence rate for total cases with days away from work, job transfer, or restriction was 2.1, a decrease of 9%. The incidence rate for cases with days away from work was 1.2 in 2007, down 8% from 2006. The incidence rate for cases with job transfer or restriction was 0.9 in 2007, down 10% from 2006. The incidence rate for other recordable cases was 2.1, unchanged from 2005.

There have been several changes that affect comparability of incidence rates from year to year. The North American Industry Classification System (NAICS) replaced the Standard Industrial Classification (SIC) system beginning with the 2003 survey of occupational injuries and illnesses. Revisions to the Occupational Safety and Health Administration's (OSHA) occupational injury and illness recordkeeping requirements became effective in 2002. Beginning with 1992, the Bureau of Labor Statistics revised its annual survey to include only nonfatal cases and stopped publishing the incidence rate of lost workdays.

OCCUPATIONAL INJURY AND ILLNESS INCIDENCE RATES, PRIVATE INDUSTRY, UNITED STATES, 1987–2007

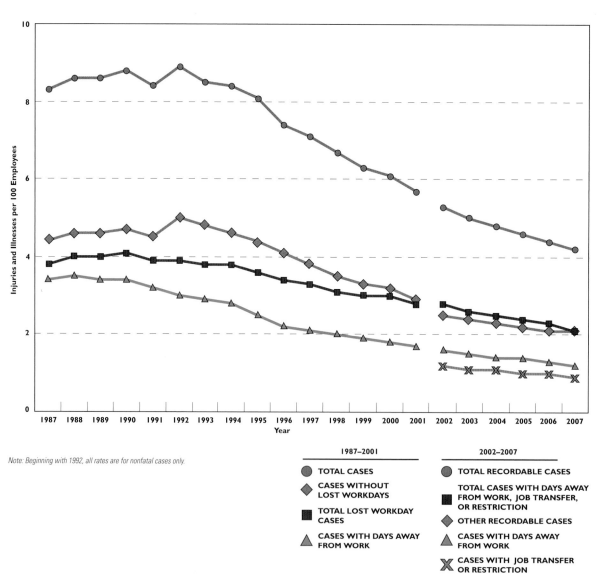

Note: Beginning with 1992, all rates are for nonfatal cases only.

1987–2001

- ● TOTAL CASES
- ◆ CASES WITHOUT LOST WORKDAYS
- ■ TOTAL LOST WORKDAY CASES
- ▲ CASES WITH DAYS AWAY FROM WORK

2002–2007

- ● TOTAL RECORDABLE CASES
- ■ TOTAL CASES WITH DAYS AWAY FROM WORK, JOB TRANSFER, OR RESTRICTION
- ◆ OTHER RECORDABLE CASES
- ▲ CASES WITH DAYS AWAY FROM WORK
- ✕ CASES WITH JOB TRANSFER OR RESTRICTION

OCCUPATIONAL INJURIES
AND ILLNESSES

61

The tables below and on pages 62–64 present the results of the 2007 Survey of Occupational Injuries and Illnesses conducted by the Bureau of Labor Statistics (BLS), U.S. Department of Labor. The survey collects data on injuries and illnesses (from the OSHA 300 Log) and employee-hours worked from a nationwide sample of about 190,300 establishments representing the private sector of the economy. The survey excludes public employees, private households, the self-employed, and farms with fewer than 11 employees. The incidence rates give the number of cases per 100 full-time workers per year using 200,000 employee-hours as the equivalent. Definitions of the terms are given in the Glossary on page 199.

Beginning with 1992 data, the BLS revised its annual survey to include only nonfatal cases and stopped publishing incidence rates of lost workdays. Beginning with 2003 data, the BLS adopted the North American Industry Classification System for publication of the incidence rates by industry.

BLS ESTIMATES OF NONFATAL OCCUPATIONAL INJURY AND ILLNESS INCIDENCE RATES AND NUMBER OF INJURIES AND ILLNESSES BY INDUSTRY SECTOR, 2007

Industry Sector	Total Recordable Cases	Cases With Days Away From Work, Job Transfer, or Restriction			Other Recordable Cases
		Total	Cases With Days Away From Work	Cases With Job Transfer or Restriction	
Incidence Rate per 100 Full-Time Workers[c]					
Private Sector[d]	**4.2**	**2.1**	**1.2**	**0.9**	**2.1**
Goods Producing[d]	5.4	2.9	1.5	1.4	2.5
Agriculture, forestry, fishing & hunting[d]	5.4	2.8	1.8	1.0	2.5
Mining	3.1	2.0	1.4	0.6	1.1
Construction	5.4	2.8	1.9	0.9	2.6
Manufacturing	5.6	3.0	1.3	1.7	2.5
Service Providing	3.8	1.9	1.1	0.8	1.9
Wholesale trade	4.0	2.4	1.3	1.1	1.6
Retail trade	4.8	2.5	1.4	1.2	2.3
Transportation and warehousing	6.4	4.3	2.7	1.6	2.1
Utilities	4.0	2.1	1.2	0.9	1.9
Information	2.0	1.1	0.7	0.4	1.0
Financial Activities	1.4	0.7	0.5	0.2	0.8
Professional and Business Services	2.1	1.0	0.6	0.4	1.1
Education and Health Services	5.2	2.4	1.3	1.0	2.9
Leisure and Hospitality	4.5	1.7	1.1	0.6	2.8
Other Services	3.1	1.5	1.0	0.5	1.7
Number of Injuries and Illnesses (in thousands)					
Private Sector[d]	**4,002.7**	**2,036.0**	**1,158.9**	**877.2**	**1,966.7**
Goods Producing[d]	1,236.1	665.3	349.4	315.8	570.8
Agriculture, forestry, fishing & hunting[d]	50.5	26.6	17.0	9.6	23.9
Mining	21.9	14.1	9.9	4.2	7.9
Construction	380.5	197.5	135.3	62.1	183.1
Manufacturing	783.1	427.1	187.2	239.9	356.0
Service Providing	2,766.6	1,370.6	809.4	561.3	1,395.9
Wholesale trade	234.9	139.3	75.2	64.0	95.6
Retail trade	587.3	309.1	166.8	142.3	278.2
Transportation and warehousing	268.0	179.4	111.1	68.3	88.5
Utilities	21.6	11.4	6.6	4.7	10.2
Information	54.7	29.1	18.6	10.5	25.7
Financial Activities	108.2	49.7	35.4	14.2	58.5
Professional and Business Services	284.5	136.2	88.3	47.9	148.3
Education and Health Services	710.0	319.5	181.7	137.8	390.5
Leisure and Hospitality	400.8	151.5	94.2	57.4	249.3
Other Services	96.6	45.7	31.5	14.2	50.9

Source: Bureau of Labor Statistics.
[a] *Industry Sector and 2 and 3 digit NAICS code totals on pages 62–64 include data for industries not shown separately.*
[b] *North American Industry Classification System, 2002 Edition, for industries shown on pages 62–64.*
[c] *Incidence Rate =* $\dfrac{Number\ of\ injuries\ \&\ illnesses \times 200,000}{Total\ hours\ worked\ by\ all\ employees\ during\ period\ covered}$
where 200,000 is the base for 100 full-time workers (working 40 hours per week, 50 weeks per year). The "Total Recordable Cases" rate is based on the number of cases with check marks in columns (G), (H), (I), and (J) of the OSHA 300 Log. The "Cases With Days Away From Work, Job Transfer, or Restriction—Total" rate is based on columns (H) and (I). The "Cases With Days Away From Work" rate is based on column (H). The "Cases With Job Transfer or Restriction" rate is based on column (I). The "Other Recordable Cases" rate is based on column (J).
[d] *Excludes farms with less than 11 employees.*
[e] *Data do not meet publication guidelines.*
[f] *Data too small to be displayed.*

OCCUPATIONAL

NATIONAL SAFETY COUNCIL® INJURY FACTS® 2009 EDITION

OCCUPATIONAL INJURIES AND ILLNESSES (CONT.)

BLS ESTIMATES OF NONFATAL OCCUPATIONAL INJURY AND ILLNESS INCIDENCE RATES FOR SELECTED INDUSTRIES, 2007

Industry[a]	NAICS Code[b]	Total Recordable Cases	Cases With Days Away From Work, Job Transfer, or Restriction			Other Recordable Cases
			Total	Cases With Days Away From Work	Cases With Job Transfer or Restriction	
PRIVATE SECTOR[d]		**4.2**	**2.1**	**1.2**	**0.9**	**2.1**
Goods Producing[d]		**5.4**	**2.9**	**1.5**	**1.4**	**2.5**
Natural Resources and Mining[d]		**4.4**	**2.5**	**1.6**	**0.8**	**1.9**
Agriculture, forestry, fishing and hunting[d]	11	5.4	2.8	1.8	1.0	2.5
Crop production	111	5.2	2.8	1.6	1.2	2.4
Animal production	112	7.0	3.6	2.3	1.3	3.4
Forestry and logging	113	5.2	2.5	2.3	0.2	2.6
Fishing, hunting, and trapping	114	3.1	1.0	0.7	0.3	2.0
Support activities for agriculture and forestry	115	4.8	2.6	1.7	0.9	2.2
Mining	21	3.1	2.0	1.4	0.6	1.1
Oil and gas extraction	211	1.7	1.2	1.0	0.2	0.5
Mining (except oil and gas)	212	3.7	2.5	1.8	0.7	1.2
Coal mining	2121	4.7	3.2	2.9	0.3	1.4
Metal ore mining	2122	3.3	2.1	1.2	0.9	1.2
Nonmetallic mineral mining and quarrying	2123	3.1	2.0	1.2	0.8	1.0
Support activities for mining	213	3.2	1.9	1.2	0.7	1.3
Construction		**5.4**	**2.8**	**1.9**	**0.9**	**2.6**
Construction of buildings	236	4.7	2.3	1.7	0.7	2.3
Residential building construction	2361	4.8	2.5	2.0	0.5	2.3
Nonresidential building construction	2362	4.5	2.1	1.2	0.9	2.3
Heavy and civil engineering construction	237	4.9	2.6	1.6	1.0	2.2
Utility system construction	2371	4.7	2.6	1.7	0.9	2.1
Land subdivision	2372	3.2	1.2	0.9	0.3	2.0
Highway, street, and bridge construction	2373	5.9	3.2	1.9	1.3	2.7
Other heavy and civil engineering construction	2379	3.5	2.0	1.3	0.8	1.4
Specialty trade contractors	238	5.7	3.0	2.1	0.9	2.7
Foundation, structure, and building exterior contractors	2381	6.8	3.9	2.6	1.3	2.9
Building equipment contractors	2382	5.9	2.8	1.9	0.8	3.1
Building finishing contractors	2383	5.2	2.9	2.1	0.8	2.2
Other specialty trade contractors	2389	4.6	2.4	1.6	0.8	2.2
Manufacturing		**5.6**	**3.0**	**1.3**	**1.7**	**2.5**
Food manufacturing	311	6.8	4.4	1.5	2.8	2.5
Animal food manufacturing	3111	5.4	2.8	1.4	1.4	2.5
Grain and oilseed milling	3112	5.5	3.1	1.4	1.7	2.3
Sugar and confectionery product manufacturing	3113	6.1	3.3	1.4	1.9	2.8
Fruit and vegetable preserving and specialty food mfg.	3114	6.2	3.6	1.4	2.2	2.5
Dairy product manufacturing	3115	8.0	5.3	2.7	2.6	2.7
Animal slaughtering and processing	3116	8.4	5.5	1.2	4.3	2.8
Seafood product preparation and packaging	3117	8.9	4.7	3.2	1.5	4.2
Bakeries and tortilla manufacturing	3118	5.2	3.5	1.6	2.0	1.6
Other food manufacturing	3119	5.3	3.5	1.5	1.9	1.9
Beverage and tobacco product manufacturing	312	7.3	5.0	2.2	2.8	2.4
Beverage manufacturing	3121	7.8	5.3	2.3	3.0	2.4
Tobacco manufacturing	3122	3.9	2.0	1.3	0.7	1.9
Textile mills	313	4.0	2.2	0.9	1.3	1.8
Fiber, yarn, and thread mills	3131	3.7	1.9	0.5	1.4	1.7
Fabric mills	3132	3.8	2.0	0.9	1.1	1.8
Textile and fabric finishing and fabric coating mills	3133	4.5	2.6	1.1	1.5	1.9
Textile product mills	314	4.2	2.4	0.9	1.6	1.8
Textile furnishings mills	3141	3.9	2.3	0.7	1.6	1.6
Other textile product mills	3149	4.7	2.7	1.2	1.5	2.0
Apparel manufacturing	315	2.6	1.4	0.6	0.7	1.3
Apparel knitting mills	3151	4.2	2.4	1.0	1.5	1.8
Cut and sew apparel manufacturing	3152	2.2	1.1	0.6	0.5	1.1
Apparel accessories and other apparel manufacturing	3159	4.0	2.0	1.0	1.0	2.1
Leather and allied product manufacturing	316	5.4	2.9	1.4	1.5	2.5
Footwear manufacturing	3162	5.6	3.1	1.4	1.7	2.5
Other leather and allied product manufacturing	3169	4.1	1.8	1.0	0.8	2.3
Wood product manufacturing	321	7.8	4.1	2.1	2.0	3.7
Sawmills and wood preservation	3211	7.7	3.9	2.5	1.4	3.7
Veneer, plywood, and engineered wood product mfg.	3212	6.4	3.4	1.4	1.9	3.1
Other wood product manufacturing	3219	8.4	4.5	2.3	2.2	4.0
Paper manufacturing	322	4.0	2.2	1.1	1.1	1.8
Pulp, paper, and paperboard mills	3221	3.5	1.9	1.1	0.8	1.6
Converted paper product manufacturing	3222	4.2	2.3	1.1	1.3	1.8
Printing and related support activities	323	3.8	2.2	1.0	1.1	1.6
Petroleum and coal products manufacturing	324	2.8	1.7	0.8	0.9	1.2
Chemical manufacturing	325	3.1	1.7	0.8	0.9	1.4
Basic chemical manufacturing	3251	2.7	1.3	0.7	0.6	1.4
Resin, synthetic rubber, and artificial and synthetic fibers and filaments manufacturing	3252	3.2	1.8	0.9	1.0	1.4
Pesticide, fertilizer, and other agricultural chemical mfg.	3253	2.8	1.7	0.9	0.8	1.1
Pharmaceutical and medicine manufacturing	3254	2.4	1.4	0.6	0.7	1.0
Paint, coating, and adhesive manufacturing	3255	4.4	2.9	1.4	1.5	1.6
Soap, cleaning compound, and toilet preparation mfg.	3256	3.8	2.3	1.1	1.3	1.5
Other chemical product and preparation manufacturing	3259	4.2	2.2	1.0	1.2	2.0

See source and footnotes on page 61.

BLS ESTIMATES OF NONFATAL OCCUPATIONAL INJURY AND ILLNESS INCIDENCE RATES FOR SELECTED INDUSTRIES, 2007, Cont.

Industry[a]	NAICS Code[b]	Total Recordable Cases	Incidence Rates[c]			Other Recordable Cases
			Cases With Days Away From Work, Job Transfer, or Restriction			
			Total	Cases With Days Away From Work	Cases With Job Transfer or Restriction	
Plastics and rubber products manufacturing	326	6.4	3.7	1.6	2.1	2.7
Plastics product manufacturing	3261	6.3	3.7	1.6	2.1	2.7
Rubber product manufacturing	3262	6.6	3.9	1.6	2.3	2.7
Nonmetallic mineral product manufacturing	327	6.5	3.9	1.9	2.0	2.7
Clay product and refractory manufacturing	3271	6.7	3.7	1.9	1.8	3.0
Glass and glass product manufacturing	3272	7.0	4.0	1.3	2.7	3.0
Cement and concrete product manufacturing	3273	6.6	4.0	2.1	2.0	2.6
Lime and gypsum product manufacturing	3274	3.1	1.6	1.3	0.3	1.5
Other nonmetallic mineral product manufacturing	3279	6.4	3.9	2.0	1.8	2.5
Primary metal manufacturing	331	8.1	4.3	2.0	2.3	3.7
Iron and steel mills and ferroalloy manufacturing	3311	4.6	2.5	1.3	1.2	2.2
Steel product manufacturing from purchased steel	3312	7.7	4.1	2.1	2.1	3.6
Alumina and aluminum production and processing	3313	6.5	3.5	1.6	1.9	3.0
Nonferrous metal (except aluminum) production and processing	3314	6.5	3.9	1.8	2.0	2.7
Foundries	3315	11.8	6.2	2.7	3.5	5.6
Fabricated metal product manufacturing	332	7.2	3.5	1.8	1.8	3.6
Forging and stamping	3321	8.3	4.1	2.0	2.1	4.2
Cutlery and handtool manufacturing	3322	6.2	2.7	1.4	1.3	3.5
Architectural and structural metals manufacturing	3323	8.7	4.4	2.2	2.3	4.3
Boiler, tank, and shipping container manufacturing	3324	7.4	3.6	1.8	1.7	3.8
Hardware manufacturing	3325	5.6	2.9	1.0	1.9	2.6
Spring and wire product manufacturing	3326	7.1	3.6	1.9	1.7	3.5
Machine shops; turned product; and screw, nut, and bolt manufacturing	3327	6.3	2.7	1.5	1.2	3.6
Coating, engraving, heat treating, and allied activities	3328	7.1	4.0	2.0	2.0	3.1
Other fabricated metal product manufacturing	3329	5.9	3.1	1.4	1.7	2.8
Machinery manufacturing	333	5.8	2.7	1.3	1.4	3.1
Agriculture, construction, and mining machinery mfg.	3331	6.3	3.1	1.4	1.7	3.2
Industrial machinery manufacturing	3332	6.3	2.5	1.3	1.1	3.8
Commercial and service machinery manufacturing	3333	4.6	2.3	1.0	1.3	2.3
Ventilation, heating, air-conditioning, and commercial refrigeration equipment manufacturing	3334	6.1	3.1	1.3	1.9	3.0
Metalworking machinery manufacturing	3335	6.0	2.5	1.4	1.1	3.5
Engine, turbine, and power transmission equipment manufacturing	3336	4.2	2.1	1.0	1.1	2.2
Other general purpose machinery manufacturing	3339	6.0	3.0	1.4	1.5	3.1
Computer and electronic product manufacturing	334	2.0	1.0	0.5	0.5	1.0
Computer and peripheral equipment manufacturing	3341	1.1	0.6	0.3	0.3	0.5
Communications equipment manufacturing	3342	1.9	1.0	0.4	0.6	0.9
Audio and video equipment manufacturing	3343	3.0	1.2	0.5	0.7	1.8
Semiconductor and other electronic component mfg.	3344	2.2	1.1	0.6	0.6	1.1
Navigational, measuring, electromedical, and control instruments manufacturing	3345	1.9	0.9	0.4	0.5	1.0
Manufacturing and reproducing magnetic and optical media	3346	2.0	1.2	0.4	0.8	0.8
Electrical equipment, appliance, and component mfg.	335	4.7	2.6	1.0	1.6	2.1
Electric lighting equipment manufacturing	3351	5.6	3.0	1.3	1.6	2.6
Household appliance manufacturing	3352	4.7	2.3	0.7	1.5	2.4
Electrical equipment manufacturing	3353	4.1	2.2	0.9	1.3	1.9
Other electrical equipment and component mfg.	3359	5.0	3.1	1.1	2.0	2.0
Transportation equipment manufacturing	336	6.9	3.6	1.4	2.3	3.2
Motor vehicle manufacturing	3361	9.3	5.0	1.5	3.5	4.3
Motor vehicle body and trailer manufacturing	3362	10.6	4.9	2.0	3.0	5.6
Motor vehicle parts manufacturing	3363	6.9	3.7	1.2	2.5	3.2
Aerospace product and parts manufacturing	3364	3.9	2.1	0.9	1.2	1.8
Railroad rolling stock manufacturing	3365	6.2	3.3	1.5	1.8	2.9
Ship and boat building	3366	8.9	5.0	2.6	2.4	3.8
Other transportation equipment manufacturing	3369	6.3	3.0	1.4	1.5	3.4
Furniture and related product manufacturing	337	6.7	3.6	1.6	2.0	3.1
Household and institutional furniture and kitchen cabinet manufacturing	3371	6.8	3.7	1.6	2.1	3.1
Office furniture (including fixtures) manufacturing	3372	6.8	3.3	1.5	1.7	3.5
Other furniture related product manufacturing	3379	5.6	3.5	1.6	1.9	2.1
Miscellaneous manufacturing	339	3.9	2.0	0.9	1.1	1.9
Medical equipment and supplies manufacturing	3391	3.2	1.6	0.7	0.9	1.6
Other miscellaneous manufacturing	3399	4.6	2.4	1.1	1.3	2.2
Service Providing		3.8	1.9	1.1	0.8	1.9
Trade, Transportation, and Utilities		4.9	2.8	1.6	1.2	2.1
Wholesale trade	42	4.0	2.4	1.3	1.1	1.6
Merchant wholesalers, durable goods	423	3.9	2.2	1.2	1.0	1.7
Merchant wholesalers, nondurable goods	424	5.1	3.3	1.7	1.6	1.8

See source and footnotes on page 61.

BLS ESTIMATES OF NONFATAL OCCUPATIONAL INJURY AND ILLNESS INCIDENCE RATES FOR SELECTED INDUSTRIES, 2007, Cont.

Industry[a]	NAICS Code[b]	Total Recordable Cases	Incidence Rates[c] Cases With Days Away From Work, Job Transfer, or Restriction — Total	Cases With Days Away From Work	Cases With Job Transfer or Restriction	Other Recordable Cases
Wholesale electronic markets and agents and brokers	425	1.8	0.9	0.6	0.3	1.0
Retail trade	44–45	4.8	2.5	1.4	1.2	2.3
Motor vehicle and parts dealers	441	4.5	1.8	1.3	0.5	2.7
Furniture and home furnishings stores	442	4.5	2.6	1.4	1.1	1.9
Electronics and appliance stores	443	2.6	1.3	(e)	0.5	1.3
Building material and garden equipment and supplies dealers	444	6.6	4.0	1.7	2.2	2.6
Food and beverage stores	445	5.9	3.1	1.7	1.4	2.8
Health and personal care stores	446	2.4	1.1	0.8	0.4	1.3
Gasoline stations	447	3.2	1.3	0.9	0.4	1.8
Clothing and clothing accessories stores	448	2.9	1.0	0.7	0.3	1.9
Sporting goods, hobby, book, and music stores	451	3.6	1.2	0.8	0.4	2.4
General merchandise stores	452	6.4	3.9	1.7	2.2	2.5
Miscellaneous store retailers	453	3.7	2.1	1.3	0.7	1.6
Nonstore retailers	454	5.0	3.1	1.8	1.3	1.9
Transportation and warehousing	48–49	6.4	4.3	2.7	1.6	2.1
Air transportation	481	9.9	7.3	5.2	2.1	2.6
Rail transportation	482	2.3	1.7	1.5	0.2	0.6
Water transportation	483	(e)	2.6	2.1	0.5	(e)
Truck transportation	484	5.6	3.5	2.6	0.9	2.1
Transit and ground passenger transportation	485	5.3	3.3	2.4	0.9	2.0
Pipeline transportation	486	2.0	0.9	0.5	0.4	1.2
Scenic and sightseeing transportation	487	4.2	2.4	2.0	0.4	1.8
Support activities for transportation	488	4.9	3.2	1.9	1.3	1.7
Couriers and messengers	492	9.8	6.8	3.3	3.5	3.0
Warehousing and storage	493	7.7	5.5	2.1	3.3	2.2
Utilities	22	4.0	2.1	1.2	0.9	1.9
Electric power generation, transmission and distribution	2211	3.6	1.8	1.0	0.7	1.9
Natural gas distribution	2212	4.7	2.9	1.6	1.3	1.8
Water, sewage and other systems	2213	5.7	3.2	2.1	1.0	2.5
Information		**2.0**	**1.1**	**0.7**	**0.4**	**1.0**
Publishing industries (except Internet)	511	1.8	0.9	0.6	0.3	0.9
Motion picture and sound recording industries	512	2.7	0.8	0.6	0.2	1.9
Broadcasting (except Internet)	515	2.4	1.4	0.7	0.6	1.1
Telecommunications	517	2.5	1.5	1.0	0.5	0.9
Internet service providers, web search portals, and data processing services	518	0.9	0.4	0.3	0.1	0.5
Other information services	519	1.2	0.6	0.5	0.1	0.6
Financial Activities		**1.4**	**0.7**	**0.5**	**0.2**	**0.8**
Finance and insurance	52	0.9	0.4	0.3	0.1	0.6
Monetary authorities	521	1.1	0.7	0.3	0.4	0.4
Credit intermediation and related activities	522	1.0	0.4	0.3	0.1	0.6
Securities, commodity contracts, and other financial investments and related activities	523	0.3	0.1	0.1	(f)	0.2
Insurance carriers and related activities	524	1.1	0.4	0.3	0.1	0.7
Funds, trusts, and other financial activities	525	1.1	0.5	0.4	0.2	0.6
Real estate and rental and leasing	53	2.9	1.6	1.0	0.5	1.4
Real estate	531	2.7	1.4	1.0	0.4	1.3
Rental and leasing services	532	3.5	1.9	1.1	0.8	1.6
Lessors of nonfinancial intangible assets (except copyrighted works)	533	1.0	0.7	0.6	0.1	0.3
Professional and Business Services		**2.1**	**1.0**	**0.6**	**0.4**	**1.1**
Professional, scientific, and technical services	54	1.3	0.5	0.3	0.2	0.8
Management of companies and enterprises	55	1.9	0.9	0.5	0.4	1.0
Administrative and support and waste management and remediation services	56	3.3	1.8	1.2	0.6	1.5
Administrative and support services	561	3.1	1.7	1.1	0.5	1.5
Waste management and remediation services	562	6.4	4.1	2.4	1.7	2.3
Education and Health Services		**5.2**	**2.4**	**1.3**	**1.0**	**2.9**
Educational services	61	2.4	1.0	0.7	0.3	1.5
Health care and social assistance	62	5.6	2.5	1.4	1.1	3.1
Ambulatory health care services	621	3.0	1.0	0.6	0.3	2.0
Hospitals	622	7.7	3.0	1.7	1.3	4.6
Nursing and residential care facilities	623	8.8	5.2	2.6	2.6	3.5
Social assistance	624	3.9	1.9	1.3	0.6	2.0
Leisure and Hospitality		**4.5**	**1.7**	**1.1**	**0.6**	**2.8**
Arts, entertainment, and recreation	71	5.3	2.5	1.4	1.1	2.8
Accommodation and food services	72	4.4	1.6	1.0	0.6	2.8
Accommodation	721	5.6	2.9	1.4	1.5	2.6
Food services and drinking places	722	4.1	1.3	0.9	0.3	2.9
Other Services, Except Public Administration		**3.1**	**1.5**	**1.0**	**0.5**	**1.7**
Repair and maintenance	811	3.9	1.8	1.4	0.5	2.0
Personal and laundry services	812	2.6	1.3	0.8	0.5	1.2
Religious, grantmaking, civic, professional, and similar organizations	813	2.8	1.2	0.8	0.4	1.6

See source and footnotes on page 61.

OCCUPATIONAL INJURIES
AND ILLNESSES (CONT.)

BLS ESTIMATES OF NONFATAL OCCUPATIONAL INJURY AND ILLNESS INCIDENCE RATES FOR SELECTED INDUSTRIES, 2007

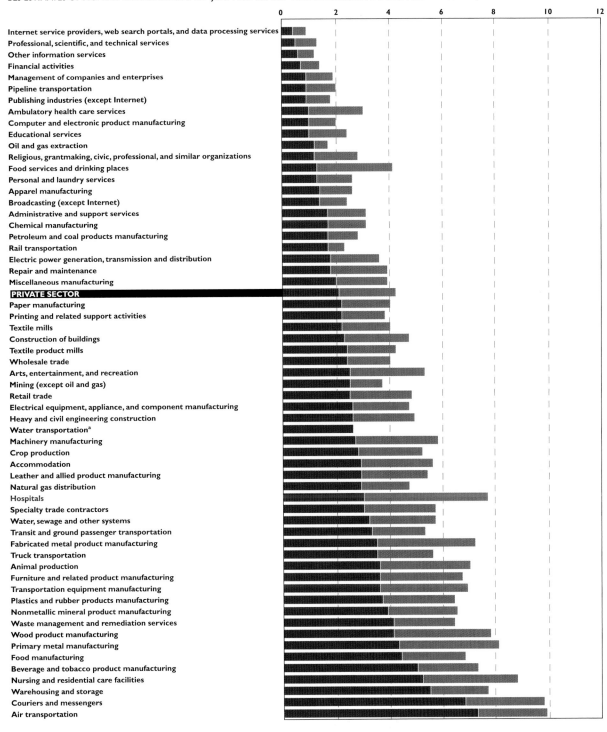

Note: Industries are shown at the 2-, 3-, or 4-digit NAICS level.
Total Cases with Days Away from Work, Job Transfer, or Restriction plus Other Recordable
Cases equals Total Recordable Cases.
[a]Data for Total Recordable Cases and Other Recordable Cases do not meet publication guidelines.

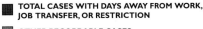 **TOTAL CASES WITH DAYS AWAY FROM WORK,
JOB TRANSFER, OR RESTRICTION**

OTHER RECORDABLE CASES

The tables on pages 67 through 82 present data on the characteristics of injured and ill workers and the injuries and illnesses that affected them. These data indicate how many workers died from on-the-job injuries and how many were affected by nonfatal injuries and illnesses. The data may be used to help set priorities for occupational safety and health programs and for benchmarking.

The fatality information covers only deaths due to injuries and comes from the Bureau of Labor Statistics (BLS) Census of Fatal Occupational Injuries. The data are for the calendar year 2006 and include wage and salary workers, the self-employed, and unpaid family workers in all types of businesses and industries.

The data on nonfatal cases cover both occupational injuries and illnesses and come from the BLS Survey of Occupational Injuries and Illnesses for 2006. The Survey also is used to produce the incidence rates shown on the preceding pages. The estimates on the following pages are the number of cases involving days away from work (with or without days of restricted work activity). The survey does not cover the self-employed or unpaid family workers or federal, state, or local government employees.

Data are presented for the sex, age, occupation, and race or ethnic origin of the worker and for the nature of injury/illness, the part of body affected, the source of injury/illness, and the event or exposure that produced the injury/illness.

The text at the top of each page describes the kind of establishments that are included in the industry sector and gives the total number of workers in the industry in 2006 and the number working in the private sector.

How to Benchmark

Incidence rates, percent distributions, or ranks may be used for benchmarking purposes. The results of the calculations described here may be compared to similar rates, percent distributions, and rankings based on data for a company.

For nonfatal cases incidence rates, multiply the number of cases by 1,000 and then divide by the *private-sector* employment given in the text at the top of the page. This will give the number of cases with days away from work per 1,000 employees per year. For fatality rates, multiply the number of fatalities by 100,000 then divide by the *total* employment given at the top of the page. This will give the number of deaths per 100,000 employees per year.

To compute percent distributions, divide number of cases for each characteristic by the total number of cases found on the first line of the table. Multiply the quotient by 100 and round to one decimal place. Percent distributions may not add to 100.0% because of unclassifiable cases not shown.

Ranks are determined by arranging the characteristics from largest to smallest within each group and then numbering consecutively starting with 1 for the largest.

Industry Sectors

Page 67 shows nonfatal injury/illness data for the private sector of the economy (excluding government entities) and fatal injury data for all industries (including government). Pages 68 through 81 present the data for industry sectors based on the North American Industry Classification System (NAICS). Page 82 presents the fatal injury data for government (the BLS Survey does not cover government entities nationwide so no nonfatal case data are available).

The nonfatal occupational injury and illness data cover only private sector employees and exclude employees in federal, state, and local government entities and the self-employed. The fatal injury data cover all workers in both the private sector and government.

There were 145,607,000 people employed in 2006, of which 124,038,000 worked in the private sector.

NUMBER OF NONFATAL OCCUPATIONAL INJURIES AND ILLNESSES INVOLVING DAYS AWAY FROM WORK[a] AND FATAL OCCUPATIONAL INJURIES BY SELECTED WORKER AND CASE CHARACTERISTICS, UNITED STATES, 2006

Characteristic	Private Industry[b,c] Nonfatal Cases	All Industries Fatalities
Total	1,183,500	5,840
Sex		
Men	775,900	5,396
Women	403,740	444
Age		
Under 16	170	11
16 to 19	39,330	127
20 to 24	132,120	390
25 to 34	270,670	1,041
35 to 44	301,700	1,288
45 to 54	266,660	1,417
55 to 64	134,030	963
65 and over	25,170	599
Occupation		
Management, business, and financial	25,810	589
Professional and related	81,190	99
Service	245,150	901
Sales and related	76,210	316
Office and administrative support	83,320	88
Farming, fishing, and forestry	14,330	297
Construction and extractive	149,910	1,273
Installation, maintenance, and repair	94,890	423
Production	171,030	285
Transportation and material moving	239,710	1,501
Military occupations	—	57
Race or ethnic origin[d]		
White, non-Hispanic	523,320	4,006
Black, non-Hispanic	94,370	565
Hispanic	158,760	990
Other, multiple, and not reported	407,060	279
Nature of injury, illness		
Sprains, strains	472,740	14
Fractures	94,110	39
Cuts, lacerations, punctures	115,210	645
Bruises, contusions	101,260	—
Heat burns	17,440	134
Chemical burns	7,490	—
Amputations	7,990	17
Carpal tunnel syndrome	13,010	—
Tendonitis	4,750	—
Multiple injuries	45,890	2,157
Soreness, Pain	105,050	—
Back pain	35,330	—
All other	198,550	2,829

Characteristic	Private Industry[b,c] Nonfatal Cases	All Industries Fatalities
Part of body affected		
Head	82,420	1,312
Eye	35,970	—
Neck	17,840	110
Trunk	401,900	901
Back	250,870	66
Shoulder	75,810	—
Upper extremities	274,180	18
Finger	106,050	—
Hand, except finger	49,480	—
Wrist	48,810	—
Lower extremities	262,180	78
Knee	95,520	8
Foot, toe	57,450	10
Body systems	18,220	972
Multiple	115,930	2,429
All other	10,840	20
Source of injury, illness		
Chemicals, chemical products	19,480	201
Containers	147,320	94
Furniture, fixtures	45,330	29
Machinery	77,500	491
Parts and materials	124,640	386
Worker motion or position	163,430	—
Floor, ground surfaces	214,580	789
Handtools	56,790	97
Vehicles	101,320	2,513
Health care patient	52,660	6
All other	180,440	1,231
Event or exposure		
Contact with object, equipment	335,460	993
Struck by object	164,670	589
Struck against object	85,710	10
Caught in object, equipment, material	59,260	391
Fall to lower level	74,280	738
Fall on same level	151,750	67
Slips, trips	35,440	—
Overexertion	284,910	10
Overexertion in lifting	150,990	6
Repetitive motion	38,310	—
Exposed to harmful substance	56,510	547
Transportation accidents	56,170	2,459
Highway accident	36,330	1,356
Nonhighway accident, except air, rail, water	8,560	345
Pedestrian, nonpassenger struck by vehicle, mobile equipment	8,400	379
Fires, explosions	2,270	202
Assault, violent act	22,430	788
By person	15,970	540
By other	6,460	248
All other	125,960	33

Source: National Safety Council tabulations of Bureau of Labor Statistics data.
Note: Because of rounding and data exclusion of nonclassifiable responses, data may not sum to the totals. Dashes (—) indicate data that do not meet publication guidelines.
[a]Days away from work include those that result in days away from work with or without restricted work activity or job transfer.
[b]Excludes farms with fewer than 11 employees.

[c]Data for mining operators in coal, metal, and nonmetal mining and for employees in railroad transportation are provided to BLS by the Mine Safety and Health Administration, U.S. Department of Labor; and the Federal Railroad Administration, U.S. Department of Transportation. Independent mining contractors are excluded from the coal, metal, and nonmetal mining industries. MSHA and FRA data do not reflect the changes in OSHA record-keeping requirements in 2002.
[d]In the fatalities column, non-Hispanic categories include cases with Hispanic origin not reported.

AGRICULTURE, FORESTRY, FISHING, HUNTING

The Agriculture, Forestry, Fishing and Hunting industry sector includes growing crops, raising animals, harvesting timber, and harvesting fish and other animals from a farm, ranch, or their natural habitats, and agricultural support services.

Employment in Agriculture, Forestry, Fishing, and Hunting totaled 2,206,000 in 2006 of which 2,155,000 were private sector employees.

NUMBER OF NONFATAL OCCUPATIONAL INJURIES AND ILLNESSES INVOLVING DAYS AWAY FROM WORK[a] AND FATAL OCCUPATIONAL INJURIES BY SELECTED WORKER AND CASE CHARACTERISTICS, UNITED STATES, AGRICULTURE, FORESTRY, FISHING, AND HUNTING, 2006

Characteristic	Nonfatal Cases[b]	Fatalities
Total	**16,890**	**655**
Sex		
Men	13,560	630
Women	3,320	25
Age		
Under 16	100	9
16 to 19	650	13
20 to 24	2,080	27
25 to 34	4,280	57
35 to 44	3,930	102
45 to 54	3,480	124
55 to 64	1,780	130
65 and over	430	193
Occupation		
Management, business, and financial	390	307
Professional and related	210	—
Service	660	—
Sales and related	30	—
Office and administrative support	260	—
Farming, fishing, and forestry	12,340	278
Construction and extractive	100	—
Installation, maintenance, and repair	490	—
Production	800	—
Transportation and material moving	1,600	58
Military occupations	—	—
Race or ethnic origin[c]		
White, non-Hispanic	4,230	517
Black, non-Hispanic	460	28
Hispanic	8,890	90
Other, multiple, and not reported	3,290	20
Nature of injury, illness		
Sprains, strains	5,130	—
Fractures	1,760	—
Cuts, lacerations, punctures	1,710	22
Bruises, contusions	1,820	—
Heat burns	180	8
Chemical burns	80	—
Amputations	170	—
Carpal tunnel syndrome	60	—
Tendonitis	80	—
Multiple injuries	820	210
Soreness, Pain	1,280	—
Back pain	*380*	—
All other	3,800	409

Characteristic	Nonfatal Cases[b]	Fatalities
Part of body affected		
Head	1,790	119
Eye	*910*	—
Neck	250	12
Trunk	5,030	141
Back	*3,140*	*7*
Shoulder	*640*	—
Upper extremities	3,780	—
Finger	*1,540*	—
Hand, except finger	*730*	—
Wrist	*530*	—
Lower extremities	3,820	7
Knee	*1,220*	—
Foot, toe	*750*	—
Body systems	290	154
Multiple	1,580	219
All other	340	—
Source of injury, illness		
Chemicals, chemical products	240	8
Containers	1,090	14
Furniture, fixtures	180	—
Machinery	1,170	84
Parts and materials	1,220	12
Worker motion or position	2,090	—
Floor, ground surfaces	3,180	22
Handtools	840	9
Vehicles	1,750	350
Health care patient	—	—
All other	5,130	155
Event or exposure		
Contact with object, equipment	5,640	212
Struck by object	*2,690*	*137*
Struck against object	*1,250*	—
Caught in object, equipment, material	*1,130*	*73*
Fall to lower level	1,390	21
Fall on same level	1,920	—
Slips, trips	590	—
Overexertion	1,850	—
Overexertion in lifting	*1,030*	—
Repetitive motion	280	—
Exposed to harmful substance	880	51
Transportation accidents	1,210	312
Highway accident	*540*	*76*
Nonhighway accident, except air, rail, water	*430*	*150*
Pedestrian, nonpassenger struck by vehicle, mobile equipment	*240*	*27*
Fires, explosions	70	11
Assault, violent act	900	46
By person	*100*	—
By other	*800*	*43*
All other	2,170	—

Source: National Safety Council tabulations of Bureau of Labor Statistics data.
Note: Because of rounding and data exclusion of nonclassifiable responses, data may not sum to the totals. Dashes (—) indicate data that do not meet publication guidelines.
[a]Days away from work include those that result in days away from work with or without restricted work activity or job transfer.
[b]Excludes farms with fewer than 11 employees.
[c]In the fatalities column, non-Hispanic categories include cases with Hispanic origin not reported.

MINING

The Mining industry sector includes extraction of naturally occurring mineral solids, such as coal and ores; liquid minerals, such as crude petroleum; and gases, such as natural gas. It also includes quarrying, well operations, beneficiating, other preparation customarily performed at the site, and mining support activities.

Mining employment in 2006 amounted to 686,000 workers of which 683,000 were private sector employees.

NUMBER OF NONFATAL OCCUPATIONAL INJURIES AND ILLNESSES INVOLVING DAYS AWAY FROM WORK[a] AND FATAL OCCUPATIONAL INJURIES BY SELECTED WORKER AND CASE CHARACTERISTICS, UNITED STATES, MINING, 2006

Characteristic	Nonfatal Cases[b]	Fatalities
Total	**9,410**	**192**
Sex		
Men	9,180	191
Women	230	—
Age		
Under 16	—	—
16 to 19	200	7
20 to 24	1,140	25
25 to 34	2,740	37
35 to 44	2,030	43
45 to 54	2,180	49
55 to 64	930	23
65 and over	90	8
Occupation		
Management, business, and financial	20	—
Professional and related	120	8
Service	20	—
Sales and related	—	—
Office and administrative support	30	—
Farming, fishing, and forestry	—	—
Construction and extractive	5,070	135
Installation, maintenance, and repair	1,040	14
Production	1,150	8
Transportation and material moving	1,930	27
Military occupations	—	—
Race or ethnic origin[c]		
White, non-Hispanic	2,670	150
Black, non-Hispanic	200	7
Hispanic	790	29
Other, multiple, and not reported	5,730	6
Nature of injury, illness		
Sprains, strains	3,100	—
Fractures	1,650	—
Cuts, lacerations, punctures	740	—
Bruises, contusions	1,150	—
Heat burns	250	7
Chemical burns	70	—
Amputations	140	—
Carpal tunnel syndrome	—	—
Tendonitis	—	—
Multiple injuries	290	73
Soreness, Pain	340	—
Back pain	160	—
All other	1,670	110

Characteristic	Nonfatal Cases[b]	Fatalities
Part of body affected		
Head	870	36
Eye	250	—
Neck	180	—
Trunk	3,100	30
Back	1,590	—
Shoulder	590	—
Upper extremities	2,150	—
Finger	920	—
Hand, except finger	480	—
Wrist	280	—
Lower extremities	2,210	—
Knee	860	—
Foot, toe	430	—
Body systems	190	43
Multiple	690	78
All other	20	—
Source of injury, illness		
Chemicals, chemical products	470	20
Containers	370	8
Furniture, fixtures	60	—
Machinery	1,080	35
Parts and materials	1,580	35
Worker motion or position	340	—
Floor, ground surfaces	1,830	7
Handtools	670	—
Vehicles	740	54
Health care patient	—	—
All other	2,260	32
Event or exposure		
Contact with object, equipment	4,210	60
Struck by object	2,140	34
Struck against object	850	—
Caught in object, equipment, material	1,130	26
Fall to lower level	630	10
Fall on same level	1,140	—
Slips, trips	80	—
Overexertion	2,020	—
Overexertion in lifting	640	—
Repetitive motion	50	—
Exposed to harmful substance	530	15
Transportation accidents	240	63
Highway accident	140	30
Nonhighway accident, except air, rail, water	40	12
Pedestrian, nonpassenger struck by vehicle, mobile equipment	40	11
Fires, explosions	40	42
Assault, violent act	20	—
By person	—	—
By other	20	—
All other	430	—

Source: National Safety Council tabulations of Bureau of Labor Statistics data.
Note: Because of rounding and data exclusion of nonclassifiable responses, data may not sum to the totals. Dashes (—) indicate data that do not meet publication guidelines.
[a] Days away from work include those that result in days away from work with or without restricted work activity or job transfer.

[b] Data for mining operators in coal, metal, and nonmetal mining are provided to BLS by the Mine Safety and Health Administration, U.S. Department of Labor. Independent mining contractors are excluded from the coal, metal, and nonmetal mining industries. MSHA data do not reflect the changes in OSHA record-keeping requirements in 2002.
[c] In the fatalities column, non-Hispanic categories include cases with Hispanic origin not reported.

CONSTRUCTION

The Construction industry sector includes establishments engaged in construction of buildings, heavy construction other than buildings, and specialty trade contractors such as plumbing, electrical, carpentry, etc.

In 2006, employment in the Construction industry totaled 11,749,000 workers of which 11,312,000 were private sector employees.

NUMBER OF NONFATAL OCCUPATIONAL INJURIES AND ILLNESSES INVOLVING DAYS AWAY FROM WORKª AND FATAL OCCUPATIONAL INJURIES BY SELECTED WORKER AND CASE CHARACTERISTICS, UNITED STATES, CONSTRUCTION, 2006

Characteristic	Nonfatal Cases	Fatalities
Total	**153,180**	**1,239**
Sex		
Men	148,530	1,224
Women	4,650	15
Age		
Under 16	—	—
16 to 19	3,680	36
20 to 24	21,980	117
25 to 34	42,170	280
35 to 44	40,330	284
45 to 54	30,850	287
55 to 64	10,520	170
65 and over	1,650	62
Occupation		
Management, business, and financial	2,180	61
Professional and related	490	10
Service	1,250	11
Sales and related	600	—
Office and administrative support	1,100	—
Farming, fishing, and forestry	30	—
Construction and extractive	124,470	986
Installation, maintenance, and repair	11,570	66
Production	5,820	26
Transportation and material moving	5,550	71
Military occupations	—	—
Race or ethnic origin[b]		
White, non-Hispanic	83,100	773
Black, non-Hispanic	6,770	87
Hispanic	33,930	354
Other, multiple, and not reported	29,390	25
Nature of injury, illness		
Sprains, strains	52,880	—
Fractures	17,670	6
Cuts, lacerations, punctures	23,930	38
Bruises, contusions	9,460	—
Heat burns	1,490	20
Chemical burns	1,070	—
Amputations	1,220	—
Carpal tunnel syndrome	890	—
Tendonitis	220	—
Multiple injuries	5,690	467
Soreness, Pain	12,030	—
Back pain	*4,050*	—
All other	26,620	702

Characteristic	Nonfatal Cases	Fatalities
Part of body affected		
Head	12,510	310
Eye	*7,050*	—
Neck	2,220	24
Trunk	44,600	153
Back	*28,020*	*15*
Shoulder	*7,630*	—
Upper extremities	38,370	—
Finger	*16,390*	—
Hand, except finger	*7,950*	—
Wrist	*4,900*	—
Lower extremities	40,150	6
Knee	*14,550*	—
Foot, toe	*7,970*	—
Body systems	1,690	247
Multiple	12,440	496
All other	1,190	—
Source of injury, illness		
Chemicals, chemical products	1,730	42
Containers	7,490	13
Furniture, fixtures	2,380	7
Machinery	10,950	149
Parts and materials	34,870	145
Worker motion or position	19,740	—
Floor, ground surfaces	28,010	408
Handtools	13,780	26
Vehicles	8,380	273
Health care patient	—	—
All other	25,860	175
Event or exposure		
Contact with object, equipment	58,440	216
Struck by object	*30,210*	*120*
Struck against object	*14,520*	—
Caught in object, equipment, material	*8,350*	*95*
Fall to lower level	18,230	424
Fall on same level	12,230	—
Slips, trips	4,220	—
Overexertion	26,680	—
Overexertion in lifting	*15,480*	—
Repetitive motion	2,640	—
Exposed to harmful substance	5,130	191
Transportation accidents	6,350	323
Highway accident	*3,840*	*152*
Nonhighway accident, except air, rail, water	*1,040*	*57*
Pedestrian, nonpassenger struck by vehicle, mobile equipment	*1,370*	*91*
Fires, explosions	540	30
Assault, violent act	460	42
By person	*150*	*19*
By other	*310*	*23*
All other	18,240	10

Source: National Safety Council tabulations of Bureau of Labor Statistics data.
Note: Because of rounding and data exclusion of nonclassifiable responses, data may not sum to the totals. Dashes (—) indicate data that do not meet publication guidelines.

ªDays away from work include those that result in days away from work with or without restricted work activity or job transfer.
[b]In the fatalities column, non-Hispanic categories include cases with Hispanic origin not reported.

MANUFACTURING

The Manufacturing industry sector includes establishments engaged in the mechanical or chemical transformation of materials, substances, or components into new products. It includes durable and nondurable goods such as food, textiles, apparel, lumber, wood products, paper and paper products, printing, chemicals and pharmaceuticals, petroleum and coal products, rubber and plastics products, metals and metal products, machinery, electrical equipment, and transportation equipment.

Manufacturing employment in 2006 was 16,377,000 workers of which 16,297,000 were private sector employees.

NUMBER OF NONFATAL OCCUPATIONAL INJURIES AND ILLNESSES INVOLVING DAYS AWAY FROM WORK[a] AND FATAL OCCUPATIONAL INJURIES BY SELECTED WORKER AND CASE CHARACTERISTICS, UNITED STATES, MANUFACTURING, 2006

Characteristic	Nonfatal Cases	Fatalities
Total	**200,970**	**456**
Sex		
Men	157,290	435
Women	43,440	21
Age		
Under 16	—	—
16 to 19	4,350	9
20 to 24	20,000	24
25 to 34	42,910	74
35 to 44	53,630	102
45 to 54	50,200	144
55 to 64	25,170	75
65 and over	2,580	28
Occupation		
Management, business, and financial	1,810	25
Professional and related	2,510	17
Service	3,790	6
Sales and related	1,220	10
Office and administrative support	7,310	10
Farming, fishing, and forestry	620	—
Construction and extractive	7,510	35
Installation, maintenance, and repair	13,620	55
Production	126,670	167
Transportation and material moving	35,550	126
Military occupations	—	—
Race or ethnic origin[b]		
White, non-Hispanic	101,550	321
Black, non-Hispanic	15,790	36
Hispanic	31,220	85
Other, multiple, and not reported	52,410	14
Nature of injury, illness		
Sprains, strains	67,810	6
Fractures	16,760	—
Cuts, lacerations, punctures	24,240	27
Bruises, contusions	16,810	—
Heat burns	3,440	17
Chemical burns	1,840	—
Amputations	3,800	—
Carpal tunnel syndrome	5,050	—
Tendonitis	1,680	—
Multiple injuries	7,130	161
Soreness, Pain	14,360	—
Back pain	4,610	—
All other	38,050	239

Characteristic	Nonfatal Cases	Fatalities
Part of body affected		
Head	15,530	105
Eye	9,550	—
Neck	2,090	5
Trunk	62,670	64
Back	34,980	5
Shoulder	13,520	—
Upper extremities	66,180	—
Finger	30,430	—
Hand, except finger	10,670	—
Wrist	11,420	—
Lower extremities	37,360	11
Knee	13,230	—
Foot, toe	9,430	—
Body systems	2,420	84
Multiple	13,170	185
All other	1,540	—
Source of injury, illness		
Chemicals, chemical products	4,380	28
Containers	23,300	15
Furniture, fixtures	5,830	—
Machinery	26,070	86
Parts and materials	36,490	51
Worker motion or position	33,820	—
Floor, ground surfaces	23,760	55
Handtools	11,350	5
Vehicles	10,490	136
Health care patient	—	—
All other	25,460	75
Event or exposure		
Contact with object, equipment	76,400	152
Struck by object	32,550	64
Struck against object	15,070	—
Caught in object, equipment, material	22,380	87
Fall to lower level	7,820	52
Fall on same level	17,810	6
Slips, trips	4,720	—
Overexertion	44,390	—
Overexertion in lifting	23,350	—
Repetitive motion	14,670	—
Exposed to harmful substance	10,670	47
Transportation accidents	4,100	125
Highway accident	1,480	60
Nonhighway accident, except air, rail, water	1,110	19
Pedestrian, nonpassenger struck by vehicle, mobile equipment	1,390	22
Fires, explosions	460	34
Assault, violent act	570	33
By person	220	16
By other	360	17
All other	19,340	—

Source: National Safety Council tabulations of Bureau of Labor Statistics data.
Note: Because of rounding and data exclusion of nonclassifiable responses, data may not sum to the totals. Dashes (—) indicate data that do not meet publication guidelines.

[a]Days away from work include those that result in days away from work with or without restricted work activity or job transfer.
[b]In the fatalities column, non-Hispanic categories include cases with Hispanic origin not reported.

WHOLESALE TRADE

Establishments in Wholesale Trade generally sell merchandise to other businesses. The merchandise includes the outputs of agriculture, mining, manufacturing, and certain information industries, such as publishing.

Wholesale Trade employed 4,562,000 people in 2006 of which 4,550,000 were private sector employees.

NUMBER OF NONFATAL OCCUPATIONAL INJURIES AND ILLNESSES INVOLVING DAYS AWAY FROM WORK[a] AND FATAL OCCUPATIONAL INJURIES BY SELECTED WORKER AND CASE CHARACTERISTICS, UNITED STATES, WHOLESALE TRADE, 2006

Characteristic	Nonfatal Cases	Fatalities
Total	**75,700**	**222**
Sex		
Men	65,860	215
Women	9,850	7
Age		
Under 16	—	—
16 to 19	2,500	5
20 to 24	7,540	14
25 to 34	18,050	42
35 to 44	21,490	43
45 to 54	15,740	58
55 to 64	7,850	36
65 and over	1,780	23
Occupation		
Management, business, and financial	1,350	11
Professional and related	560	—
Service	1,070	—
Sales and related	5,040	41
Office and administrative support	6,110	—
Farming, fishing, and forestry	590	5
Construction and extractive	1,940	—
Installation, maintenance, and repair	8,540	33
Production	9,030	14
Transportation and material moving	41,360	108
Military occupations	—	—
Race or ethnic origin[b]		
White, non-Hispanic	37,550	160
Black, non-Hispanic	5,970	22
Hispanic	9,500	33
Other, multiple, and not reported	22,670	7
Nature of injury, illness		
Sprains, strains	31,290	—
Fractures	6,230	—
Cuts, lacerations, punctures	6,450	9
Bruises, contusions	6,790	—
Heat burns	670	7
Chemical burns	760	—
Amputations	370	—
Carpal tunnel syndrome	900	—
Tendonitis	170	—
Multiple injuries	2,930	89
Soreness, Pain	7,140	—
Back pain	2,830	—
All other	12,030	111

Characteristic	Nonfatal Cases	Fatalities
Part of body affected		
Head	5,000	54
Eye	2,000	—
Neck	1,030	5
Trunk	28,260	28
Back	17,510	—
Shoulder	5,400	—
Upper extremities	15,230	—
Finger	5,970	—
Hand, except finger	2,540	—
Wrist	3,110	—
Lower extremities	18,450	—
Knee	6,430	—
Foot, toe	5,270	—
Body systems	860	32
Multiple	6,350	99
All other	520	—
Source of injury, illness		
Chemicals, chemical products	1,230	9
Containers	14,900	5
Furniture, fixtures	1,470	—
Machinery	4,170	23
Parts and materials	9,620	19
Worker motion or position	11,920	—
Floor, ground surfaces	10,280	22
Handtools	3,140	—
Vehicles	10,610	118
Health care patient	—	—
All other	8,350	22
Event or exposure		
Contact with object, equipment	21,970	53
Struck by object	11,290	34
Struck against object	4,960	—
Caught in object, equipment, material	4,230	19
Fall to lower level	4,620	16
Fall on same level	6,590	5
Slips, trips	2,320	—
Overexertion	19,900	—
Overexertion in lifting	11,590	—
Repetitive motion	2,240	—
Exposed to harmful substance	2,650	18
Transportation accidents	5,410	109
Highway accident	3,570	80
Nonhighway accident, except air, rail, water	930	7
Pedestrian, nonpassenger struck by vehicle, mobile equipment	690	12
Fires, explosions	90	6
Assault, violent act	460	12
By person	230	5
By other	220	7
All other	9,460	—

Source: National Safety Council tabulations of Bureau of Labor Statistics data.
Note: Because of rounding and data exclusion of nonclassifiable responses, data may not sum to the totals. Dashes (—) indicate data that do not meet publication guidelines.

[a] Days away from work include those that result in days away from work with or without restricted work activity or job transfer.
[b] In the fatalities column, non-Hispanic categories include cases with Hispanic origin not reported.

RETAIL TRADE

Establishments in Retail Trade generally sell merchandise in small quantities for personal or household consumption. This sector includes both store and nonstore retailers.

Retail Trade employed 16,765,000 people in 2006 of which 16,673,000 were private sector employees.

NUMBER OF NONFATAL OCCUPATIONAL INJURIES AND ILLNESSES INVOLVING DAYS AWAY FROM WORK[a] AND FATAL OCCUPATIONAL INJURIES BY SELECTED WORKER AND CASE CHARACTERISTICS, UNITED STATES, RETAIL TRADE, 2006

Characteristic	Nonfatal Cases	Fatalities
Total	**162,800**	**359**
Sex		
Men	95,720	308
Women	67,030	51
Age		
Under 16	—	—
16 to 19	10,530	6
20 to 24	21,920	20
25 to 34	33,260	55
35 to 44	37,130	79
45 to 54	33,750	89
55 to 64	18,840	65
65 and over	5,190	45
Occupation		
Management, business, and financial	2,560	10
Professional and related	2,160	—
Service	13,830	14
Sales and related	58,210	202
Office and administrative support	21,030	15
Farming, fishing, and forestry	160	—
Construction and extractive	2,320	5
Installation, maintenance, and repair	17,970	25
Production	7,200	9
Transportation and material moving	37,170	75
Military occupations	—	—
Race or ethnic origin[b]		
White, non-Hispanic	70,990	204
Black, non-Hispanic	8,820	40
Hispanic	12,680	48
Other, multiple, and not reported	70,300	67
Nature of injury, illness		
Sprains, strains	71,040	—
Fractures	11,370	5
Cuts, lacerations, punctures	16,590	147
Bruises, contusions	15,340	—
Heat burns	1,310	—
Chemical burns	740	—
Amputations	610	—
Carpal tunnel syndrome	1,340	—
Tendonitis	630	—
Multiple injuries	5,710	89
Soreness, Pain	13,470	—
Back pain	*4,350*	*—*
All other	24,650	115

Characteristic	Nonfatal Cases	Fatalities
Part of body affected		
Head	11,420	104
Eye	*3,920*	*—*
Neck	2,420	7
Trunk	58,830	86
Back	*37,110*	*6*
Shoulder	*11,040*	*—*
Upper extremities	35,560	—
Finger	*13,600*	*—*
Hand, except finger	*6,620*	*—*
Wrist	*6,600*	*—*
Lower extremities	36,370	7
Knee	*13,510*	*—*
Foot, toe	*9,620*	*—*
Body systems	1,830	32
Multiple	14,400	120
All other	1,960	—
Source of injury, illness		
Chemicals, chemical products	2,170	11
Containers	33,980	5
Furniture, fixtures	10,260	—
Machinery	10,300	6
Parts and materials	13,580	20
Worker motion or position	20,710	—
Floor, ground surfaces	29,010	29
Handtools	7,670	13
Vehicles	13,760	124
Health care patient	—	—
All other	21,370	150
Event or exposure		
Contact with object, equipment	47,090	25
Struck by object	*24,780*	*16*
Struck against object	*12,640*	*—*
Caught in object, equipment, material	*6,090*	*9*
Fall to lower level	8,560	21
Fall on same level	22,700	10
Slips, trips	4,300	—
Overexertion	47,350	—
Overexertion in lifting	*29,760*	*—*
Repetitive motion	4,400	—
Exposed to harmful substance	4,500	13
Transportation accidents	5,780	113
Highway accident	*3,400*	*76*
Nonhighway accident, except air, rail, water	*840*	*10*
Pedestrian, nonpassenger struck by vehicle, mobile equipment	*1,420*	*16*
Fires, explosions	310	8
Assault, violent act	1,530	169
By person	*960*	*141*
By other	*570*	*28*
All other	16,280	—

Source: National Safety Council tabulations of Bureau of Labor Statistics data.
Note: Because of rounding and data exclusion of nonclassifiable responses, data may not sum to the totals. Dashes (—) indicate data that do not meet publication guidelines.

[a]Days away from work include those that result in days away from work with or without restricted work activity or job transfer.
[b]In the fatalities column, non-Hispanic categories include cases with Hispanic origin not reported.

TRANSPORTATION AND WAREHOUSING

This industry sector includes transportation of cargo and passengers, warehousing and storage of goods, scenic and sightseeing transportation, and support activities related to transportation by rail, highway, air, water, or pipeline.

Employment in the Transportation and Warehousing industry sector totaled 6,269,000 in 2006 of which 5,112,000 were private sector employees.

NUMBER OF NONFATAL OCCUPATIONAL INJURIES AND ILLNESSES INVOLVING DAYS AWAY FROM WORK[a] AND FATAL OCCUPATIONAL INJURIES BY SELECTED WORKER AND CASE CHARACTERISTICS, UNITED STATES, TRANSPORTATION AND WAREHOUSING,[b] 2006

Characteristic	Nonfatal Cases	Fatalities
Total	**109,800**	**860**
Sex		
Men	84,170	820
Women	22,100	40
Age		
Under 16	—	—
16 to 19	1,940	6
20 to 24	7,530	27
25 to 34	22,230	133
35 to 44	31,620	200
45 to 54	29,460	257
55 to 64	13,750	176
65 and over	2,020	59
Occupation		
Management, business, and financial	420	6
Professional and related	240	—
Service	7,290	6
Sales and related	550	—
Office and administrative support	10,030	6
Farming, fishing, and forestry	50	—
Construction and extractive	1,070	6
Installation, maintenance, and repair	6,970	28
Production	2,410	—
Transportation and material moving	80,520	798
Military occupations	—	—
Race or ethnic origin[c]		
White, non-Hispanic	31,080	613
Black, non-Hispanic	7,290	115
Hispanic	6,340	94
Other, multiple, and not reported	65,090	38
Nature of injury, illness		
Sprains, strains	52,030	—
Fractures	8,750	—
Cuts, lacerations, punctures	4,860	47
Bruises, contusions	11,310	—
Heat burns	300	37
Chemical burns	400	—
Amputations	260	—
Carpal tunnel syndrome	400	—
Tendonitis	230	—
Multiple injuries	4,520	428
Soreness, Pain	10,150	—
Back pain	3,820	—
All other	16,580	339

Characteristic	Nonfatal Cases	Fatalities
Part of body affected		
Head	6,450	152
Eye	2,060	—
Neck	2,480	15
Trunk	42,160	117
Back	24,580	5
Shoulder	9,990	—
Upper extremities	17,650	—
Finger	4,510	—
Hand, except finger	2,910	—
Wrist	3,680	—
Lower extremities	27,510	9
Knee	9,390	—
Foot, toe	6,220	—
Body systems	1,060	89
Multiple	11,550	469
All other	940	7
Source of injury, illness		
Chemicals, chemical products	1,060	14
Containers	24,040	19
Furniture, fixtures	2,530	—
Machinery	2,930	13
Parts and materials	9,220	27
Worker motion or position	14,110	—
Floor, ground surfaces	18,710	25
Handtools	1,800	—
Vehicles	23,830	691
Health care patient	130	—
All other	11,440	68
Event or exposure		
Contact with object, equipment	23,270	87
Struck by object	11,420	53
Struck against object	6,370	—
Caught in object, equipment, material	3,910	34
Fall to lower level	8,910	18
Fall on same level	11,450	—
Slips, trips	3,180	—
Overexertion	31,440	—
Overexertion in lifting	14,870	—
Repetitive motion	1,960	—
Exposed to harmful substance	2,690	32
Transportation accidents	12,460	650
Highway accident	7,700	463
Nonhighway accident, except air, rail, water	2,050	17
Pedestrian, nonpassenger struck by vehicle, mobile equipment	1,150	69
Fires, explosions	70	8
Assault, violent act	910	58
By person	450	41
By other	470	17
All other	13,450	—

Source: National Safety Council tabulations of Bureau of Labor Statistics data.
Note: Because of rounding and data exclusion of nonclassifiable responses, data may not sum to the totals. Dashes (—) indicate data that do not meet publication guidelines.
[a] Days away from work include those that result in days away from work with or without restricted work activity or job transfer.

[b] Data for employees in railroad transportation are provided to BLS by the Federal Railroad Administration, U.S. Department of Transportation. FRA data do not reflect the changes in OSHA record-keeping requirements in 2002.
[c] In the fatalities column, non-Hispanic categories include cases with Hispanic origin not reported.

UTILITIES

The Utilities sector includes establishments that provide electric power generation, transmission, and distribution; natural gas distribution; steam supply; water treatment and distribution; and sewage collection, treatment, and disposal.

The Utilities sector employed 1,186,000 people in 2006, of which 844,000 were private sector employees.

NUMBER OF NONFATAL OCCUPATIONAL INJURIES AND ILLNESSES INVOLVING DAYS AWAY FROM WORK[a] AND FATAL OCCUPATIONAL INJURIES BY SELECTED WORKER AND CASE CHARACTERISTICS, UNITED STATES, UTILITIES, 2006

Characteristic	Nonfatal Cases	Fatalities
Total	**6,210**	**53**
Sex		
Men	5,610	50
Women	590	—
Age		
Under 16	—	—
16 to 19	—	—
20 to 24	320	—
25 to 34	1,140	9
35 to 44	1,760	11
45 to 54	1,850	20
55 to 64	1,030	9
65 and over	30	—
Occupation		
Management, business, and financial	100	—
Professional and related	260	—
Service	130	—
Sales and related	40	—
Office and administrative support	940	—
Farming, fishing, and forestry	—	—
Construction and extractive	830	10
Installation, maintenance, and repair	2,780	30
Production	780	—
Transportation and material moving	330	—
Military occupations	—	—
Race or ethnic origin[b]		
White, non-Hispanic	2,520	44
Black, non-Hispanic	300	—
Hispanic	260	—
Other, multiple, and not reported	3,100	—
Nature of injury, illness		
Sprains, strains	3,020	—
Fractures	430	—
Cuts, lacerations, punctures	310	—
Bruises, contusions	400	—
Heat burns	80	—
Chemical burns	30	—
Amputations	20	—
Carpal tunnel syndrome	120	—
Tendonitis	20	—
Multiple injuries	150	19
Soreness, Pain	420	—
Back pain	*130*	—
All other	1,200	31

Characteristic	Nonfatal Cases	Fatalities
Part of body affected		
Head	290	8
Eye	*130*	—
Neck	130	—
Trunk	2,140	7
Back	*1,260*	—
Shoulder	*540*	—
Upper extremities	1,060	—
Finger	*260*	—
Hand, except finger	*170*	—
Wrist	*250*	—
Lower extremities	1,600	—
Knee	*740*	—
Foot, toe	*200*	—
Body systems	150	17
Multiple	800	18
All other	40	—
Source of injury, illness		
Chemicals, chemical products	70	—
Containers	240	—
Furniture, fixtures	30	—
Machinery	270	—
Parts and materials	850	10
Worker motion or position	1,490	—
Floor, ground surfaces	1,230	7
Handtools	400	—
Vehicles	500	18
Health care patient	—	—
All other	1,120	11
Event or exposure		
Contact with object, equipment	1,140	8
Struck by object	*510*	*6*
Struck against object	*390*	—
Caught in object, equipment, material	*160*	—
Fall to lower level	530	6
Fall on same level	560	—
Slips, trips	260	—
Overexertion	1,250	—
Overexertion in lifting	*480*	—
Repetitive motion	300	—
Exposed to harmful substance	450	16
Transportation accidents	350	17
Highway accident	*280*	*9*
Nonhighway accident, except air, rail, water	*20*	—
Pedestrian, nonpassenger struck by vehicle, mobile equipment	*30*	—
Fires, explosions	30	—
Assault, violent act	140	—
By person	*30*	—
By other	*110*	—
All other	1,200	—

Source: National Safety Council tabulations of Bureau of Labor Statistics data.
Note: Because of rounding and data exclusion of nonclassifiable responses, data may not sum to the totals. Dashes (—) indicate data that do not meet publication guidelines.

[a]Days away from work include those that result in days away from work with or without restricted work activity or job transfer.
[b]In the fatalities column, non-Hispanic categories include cases with Hispanic origin not reported.

The Information sector includes establishments that (a) produce and distribute information and cultural products, (b) provide the means to transmit or distribute these products as well as data or communications, and (c) process data. Included are both traditional and Internet publishing and broadcasting, motion pictures and sound recordings, telecommunications, Internet service providers, Web search portals, data processing, and information services.

The Information sector employed 3,573,000 people in 2006 of which 3,374,000 were private sector employees.

NUMBER OF NONFATAL OCCUPATIONAL INJURIES AND ILLNESSES INVOLVING DAYS AWAY FROM WORKa AND FATAL OCCUPATIONAL INJURIES BY SELECTED WORKER AND CASE CHARACTERISTICS, UNITED STATES, INFORMATION, 2006

Characteristic	Nonfatal Cases	Fatalities
Total	**18,560**	**66**
Sex		
Men	12,840	52
Women	5,720	14
Age		
Under 16	—	—
16 to 19	320	—
20 to 24	960	—
25 to 34	3,970	11
35 to 44	5,590	19
45 to 54	5,130	18
55 to 64	2,200	9
65 and over	220	5
Occupation		
Management, business, and financial	600	—
Professional and related	2,160	—
Service	780	11
Sales and related	970	5
Office and administrative support	3,670	—
Farming, fishing, and forestry	—	—
Construction and extractive	150	—
Installation, maintenance, and repair	6,480	21
Production	1,820	—
Transportation and material moving	1,890	20
Military occupations	—	—
Race or ethnic originb		
White, non-Hispanic	6,230	55
Black, non-Hispanic	980	—
Hispanic	900	5
Other, multiple, and not reported	10,440	—
Nature of injury, illness		
Sprains, strains	7,850	—
Fractures	1,610	—
Cuts, lacerations, punctures	910	6
Bruises, contusions	1,570	—
Heat burns	50	—
Chemical burns	20	—
Amputations	40	—
Carpal tunnel syndrome	420	—
Tendonitis	100	—
Multiple injuries	810	32
Soreness, Pain	1,820	—
Back pain	520	—
All other	3,340	28

Characteristic	Nonfatal Cases	Fatalities
Part of body affected		
Head	1,090	19
Eye	320	—
Neck	400	—
Trunk	5,790	6
Back	3,670	—
Shoulder	1,200	—
Upper extremities	3,700	—
Finger	1,000	—
Hand, except finger	560	—
Wrist	930	—
Lower extremities	4,400	—
Knee	1,830	—
Foot, toe	760	—
Body systems	400	9
Multiple	2,610	31
All other	180	—
Source of injury, illness		
Chemicals, chemical products	140	—
Containers	1,540	—
Furniture, fixtures	610	—
Machinery	1,020	—
Parts and materials	1,060	5
Worker motion or position	4,100	—
Floor, ground surfaces	4,690	9
Handtools	360	—
Vehicles	1,860	40
Health care patient	—	—
All other	3,170	6
Event or exposure		
Contact with object, equipment	3,410	7
Struck by object	1,410	—
Struck against object	1,120	—
Caught in object, equipment, material	710	—
Fall to lower level	1,760	8
Fall on same level	3,190	—
Slips, trips	700	—
Overexertion	3,070	—
Overexertion in lifting	1,470	—
Repetitive motion	1,150	—
Exposed to harmful substance	770	5
Transportation accidents	1,370	40
Highway accident	1,130	29
Nonhighway accident, except air, rail, water	160	—
Pedestrian, nonpassenger struck by vehicle, mobile equipment	60	5
Fires, explosions	—	—
Assault, violent act	250	5
By person	100	—
By other	150	—
All other	2,880	—

Source: National Safety Council tabulations of Bureau of Labor Statistics data.
Note: Because of rounding and data exclusion of nonclassifiable responses, data may not sum to the totals. Dashes (—) indicate data that do not meet publication guidelines.

aDays away from work include those that result in days away from work with or without restricted work activity or job transfer.
bIn the fatalities column, non-Hispanic categories include cases with Hispanic origin not reported.

FINANCIAL ACTIVITIES

Financial Activities includes the Finance and Insurance sector and the Real Estate and Rental and Leasing sector. Included are banks and other savings institutions; securities and commodities brokers, dealers, exchanges, and services; insurance carriers, brokers, and agents; real estate operators, developers, agents, and brokers; and establishments that rent and lease goods such as automobiles, computers, and household and industrial machinery and equipment.

Financial Activities had 10,491,000 workers in 2006 of which 10,239,000 were private sector employees.

NUMBER OF NONFATAL OCCUPATIONAL INJURIES AND ILLNESSES INVOLVING DAYS AWAY FROM WORK[a] AND FATAL OCCUPATIONAL INJURIES BY SELECTED WORKER AND CASE CHARACTERISTICS, UNITED STATES, FINANCIAL ACTIVITIES, 2006

Characteristic	Nonfatal Cases	Fatalities
Total	**33,300**	**126**
Sex		
Men	18,250	107
Women	15,050	19
Age		
Under 16	—	—
16 to 19	320	—
20 to 24	2,350	6
25 to 34	7,860	14
35 to 44	8,990	29
45 to 54	7,800	30
55 to 64	4,230	27
65 and over	1,610	19
Occupation		
Management, business, and financial	4,450	43
Professional and related	1,360	—
Service	6,530	8
Sales and related	2,010	31
Office and administrative support	8,160	6
Farming, fishing, and forestry	—	—
Construction and extractive	830	—
Installation, maintenance, and repair	4,780	18
Production	510	—
Transportation and material moving	4,490	13
Military occupations	—	—
Race or ethnic origin[b]		
White, non-Hispanic	13,790	96
Black, non-Hispanic	3,700	5
Hispanic	4,770	20
Other, multiple, and not reported	11,040	5
Nature of injury, illness		
Sprains, strains	13,210	—
Fractures	2,260	—
Cuts, lacerations, punctures	1,650	34
Bruises, contusions	3,140	—
Heat burns	210	—
Chemical burns	90	—
Amputations	310	—
Carpal tunnel syndrome	830	—
Tendonitis	90	—
Multiple injuries	2,150	44
Soreness, Pain	2,690	—
Back pain	920	—
All other	6,670	45

Characteristic	Nonfatal Cases	Fatalities
Part of body affected		
Head	2,370	32
Eye	740	—
Neck	620	—
Trunk	10,930	18
Back	7,180	—
Shoulder	1,640	—
Upper extremities	5,110	—
Finger	1,580	—
Hand, except finger	640	—
Wrist	1,560	—
Lower extremities	8,630	—
Knee	2,680	—
Foot, toe	2,340	—
Body systems	1,070	20
Multiple	4,390	51
All other	170	—
Source of injury, illness		
Chemicals, chemical products	820	—
Containers	3,010	—
Furniture, fixtures	2,610	—
Machinery	1,820	5
Parts and materials	1,700	5
Worker motion or position	5,570	—
Floor, ground surfaces	8,580	18
Handtools	1,150	—
Vehicles	3,160	41
Health care patient	140	—
All other	4,750	49
Event or exposure		
Contact with object, equipment	7,680	7
Struck by object	3,610	—
Struck against object	2,590	—
Caught in object, equipment, material	770	—
Fall to lower level	2,700	14
Fall on same level	5,670	—
Slips, trips	1,190	—
Overexertion	5,750	—
Overexertion in lifting	3,070	—
Repetitive motion	1,620	—
Exposed to harmful substance	1,690	11
Transportation accidents	2,230	43
Highway accident	1,760	20
Nonhighway accident, except air, rail, water	130	—
Pedestrian, nonpassenger struck by vehicle, mobile equipment	270	—
Fires, explosions	20	—
Assault, violent act	920	44
By person	850	30
By other	70	14
All other	3,820	—

Source: National Safety Council tabulations of Bureau of Labor Statistics data.
Note: Because of rounding and data exclusion of nonclassifiable responses, data may not sum to the totals. Dashes (—) indicate data that do not meet publication guidelines.

[a]Days away from work include those that result in days away from work with or without restricted work activity or job transfer.
[b]In the fatalities column, non-Hispanic categories include cases with Hispanic origin not reported.

PROFESSIONAL AND BUSINESS SERVICES

The Professional and Business Services sector includes legal, accounting, architectural, engineering, computer, consulting, research, advertising, photographic, translation and interpretation, veterinary, and other professional scientific and technical services. Also included are business management and administrative and support activities and waste management and remediation services.

Professional and Business Services employed 14,867,000 people in 2006 of which 14,475,000 were private sector employees.

NUMBER OF NONFATAL OCCUPATIONAL INJURIES AND ILLNESSES INVOLVING DAYS AWAY FROM WORK[a] AND FATAL OCCUPATIONAL INJURIES BY SELECTED WORKER AND CASE CHARACTERISTICS, UNITED STATES, PROFESSIONAL AND BUSINESS SERVICES, 2006

Characteristic	Nonfatal Cases	Fatalities
Total	**89,940**	**459**
Sex		
Men	61,070	431
Women	28,870	28
Age		
Under 16	—	—
16 to 19	2,490	16
20 to 24	11,950	42
25 to 34	23,830	87
35 to 44	22,370	104
45 to 54	18,180	99
55 to 64	8,230	72
65 and over	1,650	39
Occupation		
Management, business, and financial	2,650	20
Professional and related	8,060	23
Service	32,630	255
Sales and related	2,830	6
Office and administrative support	9,510	11
Farming, fishing, and forestry	270	—
Construction and extractive	3,640	24
Installation, maintenance, and repair	6,620	13
Production	6,420	18
Transportation and material moving	17,070	86
Military occupations	—	—
Race or ethnic origin[b]		
White, non-Hispanic	37,800	273
Black, non-Hispanic	7,740	61
Hispanic	16,510	114
Other, multiple, and not reported	27,900	11
Nature of injury, illness		
Sprains, strains	32,910	—
Fractures	6,350	—
Cuts, lacerations, punctures	8,900	41
Bruises, contusions	7,540	—
Heat burns	690	7
Chemical burns	690	—
Amputations	440	—
Carpal tunnel syndrome	790	—
Tendonitis	440	—
Multiple injuries	3,820	165
Soreness, Pain	8,550	—
Back pain	2,290	—
All other	18,820	244

Characteristic	Nonfatal Cases	Fatalities
Part of body affected		
Head	6,880	114
Eye	2,860	—
Neck	1,050	7
Trunk	26,940	58
Back	16,550	—
Shoulder	4,370	—
Upper extremities	18,440	—
Finger	6,980	—
Hand, except finger	3,350	—
Wrist	3,010	—
Lower extremities	21,980	—
Knee	7,420	—
Foot, toe	4,380	—
Body systems	1,970	90
Multiple	11,480	183
All other	1,200	—
Source of injury, illness		
Chemicals, chemical products	1,920	18
Containers	10,090	5
Furniture, fixtures	3,390	—
Machinery	5,230	44
Parts and materials	6,420	17
Worker motion or position	11,890	—
Floor, ground surfaces	17,050	81
Handtools	3,700	9
Vehicles	9,550	170
Health care patient	690	—
All other	20,010	114
Event or exposure		
Contact with object, equipment	25,260	71
Struck by object	11,650	49
Struck against object	7,750	—
Caught in object, equipment, material	3,720	21
Fall to lower level	7,320	78
Fall on same level	10,660	7
Slips, trips	2,980	—
Overexertion	16,130	—
Overexertion in lifting	8,440	—
Repetitive motion	2,560	—
Exposed to harmful substance	5,660	59
Transportation accidents	6,510	185
Highway accident	4,520	95
Nonhighway accident, except air, rail, water	760	33
Pedestrian, nonpassenger struck by vehicle, mobile equipment	1,030	35
Fires, explosions	320	5
Assault, violent act	2,990	52
By person	860	34
By other	2,140	18
All other	9,540	—

Source: National Safety Council tabulations of Bureau of Labor Statistics data.
Note: Because of rounding and data exclusion of nonclassifiable responses, data may not sum to the totals. Dashes (—) indicate data that do not meet publication guidelines.

[a] Days away from work include those that result in days away from work with or without restricted work activity or job transfer.
[b] In the fatalities column, non-Hispanic categories include cases with Hispanic origin not reported.

EDUCATIONAL AND HEALTH SERVICES

Educational services includes instruction and training through schools, colleges, universities, and training centers. Health services includes ambulatory health care facilities, hospitals, nursing and residential care facilities, and social assistance for individuals, families, and communities.

Educational and Health Services employed 29,939,000 people in 2006 of which 19,551,000 were private sector employees.

NUMBER OF NONFATAL OCCUPATIONAL INJURIES AND ILLNESSES INVOLVING DAYS AWAY FROM WORK[a] AND FATAL OCCUPATIONAL INJURIES BY SELECTED WORKER AND CASE CHARACTERISTICS, UNITED STATES, EDUCATIONAL AND HEALTH SERVICES, 2006

Characteristic	Nonfatal Cases	Fatalities
Total	**182,210**	**178**
Sex		
Men	36,800	100
Women	145,370	78
Age		
Under 16	—	—
16 to 19	3,150	—
20 to 24	15,420	15
25 to 34	38,900	20
35 to 44	44,490	40
45 to 54	46,310	56
55 to 64	26,880	26
65 and over	4,820	18
Occupation		
Management, business, and financial	4,420	12
Professional and related	58,800	—
Service	97,140	126
Sales and related	570	—
Office and administrative support	11,560	6
Farming, fishing, and forestry	20	—
Construction and extractive	850	—
Installation, maintenance, and repair	3,200	—
Production	1,750	—
Transportation and material moving	3,600	25
Military occupations	—	—
Race or ethnic origin[b]		
White, non-Hispanic	80,590	137
Black, non-Hispanic	26,340	20
Hispanic	14,400	10
Other, multiple, and not reported	60,890	11
Nature of injury, illness		
Sprains, strains	89,950	—
Fractures	10,590	—
Cuts, lacerations, punctures	5,900	21
Bruises, contusions	15,710	—
Heat burns	2,130	—
Chemical burns	780	—
Amputations	90	—
Carpal tunnel syndrome	1,210	—
Tendonitis	680	—
Multiple injuries	7,860	87
Soreness, Pain	21,370	—
Back pain	*7,950*	—
All other	25,950	61

Characteristic	Nonfatal Cases	Fatalities
Part of body affected		
Head	9,940	21
Eye	*3,410*	—
Neck	3,560	—
Trunk	74,870	23
Back	*52,730*	—
Shoulder	*12,300*	—
Upper extremities	28,750	—
Finger	*7,620*	—
Hand, except finger	*4,560*	—
Wrist	*7,230*	—
Lower extremities	34,650	5
Knee	*14,650*	—
Foot, toe	*5,570*	—
Body systems	4,180	28
Multiple	24,650	96
All other	1,610	—
Source of injury, illness		
Chemicals, chemical products	3,250	16
Containers	10,620	—
Furniture, fixtures	8,840	—
Machinery	4,010	—
Parts and materials	1,920	—
Worker motion or position	22,220	—
Floor, ground surfaces	39,420	17
Handtools	2,250	—
Vehicles	9,640	95
Health care patient	51,480	5
All other	28,550	37
Event or exposure		
Contact with object, equipment	24,130	5
Struck by object	*12,530*	—
Struck against object	*7,630*	—
Caught in object, equipment, material	*2,570*	—
Fall to lower level	6,410	10
Fall on same level	33,450	6
Slips, trips	5,730	—
Overexertion	63,380	—
Overexertion in lifting	*28,720*	—
Repetitive motion	3,860	—
Exposed to harmful substance	10,110	23
Transportation accidents	6,260	94
Highway accident	*5,330*	*48*
Nonhighway accident, except air, rail, water	*410*	—
Pedestrian, nonpassenger struck by vehicle, mobile equipment	*300*	*6*
Fires, explosions	120	—
Assault, violent act	10,950	36
By person	*10,400*	*25*
By other	*550*	*11*
All other	17,810	—

Source: National Safety Council tabulations of Bureau of Labor Statistics data.
Note: Because of rounding and data exclusion of nonclassifiable responses, data may not sum to the totals. Dashes (—) indicate data that do not meet publication guidelines.

[a]Days away from work include those that result in days away from work with or without restricted work activity or job transfer.
[b]In the fatalities column, non-Hispanic categories include cases with Hispanic origin not reported.

LEISURE AND HOSPITALITY

The Leisure sector includes establishments that provide arts, entertainment, and recreation experiences such as theatre, dance, music, and spectator sports, museums, zoos, amusement and theme parks, casinos, golf courses, ski areas, marinas, and fitness and sports centers. The

Hospitality sector includes hotels and other traveler accommodations, food services, and drinking places.

The Leisure and Hospitality sector employed 12,145,000 people in 2006 of which 11,720,000 were private sector employees.

NUMBER OF NONFATAL OCCUPATIONAL INJURIES AND ILLNESSES INVOLVING DAYS AWAY FROM WORK[a] AND FATAL OCCUPATIONAL INJURIES BY SELECTED WORKER AND CASE CHARACTERISTICS, UNITED STATES, LEISURE AND HOSPITALITY, 2006

Characteristic	Nonfatal Cases	Fatalities
Total	**96,910**	**265**
Sex		
Men	47,660	212
Women	49,240	53
Age		
Under 16	60	—
16 to 19	8,300	10
20 to 24	15,960	26
25 to 34	23,260	66
35 to 44	21,460	53
45 to 54	15,670	43
55 to 64	8,790	43
65 and over	2,450	24
Occupation		
Management, business, and financial	3,640	50
Professional and related	3,010	—
Service	74,590	154
Sales and related	3,140	11
Office and administrative support	1,940	—
Farming, fishing, and forestry	240	—
Construction and extractive	700	—
Installation, maintenance, and repair	2,580	13
Production	2,740	—
Transportation and material moving	4,290	31
Military occupations	—	—
Race or ethnic origin[b]		
White, non-Hispanic	35,210	157
Black, non-Hispanic	8,160	43
Hispanic	15,230	34
Other, multiple, and not reported	38,320	31
Nature of injury, illness		
Sprains, strains	31,850	—
Fractures	6,540	—
Cuts, lacerations, punctures	15,900	110
Bruises, contusions	8,370	—
Heat burns	6,130	5
Chemical burns	860	—
Amputations	450	—
Carpal tunnel syndrome	650	—
Tendonitis	270	—
Multiple injuries	3,010	50
Soreness, Pain	8,820	—
Back pain	2,750	—
All other	14,060	100

Characteristic	Nonfatal Cases	Fatalities
Part of body affected		
Head	6,420	65
Eye	1,940	—
Neck	1,160	11
Trunk	27,110	60
Back	17,260	—
Shoulder	4,770	—
Upper extremities	31,250	—
Finger	12,710	—
Hand, except finger	7,300	—
Wrist	4,150	—
Lower extremities	19,490	—
Knee	7,010	—
Foot, toe	3,310	—
Body systems	1,640	37
Multiple	9,130	83
All other	720	7
Source of injury, illness		
Chemicals, chemical products	1,690	12
Containers	14,200	—
Furniture, fixtures	6,090	—
Machinery	6,540	9
Parts and materials	2,660	10
Worker motion or position	11,440	—
Floor, ground surfaces	24,110	25
Handtools	7,490	15
Vehicles	4,370	59
Health care patient	—	—
All other	18,300	132
Event or exposure		
Contact with object, equipment	28,820	14
Struck by object	15,210	8
Struck against object	8,960	—
Caught in object, equipment, material	3,200	—
Fall to lower level	4,240	19
Fall on same level	20,750	5
Slips, trips	4,460	—
Overexertion	14,930	—
Overexertion in lifting	8,850	—
Repetitive motion	1,780	—
Exposed to harmful substance	9,650	20
Transportation accidents	2,520	62
Highway accident	1,570	23
Nonhighway accident, except air, rail, water	580	15
Pedestrian, nonpassenger struck by vehicle, mobile equipment	240	5
Fires, explosions	170	8
Assault, violent act	1,690	134
By person	1,310	114
By other	380	20
All other	7,900	—

Source: National Safety Council tabulations of Bureau of Labor Statistics data.
Note: Because of rounding and data exclusion of nonclassifiable responses, data may not sum to the totals. Dashes (—) indicate data that do not meet publication guidelines.

[a]Days away from work include those that result in days away from work with or without restricted work activity or job transfer.
[b]In the fatalities column, non-Hispanic categories include cases with Hispanic origin not reported.

OTHER SERVICES

The Other Services sector includes repair and maintenance of equipment and machinery and personal and household goods, personal care and laundry services, and religious, grant making, civic, professional, and similar organizations.

The Other Services sector employed 7,088,000 people in 2006 of which 7,053,000 were private sector employees.

NUMBER OF NONFATAL OCCUPATIONAL INJURIES AND ILLNESSES INVOLVING DAYS AWAY FROM WORK[a] AND FATAL OCCUPATIONAL INJURIES BY SELECTED WORKER AND CASE CHARACTERISTICS, UNITED STATES, OTHER SERVICES (EXCEPT PUBLIC ADMINISTRATION), 2006

Characteristic	Nonfatal Cases	Fatalities
Total	**27,640**	**183**
Sex		
Men	19,350	164
Women	8,290	19
Age		
Under 16	—	—
16 to 19	880	6
20 to 24	2,960	11
25 to 34	6,070	33
35 to 44	6,880	43
45 to 54	6,070	37
55 to 64	3,820	24
65 and over	660	29
Occupation		
Management, business, and financial	1,230	16
Professional and related	1,250	—
Service	5,440	41
Sales and related	990	—
Office and administrative support	1,660	—
Farming, fishing, and forestry	—	—
Construction and extractive	430	5
Installation, maintenance, and repair	8,230	83
Production	3,930	12
Transportation and material moving	4,350	23
Military occupations	—	—
Race or ethnic origin[b]		
White, non-Hispanic	16,010	112
Black, non-Hispanic	1,840	37
Hispanic	3,350	25
Other, multiple, and not reported	6,430	9
Nature of injury, illness		
Sprains, strains	10,670	—
Fractures	2,130	—
Cuts, lacerations, punctures	3,120	37
Bruises, contusions	1,840	—
Heat burns	490	—
Chemical burns	70	—
Amputations	70	—
Carpal tunnel syndrome	350	—
Tendonitis	150	—
Multiple injuries	1,020	42
Soreness, Pain	2,610	—
Back pain	560	—
All other	5,110	98

Characteristic	Nonfatal Cases	Fatalities
Part of body affected		
Head	1,860	51
Eye	850	—
Neck	250	—
Trunk	9,460	41
Back	5,290	—
Shoulder	2,170	—
Upper extremities	6,950	—
Finger	2,520	—
Hand, except finger	1,020	—
Wrist	1,160	—
Lower extremities	5,550	—
Knee	2,010	—
Foot, toe	1,200	—
Body systems	460	32
Multiple	2,680	55
All other	420	—
Source of injury, illness		
Chemicals, chemical products	290	10
Containers	2,440	—
Furniture, fixtures	1,070	—
Machinery	1,940	13
Parts and materials	3,460	12
Worker motion or position	3,990	—
Floor, ground surfaces	4,730	23
Handtools	2,180	5
Vehicles	2,680	66
Health care patient	190	—
All other	4,660	51
Event or exposure		
Contact with object, equipment	8,000	43
Struck by object	4,680	34
Struck against object	1,600	—
Caught in object, equipment, material	900	8
Fall to lower level	1,170	19
Fall on same level	3,650	—
Slips, trips	710	—
Overexertion	6,750	—
Overexertion in lifting	3,230	—
Repetitive motion	770	—
Exposed to harmful substance	1,120	18
Transportation accidents	1,380	44
Highway accident	1,090	26
Nonhighway accident, except air, rail, water	50	—
Pedestrian, nonpassenger struck by vehicle, mobile equipment	190	12
Fires, explosions	—	13
Assault, violent act	630	43
By person	330	31
By other	310	12
All other	3,440	—

Source: National Safety Council tabulations of Bureau of Labor Statistics data.
Note: Because of rounding and data exclusion of nonclassifiable responses, data may not sum to the totals. Dashes (—) indicate data that do not meet publication guidelines.

[a]Days away from work include those that result in days away from work with or without restricted work activity or job transfer.
[b]In the fatalities column, non-Hispanic categories include cases with Hispanic origin not reported.

GOVERNMENT

Government includes public employees at all levels from federal (civilian and military) to state, county, and municipal.

Government employment totaled 21,569,000 in 2006.

NUMBER OF NONFATAL OCCUPATIONAL INJURIES AND ILLNESSES INVOLVING DAYS AWAY FROM WORK[a] AND FATAL OCCUPATIONAL INJURIES BY SELECTED WORKER AND CASE CHARACTERISTICS, UNITED STATES, GOVERNMENT, 2006

Characteristic	Nonfatal Cases	Fatalities
Total	([b])	520
Sex		
Men		451
Women		69
Age		
Under 16		—
16 to 19		9
20 to 24		29
25 to 34		123
35 to 44		134
45 to 54		102
55 to 64		78
65 and over		45
Occupation		
Management, business, and financial		24
Professional and related		26
Service		265
Sales and related		—
Office and administrative support		25
Farming, fishing, and forestry		—
Construction and extractive		55
Installation, maintenance, and repair		16
Production		12
Transportation and material moving		36
Military occupations		57
Race or ethnic origin[c]		
White, non-Hispanic		390
Black, non-Hispanic		58
Hispanic		43
Other, multiple, and not reported		29
Nature of injury, illness		
Sprains, strains		—
Fractures		8
Cuts, lacerations, punctures		103
Bruises, contusions		—
Heat burns		16
Chemical burns		—
Amputations		—
Carpal tunnel syndrome		—
Tendonitis		—
Multiple injuries		199
Soreness, Pain		—
Back pain		—
All other		192

Characteristic	Nonfatal Cases	Fatalities
Part of body affected		
Head		119
Eye		—
Neck		13
Trunk		68
Back		6
Shoulder		—
Upper extremities		—
Finger		—
Hand, except finger		—
Wrist		—
Lower extremities		14
Knee		—
Foot, toe		—
Body systems		57
Multiple		244
All other		—
Source of injury, illness		
Chemicals, chemical products		6
Containers		6
Furniture, fixtures		—
Machinery		16
Parts and materials		15
Worker motion or position		—
Floor, ground surfaces		40
Handtools		—
Vehicles		275
Health care patient		—
All other		152
Event or exposure		
Contact with object, equipment		32
Struck by object		22
Struck against object		—
Caught in object, equipment, material		9
Fall to lower level		21
Fall on same level		15
Slips, trips		—
Overexertion		—
Overexertion in lifting		—
Repetitive motion		—
Exposed to harmful substance		27
Transportation accidents		277
Highway accident		168
Nonhighway accident, except air, rail, water		12
Pedestrian, nonpassenger struck by vehicle, mobile equipment		61
Fires, explosions		30
Assault, violent act		111
By person		79
By other		32
All other		—

Source: National Safety Council tabulations of Bureau of Labor Statistics data.
Note: Because of rounding and data exclusion of nonclassifiable responses, data may not sum to the totals. Dashes (—) indicate data that do not meet publication guidelines.
[a]Days away from work include those that result in days away from work with or without restricted work activity or job transfer.

[b]Data for government entities not collected in the national BLS Survey of Occupational Injuries and Illnesses.
[c]In the fatalities column, non-Hispanic categories include cases with Hispanic origin not reported.

OCCUPATIONAL HEALTH

More than 35,000 new skin diseases or disorders cases in 2007.

Approximately 206,300 occupational illnesses were recognized or diagnosed by private employers in 2007 according to the Bureau of Labor Statistics (BLS), a decrease of 10% from 2006. The overall incidence rate of occupational illness for all workers was 21.8 per 10,000 full-time workers. Of the major industry sectors, manufacturing had the highest overall rate for total cases in 2007, 50.5 per 10,000 full-time workers. Utilities had the second highest incidence rate, 38.9, followed by agriculture, forestry, fishing, and hunting with a rate of 33.7. Workers in agriculture, forestry, fishing, and hunting had the highest illness rates for skin diseases and disorders, while workers in education and health services had the highest rate for respiratory conditions. Workers in utilities had the highest rates for poisoning, while manufacturing had the highest rates in the hearing loss and "all other illnesses" categories.

Manufacturing accounted for about 34% of new illness cases in 2007. Skin diseases or disorders were the most common illness with 35,300 new cases, followed by

hearing loss with 23,000, respiratory conditions with 16,700, and poisonings with 3,400. Since the revised recordkeeping guidelines that became effective January 1, 2002, no longer provide categories to separately record cases such as disorders associated with repeated trauma or disorders due to physical agents, these cases are now being captured in the "all other illnesses" category, which accounted for 127,900 or about 62% of all new illness cases in 2007.

The table below shows the number of occupational illnesses and the incidence rate per 10,000 full-time workers as measured by the 2007 BLS survey. To convert these to incidence rates per 100 full-time workers, which are comparable to other published BLS rates, divide the rates in the table by 100. The BLS survey records illnesses only for the year in which they are recognized or diagnosed as work-related. Since only recognized cases are included, the figures underestimate the incidence of occupational illness.

NONFATAL OCCUPATIONAL ILLNESS INCIDENCE RATES AND NUMBER OF ILLNESSES BY TYPE OF ILLNESS AND INDUSTRY SECTOR, 2007

Industry Sector	All Illnesses	Skin Diseases, Disorders	Respiratory Conditions	Poisoning	Hearing Loss	All Other Occupational Illnesses
Incidence Rate per 10,000 Full-Time Workers						
Private Sector[a,b]	**21.8**	**3.7**	**1.8**	**0.4**	**2.4**	**13.5**
Goods Producing[a,b]	36.7	5.5	1.8	0.3	8.5	20.6
Agriculture, forestry, fishing & hunting[a]	33.7	12.3	1.5	0.7	2.0	17.1
Mining[b,c]	9.0	1.3	1.4	(d)	2.4	3.7
Construction	12.5	3.6	1.2	0.5	0.3	6.9
Manufacturing	50.5	6.2	2.1	0.3	13.3	28.5
Service providing	17.0	3.2	1.8	0.4	0.5	11.2
Wholesale trade	8.7	1.6	0.8	0.1	0.8	5.4
Retail trade	14.7	2.6	1.2	0.4	0.2	10.3
Transportation and warehousing	23.5	2.5	1.6	0.4	3.0	15.9
Utilities	38.9	8.0	1.5	0.9	12.1	16.4
Information	14.0	1.7	1.2	0.8	1.4	9.0
Financial activities	10.0	0.8	0.7	0.1	0.1	8.4
Professional and business services	13.1	2.6	1.3	0.2	0.2	8.8
Education and health services	31.2	5.7	4.1	0.3	0.1	20.9
Leisure and hospitality	14.4	4.6	1.3	(d)	0.1	7.7
Other services	11.4	2.6	1.9	(d)	0.4	6.1
Number of Illnesses (in thousands)						
Private Sector[a,b]	**206.3**	**35.3**	**16.7**	**3.4**	**23.0**	**127.9**
Goods producing[a,b]	83.8	12.6	4.1	0.8	19.4	47.0
Agriculture, forestry, fishing & hunting[a]	3.2	1.2	0.1	0.1	0.2	1.6
Mining[b,c]	0.6	0.1	0.1	(d)	0.2	0.3
Construction	8.9	2.6	0.8	0.3	0.2	4.9
Manufacturing	71.1	8.8	3.0	0.4	18.8	40.2
Service providing	122.5	22.7	12.6	2.6	3.7	80.9
Wholesale trade	5.1	0.9	0.5	0.1	0.4	3.1
Retail trade	17.9	3.1	1.5	0.5	0.2	12.5
Transportation and warehousing	9.9	1.1	0.7	0.2	1.3	6.7
Utilities	2.1	0.4	0.1	(e)	0.7	0.9
Information	3.7	0.4	0.3	0.2	0.4	2.4
Financial activities	7.6	0.6	0.5	0.1	(e)	6.3
Professional and business services	17.8	3.6	1.8	0.2	0.3	11.9
Education and health services	42.2	7.7	5.6	0.4	0.2	28.3
Leisure and hospitality	12.8	4.1	1.2	(d)	0.1	6.8
Other services	3.5	0.8	0.6	(d)	0.1	1.9

Source: Bureau of Labor Statistics, U.S. Department of Labor. Components may not add to totals due to rounding.
[a] *Private sector includes all industries except government, but excludes farms with less than 11 employees.*
[b] *Data for mining do not reflect the changes OSHA made to its recordkeeping requirements effective January 1, 2002; therefore, estimates for this industry are not comparable with estimates for other industries.*
[c] *Mining includes quarrying and oil and gas extraction.*
[d] *Data do not meet publication guidelines.*
[e] *Data too small to be displayed.*

NATIONAL SAFETY COUNCIL

INJURY FACTS®

Between 1912 and 2007, motor-vehicle deaths per 10,000 registered vehicles were reduced 95%, from 33 to less than 2. In 1912, there were 3,100 fatalities when the number of registered vehicles totaled only 950,000. In 2007, there were 43,100 fatalities, but registrations soared to 256 million.

While mileage data were not available in 1912, the 2007 mileage death rate of 1.44 per 100,000,000 vehicle miles was down 3% from the revised 2006 rate of 1.48, and is the lowest on record. Disabling injuries in motor-vehicle accidents totaled 2,300,000 in 2007, and total motor-vehicle costs were estimated at $257.7 billion. Costs include wage and productivity losses, medical expenses, administrative expenses, motor-vehicle property damage, and employer costs.

Motor-vehicle deaths decreased 3% from 2006 to 2007 and 2% from 2005 to 2006. Miles traveled was down

about 1%, the number of registered vehicles increased 2%, and the population increased 1%. As a result, the mileage death rate was down 3%, the registration death rate was down 5%, and the population death rate was down 4% from 2006 to 2007.

Compared with 1997, 2007 motor-vehicle deaths decreased by about 1%. However, mileage, registration, and population death rates were all sharply lower in 2007 compared to 1997 (see chart on next page).

The word "accident" may be used in this section as well as the word "crash." When used, "accident" has a specific meaning as defined in the *Manual on Classification of Motor Vehicle Traffic Accidents, ANSI D16.1-2007.* "Crash" is generally used by the National Highway Traffic Safety Administration to mean the same as accident, but it is not formally defined.

Deaths **43,100**
Disabling injuries **2,300,000**
Cost . . . . **$257.7 billion**
Motor-vehicle mileage . . . . **2,996 billion**
Registered vehicles in the United States **255,700,000**
Licensed drivers in the United States **205,100,000**
Death rate per 100,000,000 vehicle miles **1.44**
Death rate per 10,000 registered vehicles **1.69**
Death rate per 100,000 population **14.3**

MOTOR-VEHICLE ACCIDENT OUTCOMES, UNITED STATES, 2007

Severity	Deaths or Injuries	Accidents or Crashes	Drivers (Vehicles) Involved
Fatal (within 1 year)	43,100	39,100	58,400
Disabling injury	2,300,000	1,600,000	2,800,000
Property damage (including unreported) and nondisabling injury		9,000,000	15,200,000
Total		**10,600,000**	**18,100,000**
Fatal (within 30 days)	41,059	37,248	55,681
Injury (disabling and nondisabling)	2,491,000	1,711,000	3,057,000
Police-reported property damage		4,275,000	7,411,000
Total		**6,024,000**	**10,524,000**

Source: National Safety Council estimates (top half) and National Highway Traffic Safety Administration (bottom half).

TRAVEL, DEATHS, AND DEATH RATES, UNITED STATES, 1925–2007

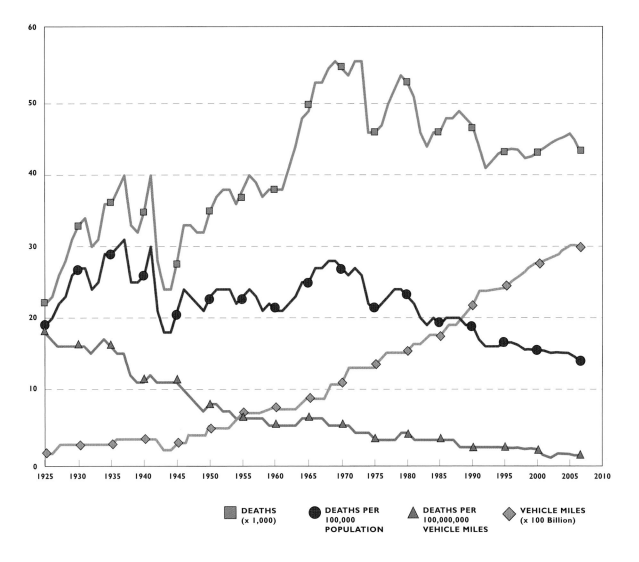

| ■ | **DEATHS**
(x 1,000) | ● | **DEATHS PER**
100,000
POPULATION | ▲ | **DEATHS PER**
100,000,000
VEHICLE MILES | ◆ | **VEHICLE MILES**
(x 100 Billion) |

DEATHS DUE TO MOTOR-VEHICLE ACCIDENTS, 2007

TYPE OF EVENT AND AGE OF VICTIM

All Motor-Vehicle Accidents

Includes deaths involving mechanically or electrically powered highway-transport vehicles in motion (except those on rails), both on and off the highway or street.

	Total	Change from 2006	Death Rate[a]
Deaths	43,100	–3%	14.3
Nonfatal injuries	2,300,000		

Age	0–4	5–14	15–24	25–44	45–64	65–74	75+
Deaths	600	1,200	10,500	13,300	10,800	2,900	3,800

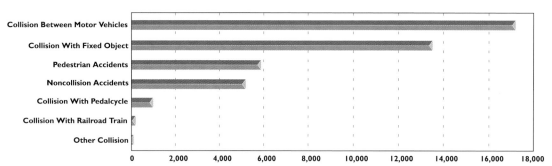

Collision Between Motor Vehicles

Includes deaths from collisions of two or more motor vehicles. Motorized bicycles and scooters, trolley buses, and farm tractors or road machinery traveling on highways are motor vehicles.

	Total	Change from 2006	Death Rate[a]
Deaths	17,200	–5%	5.7
Nonfatal injuries	1,680,000		

Age	0–4	5–14	15–24	25–44	45–64	65–74	75+
Deaths	250	350	3,800	5,000	4,400	1,400	2,000

Collision with Fixed Object

Includes deaths from collisions in which the first harmful event is the striking of a fixed object such as a guardrail, abutment, impact attenuator, etc.

	Total	Change from 2006	Death Rate[a]
Deaths	13,500	–1%	4.5
Nonfatal injuries	360,000		

Age	0–4	5–14	15–24	25–44	45–64	65–74	75+
Deaths	90	210	4,400	4,500	2,900	600	800

Pedestrian Accidents

Includes all deaths of persons struck by motor vehicles, either on or off a street or highway, regardless of the circumstances of the accident.

	Total	Change from 2006	Death Rate[a]
Deaths	5,900	–2%	2.0
Nonfatal injuries	85,000		

Age	0–4	5–14	15–24	25–44	45–64	65–74	75+
Deaths	180	270	700	1,600	1,900	500	750

See footnotes on page 89.

Noncollision Accidents

Includes deaths from accidents in which the first injury or damage-producing event was an overturn, jackknife, or other type of noncollision.

	Total	Change from 2006	Death Rate[a]
Deaths	5,200	–2%	1.7
Nonfatal injuries	110,000		

Collision with Pedalcycle

Includes deaths of pedalcyclists and motor-vehicle occupants from collisions between pedalcycles and motor vehicles on streets, highways, private driveways, parking lots, etc.

	Total	Change from 2006	Death Rate[a]
Deaths	1,000	–9%	0.3
Nonfatal injuries	59,000		

Collision with Railroad Train

Includes deaths from collisions of motor vehicles (moving or stalled) and railroad vehicles at public or private grade crossings. In other types of accidents, classification requires motor vehicle to be in motion.

	Total	Change from 2006	Death Rate[a]
Deaths	200	–33%	0.1
Nonfatal injuries	1,000		

Other Collision

Includes deaths from motor-vehicle collisions not specified in other categories above. Most of the deaths arose out of accidents involving animals or animal-drawn vehicles.

	Total	Change from 2006	Death Rate[a]
Deaths	100	0%	(c)
Nonfatal Injuries	5,000		

Note: Procedures and benchmarks for estimating deaths by type of accident and age were changed in 1990. Estimates for 1987 and later years are not comparable to earlier years. The noncollision and fixed object categories were most affected by the changes.
[a]*Deaths per 100,000 population.*
[b]*Deaths per 100,000 population in each age group.*
[c]*Death rate was less than 0.05.*

With the lone exception of cancer deaths at age 7, motor-vehicle crashes were the leading cause of death for people between the ages of 3 and 34 in 2005. Motor-vehicle crashes were also the leading cause of unintentional-injury (accidental) death for persons one year of age, for each single year of age from 3 to 39, for age 42, and again for each single year of age from 52 to 72. This is a summary of the most important issues that affect traffic safety.

Occupant protection. Forty-nine states and the District of Columbia have mandatory belt use laws in effect, with the laws in 26 of the states and the District of Columbia allowing standard (primary) enforcement. Seat belt use was 83% overall in 2008, statistically unchanged from the 82% use rate in 2007. In 2007, belt use was significantly higher in states with standard (primary) enforcement (87%) than in states with secondary enforcement (73%). More than half (54%) of the passenger vehicle occupants killed in 2007 were unrestrained. Use of DOT-compliant motorcycle helmets increased 5 percentage points to 63% in 2008, although use has declined 8 percentage points from 71% in 2000.

Alcohol. All states and the District of Columbia have 21-year-old minimum drinking age laws and have by law created a threshold making it illegal to drive while alcohol impaired (i.e., with a BAC of 0.08 g/dl or higher). Traffic fatalities in alcohol-impaired crashes as a percentage of total traffic fatalities rose slightly to 31.7% in 2007. Young drivers aged 21 to 34 made up 30% of drivers involved in fatal crashes, but comprised 44% of those who were alcohol-impaired. Overall, about 12,998 people were killed in alcohol-impaired crashes in 2007, a reduction of 3.7% from 2006.

Speeding. Excessive speed was a factor in 32% of all traffic fatalities in 2007. Similar to alcohol-impaired crashes, the total number of fatal crashes attributable to speeding declined over 3% from 2006 to 2007, but the percentage of speeding related fatalities among overall fatalities remained unchanged. It has been estimated that speeding-related crashes cost the nation over $40 billion annually.

Distracted driving. Recent studies indicate that from 1995–2003 over 10% of drivers involved in fatal crashes were distracted at the time of their crash involvement. About 70% of the distracted driver crashes involved non-collision (single-vehicle) or rear-end crashes. The leading sources of distraction included objects, persons, or events outside the vehicle or other vehicle occupants, followed by reaching for an object, a moving object in the vehicle, a cell phone, adjusting the radio/cassette/CD player, eating/drinking, adjusting the climate control, and smoking. Observational studies indicated that about 6% of drivers were observed using a hand-held cell phone in 2007, an increase from the 5% observed in 2006. Hand-held phone use was highest in 2007 among young drivers 16–24 years old.

Large trucks. About 75% of the 4,808 fatalities in 2007 resulting from traffic crashes involving large trucks (gross vehicle weight rating greater than 10,000 pounds) were occupants of vehicles other than the large truck. Large trucks were more likely to be involved in a multiple vehicle fatal crash than passenger vehicles— 82% versus 59%, respectively.

Motorcycles. Fatalities among motorcycle riders and passengers have increased by 144% between 1997 and 2007, while nonfatal injuries have increased by 94% over the same period. The motorcycle death rate per 100 million miles travelled improved for the first time in 10 years, decreasing from 43.77 in 2005 to 39.00 in 2006. Nearly half of the fatally injured riders were 40 years of age or older in 2007. Speeding was a factor in 36% of fatal motorcycle crashes, compared to 24% for fatal passenger car crashes.

Young drivers. The number of fatal crashes involving drivers 15 to 20 years old numbered 6,552 in 2007, a 7% reduction from 2006. Young driver fatalities decreased nearly 9% from 2006 to 2007, while passenger fatalities in vehicles with young drivers decreased about 6%. According to the latest 2005 mortality figures, motor-vehicle crashes are the leading cause of death for 15 to 20 year olds. According to recent studies, the most comprehensive graduated driver licensing (GDL) programs are associated with crash involvement rates about 20% lower for 16-year-olds than comparable crash involvement rates without GDL programs.

Pedestrians. There were about 5,900 pedestrian deaths and 85,000 injuries in motor-vehicle accidents in 2007. The majority (about 61%) of pedestrian deaths and injuries occur when pedestrians improperly cross roadways or intersections or dart/run into streets. Pedestrians in age groups beginning with those aged 15 and older are more likely to cross improperly, while those in younger age groups are more likely to dart/run into the roadway.

ESTIMATING MOTOR-VEHICLE CRASH COSTS

There are two methods commonly used to measure the costs of motor-vehicle crashes. One is the economic cost framework and the other is the *comprehensive cost* framework.

Economic costs may be used by a community or state to estimate the economic impact of motor-vehicle crashes that occurred within its jurisdiction in a given time period. It is a measure of the productivity lost and expenses incurred because of the crashes. Economic costs, however, should not be used for cost-benefit analysis because they do not reflect what society is willing to pay to prevent a statistical fatality or injury.

There are five economic cost components: (a) wage and productivity losses, which include wages, fringe benefits, household production, and travel delay; (b) medical expenses including emergency service costs; (c) administrative expenses, which include the administrative cost of private and public insurance plus police and legal costs; (d) motor-vehicle damage including the value of damage to property; and (e) uninsured employer costs for crashes involving workers.

The information below shows the average economic costs in 2007 per death (*not* per fatal crash), per injury (*not* per injury crash), and per property damage crash.

ECONOMIC COSTS, 2007

Death	**$1,130,000**
Nonfatal Disabling Injury	**$61,600**
Incapacitating injury[a]	$65,000
Nonincapacitating evident injury[a]	$21,000
Possible injury[a]	$11,900
Property Damage Crash (including minor injuries)	**$7,500**

Comprehensive costs include not only the economic cost components, but also a measure of the value of lost quality of life associated with the deaths and injuries, that is, what society is willing to pay to prevent them. The values of lost quality of life were obtained through empirical studies of what people actually pay to reduce their safety and health risks, such as through the purchase of air bags or smoke detectors.

Comprehensive costs should be used for cost-benefit analysis, but because the lost quality of life represents only a dollar equivalence of intangible qualities, they do not represent real economic losses and should not be used to determine the economic impact of past crashes.

The information below shows the average comprehensive costs in 2007 on a per person basis.

COMPREHENSIVE COSTS, 2007

Death	**$4,100,000**
Incapacitating injury[a]	$208,500
Nonincapacitating evident injury[a]	$53,200
Possible injury[a]	$25,300
No Injury	**$2,300**

Source: National Safety Council estimates (see the Technical Appendix) and Children's Safety Network Economics and Insurance Resource Center, Pacific Institute for Research and Evaluation.
Note: The National Safety Council's cost estimating procedures were extensively revised for the 1993 edition and additional revisions were made for the 2005–2006 edition. The costs are not comparable to those of prior years.
[a]Manual on Classification of Motor Vehicle Traffic Accidents, ANSI D16.1-2007 *(7th ed.). (2007). Itasca, IL: National Safety Council..*

STATE LAWS

All states and the District of Columbia have 21-year-old drinking age and child safety seat laws. Breath alcohol ignition interlock device laws are in effect in 46 states. Mandatory belt use laws are in effect in 49 states plus the District of Columbia, of which 26 states and D.C. are standard enforcement. Graduated licensing is in effect in some form in all states and the District of Columbia.

STATE LAWS

State	Alcohol Laws				Mandatory Belt Use Law		Graduated Licensing Laws				
	Administrative License Revocation[a]	BAC Limit[b]	Zero Tolerance Limit[c] for Minors	Alcohol Ignition Interlock Device[d]	Enforcement	Seating Positions Covered by Law	Minimum Instructional Permit Period[e]	Minimum Hours of Supervised Driving[f]	Passenger Restrictions	Nighttime Driving Restrictions	Unrestricted License Minimum Age[g]
Alabama	1996	0.08	0.02	no	standard	front	6 mo.	30/–	yes	yes	16 yrs.
Alaska	1983	0.08	0.00	yes	standard	all	6 mo.	40/10	yes	yes	16yrs., 6 mo.
Arizona	1992	0.08	0.00	yes	secondary	front	6 mo.	25/5	yes	yes	16 yrs.
Arkansas	1995	0.08	0.02	yes	secondary	front	until 16 yrs.	none	no	no	18 yrs.
California	1989	0.08	0.01	yes[h]	standard	all	6 mo.	50/10	yes	yes	16 yrs.
Colorado	1983	0.08	0.02	yes[h]	secondary	front	12 mo.	50/10	yes	yes	17 yrs.
Connecticut	1990	0.08	0.02	yes[h]	standard	front[i]	6 mo.	40/0	yes	yes	16yrs., 4 mo.
Delaware	yes	0.08	0.02	yes[h]	standard	all	12 mo.	50/10	yes	yes	17 yrs.
Dist. of Columbia	yes	0.08	0.00	no	standard	all	6 mo.	0/10	yes	yes	18 yrs.
Florida	1990	0.08	0.02	yes[h]	secondary[k]	front	12 mo.	50/10	no	yes	18 yrs.
Georgia	1995	0.08	0.02	yes[h]	standard	front[i]	12 mo.	40/6	yes	yes	18 yrs.
Hawaii	1990	0.08	0.02	no	standard	front[i]	6 mo.	50/10	yes	yes	17 yrs.
Idaho	1994	0.08	0.02	yes	secondary	all	6 mo.	50/10	yes	yes	16 yrs.
Illinois	1986	0.08	0.00	yes[h]	standard	front	9 mo.	50/10	yes	yes	18 yrs.
Indiana	yes	0.08	0.02	yes[h]	standard	all	2 mo.	none	yes	yes	18 yrs.
Iowa	1982	0.08	0.02	yes	standard	front	6 mo.	20/2	no	yes	17 yrs.
Kansas	1988	0.08	0.02	yes[h]	secondary	front	6 mo.	50/10	no	no	16yrs.
Kentucky	no	0.08	0.02	yes[h]	standard	all	180 days	60/10	yes	yes	17 yrs.
Louisiana	1984	0.08	0.02	yes	standard	front[i]	3 mo.	none	yes	yes	17 yrs.
Maine	1984	0.08	0.00	yes[h]	standard	all	6 mo.	35/5	yes	yes	16yrs., 6 mo.
Maryland	1989	0.08[l]	0.02	yes[h]	standard	front[i]	6 mo.	60/10	yes	yes	17yrs., 9 mo.
Massachusetts	1994	0.08	0.02	yes[h]	secondary	all	6 mo.	40/–	yes	yes	18 yrs.
Michigan	no	0.08	0.02	yes[h]	standard	front[i]	6 mo.	50/10	no	yes	17 yrs.
Minnesota	1976	0.08	0.00	yes[h]	secondary	front[i]	6 mo.	30/10	yes	yes	17 yrs.
Mississippi	1983	0.08	0.02	yes[h]	standard	front	6 mo.	none	no	yes	16 yrs.
Missouri	1987	0.08	0.02	yes[h]	secondary	front[i]	6 mo.	40/10	yes	yes	18 yrs.
Montana	1947	0.08	0.02	yes[h]	secondary	all	6 mo.	50/10	yes	yes	18 yrs.
Nebraska	1993	0.08	0.02	yes	secondary	front[i]	6 mo.	50/10	yes	yes	17 yrs.
Nevada	1983	0.08	0.02	yes[h]	secondary	all	6 mo.	50/10	yes	yes	18 yrs.
New Hampshire	1993	0.08	0.02	yes[h]	(k)	(k)	6 mo.	20/–	no	yes	18 yrs.
New Jersey	no	0.08	0.01	yes[h]	standard	front	12 mo.	none	yes	yes	18 yrs.
New Mexico	1984	0.08	0.02	yes	standard	all	6 mo.	50/10	yes	yes	16yrs., 6mo.
New York	1994[n]	0.08[l]	0.02	yes[h]	standard	front[i]	6 mo.	20/–	yes	yes	18 yrs.
North Carolina	1983	0.08	0.00	yes[h]	standard	all	12 mo.	none	yes	yes	16yrs., 6mo.
North Dakota	1983	0.08	0.02	yes[h]	secondary	front	6 mo.	none	no	no	16 yrs.
Ohio	1993	0.08	0.02	yes	secondary	front	6 mo.	50/10	no	yes	18 yrs.
Oklahoma	1983	0.08	0.00	yes	standard	front	6 mo.	40/10	yes	yes	18 yrs.
Oregon	1983	0.08	0.00	yes	standard	all	6 mo.	100/–	yes	yes	18 yrs.
Pennsylvania	no	0.08	0.02	yes[h]	secondary	front[i]	6 mo.	50/–	yes	yes	17yrs., 6mo.
Rhode Island	no	0.08	0.02	yes[h]	secondary	all	6 mo.	50/10	yes	yes	17yrs., 6mo.
South Carolina	1998	0.08	0.02	yes	standard	front[i]	180 days	40/10	yes	yes	17 yrs.
South Dakota	no	0.08	0.02	no	secondary	front	6 mo.	none	no	yes	16 yrs.
Tennessee	no	0.08	0.02	yes	standard	all	6 mo.	50/10	yes	yes	17 yrs.
Texas	1995	0.08	0.00	yes[h]	standard	front[i]	6 mo.	none	yes	yes	18 yrs.
Utah	1983	0.08	0.00	yes	secondary[k]	all	6 mo.	40/10	yes	yes	17 yrs.
Vermont	1969[n]	0.08	0.02	no	secondary	all	12 mo.	40/10	yes	no	16yrs., 6 mo.
Virginia	1995	0.08	0.02	yes	secondary	front[i]	9 mo.	40/10	yes	yes	18 yrs.
Washington	1998	0.08	0.02	yes	standard	all	6 mo.	50/10	yes	yes	18 yrs.
West Virginia	1981	0.08	0.02	yes	secondary	front[i]	6 mo.	30/–	yes	yes	18 yrs.
Wisconsin	1988	0.08	0.00	yes[h]	secondary	front[j]	12 mo.	30/10	yes	yes	18 yrs.
Wyoming	1973	0.08	0.02	yes	secondary	all	10 days	50/10	yes	yes	17 yrs.

Source: National Safety Council survey of state officials. Laws as of August 2008.
Note: California and Indiana did not respond to the 2008 survey. Data for these states are for 2007.
[a] Year original law became effective, not when grandfather clauses expired.
[b] Blood alcohol concentration that constitutes the threshold of legal intoxication.
[c] Blood alcohol concentration that constitutes "zero tolerance" threshold for minors (<21 years of age unless otherwise noted).
[d] Instruments designed to prevent drivers from starting their cars when breath alcohol content is at or above a set point.
[e] Minimum instructional periods often include time spent in driver's education classes.
[f] Figures shown as follows: Total hours/Nighttime hours. For example, 25/5 means 25 hours of supervised driving, 5 of which must be at night. Some states (GA, OR, WV) have lower requirements if driver ed is taken while other states require drivers ed in addition to supervision requirements.

[g] Minimum age to obtain unrestricted license provided driver is crash and violation free. Alcohol restrictions still apply at least until 21.
[h] Primarily for repeat offenders.
[i] Required for certain ages at all seating positions.
[j] Belt use required in rear seat if lap/shoulder belt is available.
[k] Standard enforcement law in effect for ages under 18 (FL, NH), under 19 (UT).
[l] BAC of 0.07 is prima facia evidence of DUI (MD). BAC of 0.05–0.07 constitutes driving while ability impaired (NY).
[m] 16 years old with drivers ed.
[n] Revocation by judicial action (NY) or Department of Motor Vehicles (VT).

Seat belt use was 83% overall in 2008, statistically unchanged from the 82% use rate in 2007 and much higher than the 69% use rate in 1998. These results are from the National Occupant Protection Use Survey conducted annually by the National Highway Traffic Safety Administration.

In 2007, belt use was 87% in states with standard (primary) enforcement and 73% in states with secondary enforcement.

By vehicle type, belt use was 86% in vans and SUVs, 84% in passenger cars, and 72% in pickup trucks. Belt use was higher in fast traffic (86%) than in slow traffic (78%) and higher in heavy traffic (84%) than in light traffic (82%).

Seat belt use was greater among females (86%) than among males (79%). By age group, use was lowest among those 16-24 years old (77%) and increased with age to 88% among those 70 and older.

Overall, drivers with no passengers were less likely to use seat belts (82%) than those with at least one passenger (86%). On the other hand, drivers aged 16–24, whose overall belt use when driving alone was 79%, were less likely to wear seat belts when all their passengers were also aged 16–24 (78%) compared to having at least one passenger not in that age group (83%).

Rear-seat belt use was 76% in 2007, 11 percentage points higher than in 2006. Rear-seat belt use was higher among occupants aged 8–15 years old (84%) and 70 and older (86%) than among those 16–24 years old (72%) and 25-69 years old (70%). In the 18 states and District of Columbia that required seat belt use in all seating positions, rear-seat belt use was 88% compared to 69% in states that required only front seat use.

Child restraint use. Ninety eight percent of infants were restrained in child safety seats in 2007 as were 96% of children 1–3 years of age and 85% of children 4–7 years old. Most children were observed riding in the rear seat—95% of infants, 98% of children 1–3 years old, and 88% of children 4–7 years old.

Seat belt use by the driver strongly influences the restraint status of child passengers. When the driver was belted, 92% of child passengers under the age of 8 were restrained. When the driver was not belted, only 61% of children were restrained.

By type of vehicle, child restraint use was highest in vans and SUVs (91%), somewhat lower in passenger cars (88%), and lowest in pickup trucks (76%).

Children from 4 to 7 years old should be restrained in a front-facing safety seat or booster seat depending on the child's height and weight. The National Survey of the Use of Booster Seats (NSUBS) found that, in 2007, 37% were using booster seats, 13% were in child safety seats, 35% were in seat belts, and 15% were unrestrained.

Source: Pickrell, T. M., & Ye, T. J. (2008). Seat belt use in 2008—overall results. Traffic Safety Facts Research Note, DOT HS 811 036. Washington, DC: National Highway Traffic Safety Administration.
Glassbrenner, D., & Ye, T. J. (2007). Seat belt use in 2007—overall results. Traffic Safety Facts Research Note, DOT HS 810 841. Washington, DC: National Highway Traffic Safety Administration.
Ye, T. J., & Pickrell, T. M. (2008). Seat belt use in 2007—demographic results. Traffic Safety Facts Research Note, DOT HS 810 932. Washington, DC: National Highway Traffic Safety Administration.
Ye, T. J., & Pickrell, T. M. (2008). Seat Belt Use in Rear Seats in 2007. Traffic Safety Facts Research Note, DOT HS 810 933. Washington, DC: National Highway Traffic Safety Administration.
Ye, T. J., & Pickrell, T. M. (2008). Child restraint use in 2007—overall results. Traffic Safety Facts Research Note, DOT HS 810 931. Washington, DC: National Highway Traffic Safety Administration.
Glassbrenner, D., & Ye, T. J. (2008). Booster seat use in 2007. Traffic Safety Facts Research Note, DOT HS 810 894. Washington, DC: National Highway Traffic Safety Administration.

SEAT BELT USE, UNITED STATES, 2000–2008

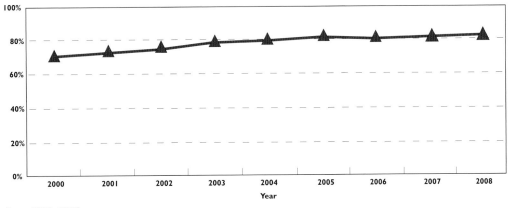

Source: NHTSA, NOPUS.

OCCUPANT PROTECTION

Safety Belts

- When used, lap/shoulder safety belts reduce the risk of fatal injury to front seat passenger car occupants by 45% and reduce the risk of moderate-to-critical injury by 50%.

- For light truck occupants, safety belts reduce the risk of fatal injury by 60% and moderate-to-critical injury by 65%.

- Forty-nine states and the District of Columbia have mandatory belt use laws in effect, the only exception being New Hampshire. Twenty-three of the states with belt use laws in effect in 2007 specified secondary enforcement (i.e., police officers are permitted to write a citation only after a vehicle is stopped for some other traffic infraction). Twenty-six states and the District of Columbia had laws that allowed primary enforcement, enabling officers to stop vehicles and write citations whenever they observe violations of the belt law.

- Safety belts saved an estimated 15,147 lives in 2007 among passenger vehicle occupants over 4 years old. *An additional* 5,024 lives could have been saved in 2007 if all passenger vehicle occupants over age 4 wore safety belts. From 1975 through 2007, an estimated 241,849 lives were saved by safety belts.

- More than half (54%) of the passenger vehicle occupants killed in 2007 were unrestrained.

- Almost two-thirds (63%) of the passenger vehicle occupants killed during the night were unrestrained, compared to 45% during the day.

PASSENGER VEHICLE OCCUPANT FATALITIES BY RESTRAINT USE[a], UNITED STATES, 2006–2007

Restraint Use	Year			
	2006		2007	
People Killed	**30,686**		**28,933**	
Restraint Used[b]	13,760	45%	13,306	46%
Restraint Not Used[b]	16,926	55%	15,627	54%
Day (6 a.m.–5:59 p.m.)				
Restraint Used[b]	8,194	54%	7,874	55%
Restraint Not Used	7,094	46%	6,344	45%
Night (6 p.m.–5:59 a.m.)				
Restraint Used[b]	5,472	36%	5,322	37%
Restraint Not Used	9,674	64%	9,142	63%

Source: National Center for Statistics and Analysis. (2008). Motor Vehicle Traffic Crash Fatality Counts and Estimates of People Injured for 2007 presentation (DOT HS 811 034). Washington, DC: National Highway Traffic Safety Administration. Accessed on 12/02/08: http://www-nrd.nhtsa.dot.gov/Pubs/811034.PDF
[a] *Occupant fatalities whose restraint use was unknown were distributed proportionally to the known use categories. Restraint use was unknown for 8% of passenger vehicle occupant fatalities in 2006 and 2007.*
[b] *Restraint Used: Use of any type of restraint, e.g., lap belt, lap/shoulder belt, child safety seat, etc.*

Air Bags

- Air bags, combined with lap/shoulder belts, offer the best available protection for passenger vehicle occupants. Recent analyses indicate a fatality-reducing effectiveness for air bags of 14% when no safety belt was used and 11% when a safety belt was used in conjunction with air bags.

- Lap/shoulder belts should always be used, even in a vehicle with an air bag. Air bags are a supplemental form of protection and most are designed to deploy only in moderate-to-severe *frontal* crashes.

- Children in rear-facing child seats should not be placed in the front seat of vehicles equipped with passenger-side air bags. The impact of the deploying air bag could result in injury to the child.

- An estimated 2,788 lives were saved by air bags in 2007 and a total of 25,282 lives were saved from 1987 through 2007.

- Beginning September 1997, all new passenger cars were required to have driver and passenger side air bags. In 1998, the same requirement went into effect for light trucks.

Child Restraints

- Child restraints saved an estimated 382 lives in 2007 among children under the age of 5.

- All states and the District of Columbia have had child restraint use laws in effect since 1985.

- Research has shown that child safety seats reduce fatal injury in passenger cars by 71% for infants (less than 1 year old), and by 54% for toddlers (1–4 years old). For infants and toddlers in light trucks, the corresponding reductions are 58% and 59%, respectively.

- In 2007, there were 322 occupant fatalities among children less than 4 years of age. Of these fatalities, 88 (27%) were totally unrestrained. Of the 274 fatalities among children 4 to 7 years of age for which restraint use was known, 117 (43%) were unrestrained.

- An estimated 8,709 lives have been saved by child restraints from 1975 through 2007.

ESTIMATED NUMBER OF LIVES SAVED BY RESTRAINT SYSTEMS, 1975–2007

Restraint Type	1975–99	2000	2001	2002	2003	2004	2005	2006	2007
Seat Belts	124,472	12,882	13,295	14,264	15,095	15,548	15,688	15,458	15,147
Child Restraints	5,324	479	388	383	447	455	424	427	382
Air Bags	5,721	1,716	1,978	2,324	2,519	2,660	2,752	2,824	2,788

Source: 1975–2002 data: National Center for Statistics and Analysis. (2007). Traffic Safety Facts 2006 Data—Occupant Protection (DOT HS 810 807). Washington, DC: National Highway Traffic Safety Administration; 2003–2007 data: National Center for Statistics and Analysis. (November 2008). Traffic Safety Facts Crash Stats—Lives Saved in 2007 by Restraint Use and Minimum Drinking Age Laws (DOT HS 811 049). Washington, DC: National Highway Traffic Safety Administration.

Motorcycle Helmets

- Motorcycle helmets are estimated to be 37% effective in preventing fatal injuries to motorcycle riders.

- It is estimated that motorcycle helmets saved the lives of 1,784 motorcyclists in 2007, an increase of more than 50% from the 1,173 lives saved in 2003. An additional 800 lives could have been saved in 2007 if all motorcyclists had worn helmets.

- Reported helmet use rates for fatally injured motorcyclists in 2007 were 59% for operators and 47% for passengers, compared with the corresponding rates of 59% and 45%, respectively, in 2006.

- In 2007, 20 states, the District of Columbia, and Puerto Rico required helmet use by all motorcycle operators and passengers. Other states either required only a subset of motorcyclists to use helmets (such as those under 18), or had no helmet requirement.

- Use of DOT-compliant helmets increased 5 percentage points to 63% in 2008, according to the National Occupant Protection Use Survey. However, motorcycle helmet use has declined by 8 percentage points from 71% in 2000.

Source: National Center for Statistics and Analysis. (November 2008). Traffic Safety Facts Crash Stats—Lives Saved in 2007 by Restraint Use and Minimum Drinking Age Laws (DOT HS 811 049). Washington, DC: National Highway Traffic Safety Administration. National Center for Statistics and Analysis. (September 2008). Traffic Safety Facts Research Note—Motorcycle Helmet Use in 2008—Overall Results (DOT HS 811 044). Washington, DC: National Highway Traffic Safety Administration. National Center for Statistics and Analysis. (2008). Traffic Safety Facts 2006 Data—Occupant Protection (DOT HS 810 807); Traffic Safety Facts 2007 Data—Motorcycles (DOT HS 810 990). Washington, DC: National Highway Traffic Safety Administration. National Center for Statistics and Analysis. (2007). Traffic Safety Facts 2006 Data—Occupant Protection (DOT HS 810 807); Traffic Safety Facts 2006 Data—Motorcycles (DOT HS 810 806). Washington, DC: National Highway Traffic Safety Administration.

ALCOHOL

According to studies conducted by the National Highway Traffic Safety Administration (NHTSA), about 12,998 people were killed in alcohol-impaired crashes in 2007, a decline of 3.7% from the 13,491 fatalities in 2006. Alcohol-impaired driving crashes are crashes that involve at least one driver or motorcycle [MC] operator with a blood alcohol concentration [BAC] of 0.08 grams per deciliter [g/dl] or greater. The following data summarizes the extent of alcohol involvement in motor-vehicle crashes involving at least one alcohol-impaired driver or MC operator:

- Traffic fatalities in alcohol-impaired driving crashes as a percentage of total traffic fatalities rose by 0.1% to 31.7% from 2006 to 2007 and increased by 1.5% from 1998 to 2007. (See corresponding chart.) In 1998, alcohol-impaired driving fatalities accounted for 30.2% of all traffic deaths.

- The alcohol-impaired driving fatality rate per 100 million vehicle miles of travel decreased to 0.43, the lowest rate on record.

- The only increase from 2006 to 2007 in the number of alcohol-impaired fatalities by age group was seen among the 45- to 64-year-old age group, which increased by about 3%. All other age groups showed decreases, ranging from –17.2% for those under 16 years of age to –1.8% for those age 21 to 24.

- About 83% of the alcohol-related fatalities in 2007 involved driver/MC operators or their passengers, while the remainder of the deaths occurred to occupants of other vehicles (11.0%), nonoccupants (5.8%), and others (0.1%)

- In 2007, while drivers age 25 to 34 constituted 19% of all drivers involved in fatal crashes, they were over-represented among the drivers/MC operators with BACs of 0.08 g/dl or greater, comprising 26% of such drivers/MC operators involved in fatal crashes. Drivers age 21 to 24 were similarly over-represented, accounting for 11% of drivers in fatal crashes and 18% of those with BACs of 0.08 g/dl or greater. The 35–44 age group was also slightly over-represented, making up 18% of drivers/MC operators in fatal crashes and 20% of those with BACs of 0.08 g/dl or greater.

PERCENT OF ALCOHOL-IMPAIRED DRIVING FATALITIES, UNITED STATES, 1998–2007

- From 2006 to 2007, the number of drivers/MC operators involved in fatal crashes that had a BAC of 0.08 g/dl or greater increased 2% in the 45–64 age group and 1% in the 21–24 age group. All other age groups showed decreases, ranging from –4% for the 25–34 age group to over 13% for the 16–20 age group. However, the only changes from 2006–2007 in the percentage distribution by age group of drivers/MC operators involved in fatal crashes with BAC 0.08 g/dl or higher were slight (1%) increases in the 21–24 and 45–64 age groups, with corresponding decreases in the 16–20 and 35–44 age groups.

- Males continue to comprise the majority—83% in 2007—of all drivers involved in fatal crashes with a BAC of 0.08 g/dl or greater. Although the percentage reduction in the total number of drivers involved in fatal crashes from 2006 to 2007 was comparable for males and females, the percent reduction in the number with BACs of 0.08 g/dl or greater was larger for females (–16%) compared to males (–1.4%).

- About 85% of drivers involved in fatal crashes in 2007 with a BAC of 0.08 g/dl or greater were driving passenger cars or light trucks (including SUVs), while a further 12% were motorcycle operators. The number of alcohol-impaired motorcycle operators increased 10% from 2006 to 2007 and they were the only category to show an increase. Nearly 60% of alcohol-impaired driver/MC operators were involved in a fatal crash on the weekend and over two-thirds of the crashes were single vehicle crashes.

- Thirty-two states showed decreases in the number of alcohol-impaired driving fatalities in 2007, as compared to 2006 (see corresponding chart).

- All states and the District of Columbia now have 21-year-old minimum drinking age laws. In 2007, all states plus the District of Columbia had by law created a threshold making it illegal to drive with a BAC of 0.08 g/dl or higher.

- The cost of alcohol-related motor-vehicle crashes is estimated by the National Safety Council at $41.0 billion in 2007.

Source: National Center for Statistics and Analysis. (2008). *2007 Traffic Safety Annual Assessment—Alcohol-Impaired Driving Fatalities.* Washington, DC: National Highway Traffic Safety Administration.

PERCENT CHANGE IN NUMBER OF ALCOHOL-IMPAIRED DRIVING FATALITIES, BY STATE, 2006–2007

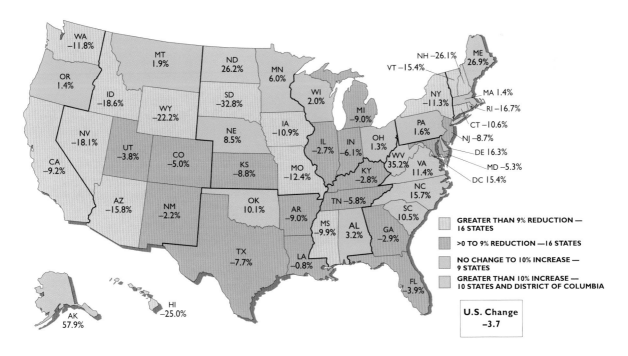

TYPE OF MOTOR-VEHICLE ACCIDENT

Although motor-vehicle deaths occur more often in collisions between motor vehicles than any other type of accident, this type represents only about 40% of the total. Collisions between a motor vehicle and a fixed object were the next most common type, with about 31% of the deaths, followed by pedestrian accidents and noncollisions (rollovers, etc.).

While collisions between motor vehicles accounted for less than half of motor-vehicle fatalities, this accident type represented 73% of injuries, 68% of injury accidents, and 70% of all accidents. Single-vehicle accidents involving collisions with fixed objects, pedestrians, and noncollisions, on the other hand,

accounted for a greater proportion of fatalities and fatal accidents compared to less serious accidents. These three accident types made up 57% of fatalities and 56% of fatal accidents, but 30% or less of injuries, injury accidents, or all accidents.

Of collisions between motor vehicles, angle collisions cause the greatest number of deaths, about 8,500 in 2007 and the greatest number of nonfatal injuries as well as fatal and injury accidents. The table below shows the estimated number of motor-vehicle deaths, injuries, fatal accidents, injury accidents, and all accidents, for various types of accidents.

MOTOR-VEHICLE DEATHS AND INJURIES AND NUMBER OF ACCIDENTS BY TYPE OF ACCIDENT, 2007

Type of Accident	Deaths	Nonfatal Injuries	Fatal Accidents	Injury Accidents	All Accidents
Total	43,100	2,300,000	39,100	1,600,000	10,600,000
Collision with—					
Pedestrian	5,900	85,000	4,500	60,000	120,000
Other motor vehicle	17,200	1,680,000	15,100	1,080,000	7,440,000
Angle collision	8,500	791,000	8,100	490,000	2,940,000
Head-on collision	4,800	124,000	4,200	66,000	270,000
Rear-end collision	2,700	675,000	1,900	463,000	3,350,000
Sideswipe and other two-vehicle collisions	1,200	90,000	900	61,000	880,000
Railroad train	200	1,000	200	1,000	2,000
Pedalcycle	1,000	59,000	1,000	40,000	88,000
Animal, animal-drawn vehicle	100	5,000	100	5,000	490,000
Fixed or other object	13,500	360,000	13,100	330,000	2,150,000
Noncollision	5,200	110,000	5,100	84,000	310,000

Source: National Safety Council estimates, based on data from the National Highway Traffic Safety Administration Fatality Analysis Reporting System and General Estimates System. Procedures for estimating the number of accidents by type were changed for the 1998 edition and are not comparable to estimates in previous editions (See Technical Appendix).

SPEEDING

Speeding is one of the major factors contributing to the occurrence of deaths, injuries, and property damage related to motor-vehicle crashes. The role of speeding in crash causation can be described in terms of its effect on the driver, the vehicle, and the road. Excessive-speed driving reduces the amount of time the driver has to react in a dangerous situation to avoid a crash. Speeding increases vehicle stopping distance and also reduces the ability of road safety structures such as guardrails, impact attenuators, crash cushions, median dividers, and concrete barriers to protect vehicle occupants in a crash.

The National Highway Traffic Safety Administration (NHTSA) estimates that speeding-related crashes[a] cost the nation $40.4 billion in 2000, or 18% of the entire cost of motor-vehicle crashes in the United States. After adjusting for inflation these economic losses are equivalent to $132.0 million per day or $5.5 million per hour.

Speeding was a factor in 32% of all traffic fatalities in 2007, killing an average of 36 vehicle occupants per day. The total number of fatal motor-vehicle crashes attributable to speeding declined over 3% from 2006 to 2007 with 12,082 and 11,659 fatal crashes respectively each year. However, the percentage of speeding-related fatalities among overall fatalities remained unchanged from 2006.

A study conducted by the Insurance Institute for Highway Safety collected speed data on urban, suburban, and rural interstates in eight metropolitan areas. On urban interstates, the average speed of passenger vehicles in 2007 exceeded the limits in all surveyed areas. On suburban and rural interstates, average speeds were faster than the limits in half of the metro areas.

[a]A crash is considered speeding related if the driver was charged with a speeding-related offense or if racing, driving too fast for conditions, or exceeding the posted speed limit was indicated as a contributing factor in the crash.

PASSENGER VEHICLE SPEEDING, 2007

	Speed Limit (mph)	Mean Speed (mph)	Percentage Going Faster Than 75 mph	Percentage Going Faster Than 80 mph
Suburban/Rural Interstates				
Albuquerque	75	74	47	14
Atlanta	65	72	27	8
Boston	65	67	11	3
Denver	75	70	11	1
Los Angeles	70	67	6	1
Omaha	75	74	46	10
Tampa	70	75	49	14
Washington, DC	65	66	7	1
Urban Interstates				
Albuquerque	65	69	38	13
Atlanta	55	65	20	4
Boston	55	62	15	4
Denver	55	56	1	<1
Los Angeles	65	67	34	12
Omaha	60	68	30	8
Tampa	55	57	1	<1
Washington, DC	55	61	5	1
Arterial Roads				
Atlanta	45	43	4	<1
Boston	45	62	99	62
Denver	40	42	3	0
Los Angeles	45	47	30	4
Omaha	45	47	19	1
Tampa	45	49	45	3
Washington, DC	45	57	85	25

Source: National Center for Statistics and Analysis. (2008). Motor Vehicle Traffic Crash Fatality Counts and Estimates of People Injured for 2007 presentation (DOT HS 811 034). Washington, DC: National Highway Traffic Safety Administration. Accessed on 12/02/08: http://www-nrd.nhtsa.dot.gov/Pubs/811034.PDF. Insurance Institute for Highway Safety (2008). Status Report, Special Issue: Speed. Vol. 43, No.1. Accessed on 12/02/08: http://www.iihs.org/sr/pdfs/sr4301.pdf.

DISTRACTED DRIVING

Driver Distraction

Driver distraction occurs when a driver's attention is diverted away from driving by a secondary task that requires focusing on an object, event, or person not related to the driving task. The most frequent secondary task is conversation with passengers, followed by eating, smoking, manipulating controls, reaching inside the vehicle, and cell phone use. It has been estimated that drivers engage in potentially distracting tasks approximately 30% of the time their vehicles are in motion.

Based on separate analyses of 1995–1999 and 2000–2003 data from the National Highway Traffic Safety Administration's Crash Worthiness Data System (CDS), it was estimated that over the entire time frame about 10.5% of drivers involved in crashes were distracted at the time of their crash involvement. About 70% of the distracted driver crashes involved non-collision (single-vehicle) or rear-end crashes. The

leading sources of distraction were an outside object/person/event or another vehicle occupant, followed by reaching for an object, a moving object in the vehicle, a cell phone, adjusting the radio/cassette/CD player, eating/drinking, adjusting climate control, and smoking.

In addition to mobile telephones and radio/CD players, other devices such as in-vehicle route guidance systems (i.e., GPS devices) have also become potential sources of distraction, as will future in-vehicle internet and e-mail access. The expansion of cell phone's capabilities to include these latter two options as well as text messaging, combined with the continually increasing number of cell phone users overall, suggest that their portion of the incidence of distracting activities and associated problems may increase.

Source: Ranney, T. A. (2008, April). Driver distraction: A review of the current state-of-knowledge (Report No. DOT HS 810 787). Washington, DC: National Highway Traffic Safety Administration.

Driver Electronic Devise Use

Six percent of drivers were observed using a hand-held cell phone in the 2007 National Occupant Protection Use Survey (NOPUS) conducted by the National Highway Traffic Safety Administration, an increase from the 5% observed in 2006. The portion of drivers using observable headsets remained unchanged at 0.6%, while the portion visibly manipulating hand-held devices increased a non-significant 0.3 percentage points to 0.7%.

Other significant increases in hand-held cell phone use from 2006 to 2007 were observed for male drivers, female drivers, drivers aged 25–69, and drivers of all races and vehicle types. Significant increases for drivers

using observable headsets occurred only among male drivers, while significant increases for drivers visibly manipulating hand-held devices were observed only for drivers aged 16–24.

Hand-held phone use was highest (9%) in 2007 among young drivers 16–24 years old and lowest among drivers aged 70 and older (1%). Use was higher among females (8%) than males (5%). Use also varied by vehicle type—7% for van and SUV drivers, 6% for pickup truck drivers, and 6% for passenger car drivers. Cell phones were in use by 8% of drivers with no passengers and 2% among drivers with at least one passenger.

Source: National Center for Statistics and Analysis (June, 2008). Driver electronic device use in 2007. Traffic Safety Facts Research Note (DOT HS 810 963). Washington, DC: National Highway Traffic Safety Administration.

DRIVER HAND-HELD PHONE USE, UNITED STATES, 2002–2007

Source: NOPUS, NHTSA, 2002–2007.

IMPROPER DRIVING

In most motor-vehicle accidents, factors are present relating to the driver, the vehicle, and the road, and it is the interaction of these factors that often sets up the series of events that result in an accident. The table below relates only to the driver, and shows the principal kinds of improper driving in accidents in 2007 as reported by police.

Exceeding the posted speed limit or driving at an unsafe speed was the most common error in fatal accidents. Right-of-way violations predominated in the injury accidents and all accidents categories.

While some drivers were under the influence of alcohol or other drugs, this represents the driver's physical condition—not a driving error. See page 96 for a discussion of alcohol involvement in traffic accidents.

Correcting the improper practices listed below could reduce the number of accidents. This does not mean, however, that road and vehicle conditions can be disregarded.

IMPROPER DRIVING REPORTED IN ACCIDENTS, 2007

Kind of Improper Driving	Fatal Accidents	Injury Accidents	All Accidents
Total	100.0%	100.0%	100.0%
Improper driving	67.3	67.6	63.7
Speed too fast or unsafe	16.9	11.4	9.5
Right of way	11.3	16.2	13.8
Failed to yield	7.5	11.9	10.5
Disregarded signal	2.4	1.5	1.1
Passed stop sign	1.4	2.8	2.2
Drove left of center	6.7	1.5	1.1
Made improper turn	4.1	4.0	4.2
Improper overtaking	0.8	0.6	0.8
Followed too closely	0.8	9.1	8.5
Other improper driving	26.7	24.8	25.8
No improper driving stated	32.7	32.4	36.3

Source: Based on reports from 21 state traffic authorities. Percents may not add to totals due to rounding.

LARGE TRUCKS

In 2007, 4,808 fatalities resulted from a traffic crash involving a large truck and 75% of these deaths were occupants of vehicles other than the large truck. An estimated 101,000 people were injured in large truck crashes in 2007. A large truck is one with gross vehicle weight rating greater than 10,000 pounds.

Large trucks were more likely to be involved in a multiple-vehicle fatal crash than passenger vehicles. In 2007, 82% of large trucks in fatal crashes were in multiple-vehicle crashes compared to 59% of passenger vehicles.

Most large truck fatal crashes occurred in rural areas (62%) and on weekdays (78%) in 2007. Nearly three quarters (74%) of the fatal crashes happened during the daytime on weekdays while on weekends over three fifths (62%) occurred at night.

Source: National Center for Statistics and Analysis. (2008). Traffic Safety Facts 2007 Data: Large Trucks. DOT HS 810 989. Washington, DC: National Highway Traffic Safety Administration.

FATALITIES IN CRASHES INVOLVING LARGE TRUCKS, UNITED STATES, 2007

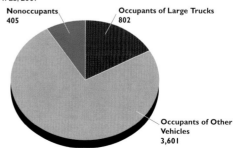

Nonoccupants 405
Occupants of Large Trucks 802
Occupants of Other Vehicles 3,601

MOTORCYCLES

Fatalities among motorcycle riders and passengers have increased 144% between 1997 and 2007. Nonfatal injuries have increased, too, from 53,000 to 103,000 over the same period.

Exposure has also increased. From 1997 through 2006 (the latest year available), the number of registered motorcycles increased more than 75% from 3.8 million to 6.7 million. Miles traveled is up 23% from 10.1 billion to 12.4 billion. Consequently, the death rate has increased 85% from 20.99 to 39.00 deaths per 100 million miles traveled.

Showing some improvement this last year, the motorcycle death rate per 100 million miles improved for the first time in 10 years from 43.77 in 2005 to 39.00 in 2006. Even with this improvement, the mileage death rate for motorcyclists was 35 times greater than for passenger cars and light trucks in 2006.

In 2007, speeding was a factor in 36% of fatal motorcycle crashes compared to 24% for fatal passenger car crashes. One fourth (26%) of motorcycle operators in fatal crashes had invalid licenses compared to 13% for passenger car drivers.

Twenty seven percent of motorcycle operators involved in fatal crashes were intoxicated (BAC ≥ .08 g/dL) compared to 23% of passenger car drivers.

Although helmet use is down from a high of 71% in 2000, the latest survey does show some improvement. The percent of helmet use increased from 58% in 2007 to 63% for 2008.

A review conducted by the National Highway Traffic Safety Administration of state-level motorcycle safety interventions found that the only intervention with proven effectiveness was state helmet use laws. The effectiveness of other interventions such as licensing and education/training was found to be uncertain.

SUMMARY OF STATE-LEVEL INTERVENTIONS TO IMPROVE MOTORCYCLE SAFETY

Intervention	Effectiveness
Helmets	
State helmet use laws	Proven
Helmet law enforcement—noncompliant helmets	Unknown
Helmet use promotion programs	Unknown
Alcohol Impairment	
Detection, sanction	Unknown
Communications	Unknown
Operator licensing and training	
Licensing	Uncertain
Education and training	Uncertain
Communications and outreach	
Campaigns to promote protective and conspicuous clothing	Unknown
Campaigns to increase other driver awareness of motorcyclists	Unknown

Proven = Demonstrated by several high-quality evaluations with consistent results
Uncertain = Limited and perhaps ambiguous evidence
Unknown = No high-quality evaluation evidence

MOTORCYCLIST DEATHS AND DEATH RATES, UNITED STATES, 1997–2007

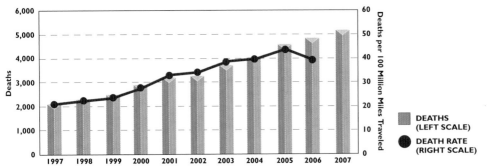

Source: *Countermeasures That Work: A Highway Safety Countermeasures Guide for State Highway Safety Offices*, Third Edition, 2008. Washington, DC: NHTSA.
National Center for Statistics and Analysis. (2007). Traffic Safety Facts 2006 Data: Motorcycles. *DOT HS 810 806*. Washington, DC: National Highway Traffic Safety Administration.
National Center for Statistics and Analysis. (2008). Traffic Safety Facts Research Note: Motorcycle Helmet Use in 2008—Overall Results. *DOT HS 811 0446*. Washington, DC: National Highway Traffic Safety Administration.

SCHOOL BUS TRANSPORTATION

School bus-related crashes killed 141 persons nationwide in 2007, according to data from the National Highway Traffic Safety Administration.

A school bus-related crash is defined by NHTSA to be any crash in which a vehicle, regardless of body design, used as a school bus is directly or indirectly involved, such as a crash involving school children alighting from a vehicle.

Over the period from 2002-2007, about 74% of the deaths in school bus-related crashes were occupants of vehicles other than the school bus and 18% were pedestrians. About 3% were school bus passengers and 3% were school bus drivers.

Of the 18 pedestrians killed in school bus-related crashes in 2007, 15 were struck by the school bus.

Out of the people injured in school bus-related crashes from 2002 through 2007, about 43% were school bus passengers, 9% were school bus drivers, and another 44% were occupants of other vehicles. The remainder were pedestrians, pedalcyclists, and other or unknown type persons.

Characteristics of school bus transportation
Forty-seven states reported that about 24.8 million public school pupils were transported at public expense and 26 states reported that public funds were used to transport another 1.0 million private school pupils. These data are prepared by *School Bus Fleet* (vol. 53, no. 11) for the 2005–2006 school year with 13 states reporting for prior school years. This compares to estimates from the U.S. Department of Education of enrollments in fall 2005 in grades K-12 of about 49.1 million public school pupils and 6.1 million private school pupils nationwide. Fifty states employed a total of 476,798 school buses, and the buses in 41 states traveled about 4.2 billion route miles.

DEATHS AND INJURIES IN SCHOOL BUS-RELATED CRASHES, UNITED STATES, 2002–2007

	2002	2003	2004	2005	2006	2007
Deaths						
Total	**129**	**140**	**133**	**134**	**150**	**141**
School bus driver	1	6	3	5	3	4
School bus passenger	2	5	4	5	5	1
Pedestrian	20	27	30	30	22	18
Pedalcyclist	5	2	3	6	2	6
Occupant of other vehicle	100	100	93	87	118	112
Other non-occupants	1	0	0	1	0	0
Injuries						
Total	**18,000**	**19,000**	**17,000**	**11,000**	**13,000**	**9,000**
School bus driver	1,000	2,000	1,000	1,000	2,000	1,000
School bus passenger	9,000	9,000	8,000	4,000	5,000	2,000
Pedestrian	1,000	(a)	1,000	(a)	(a)	(a)
Pedalcyclist	(a)	(a)	(a)	(a)	(a)	(a)
Occupant of other vehicle	7,000	8,000	7,000	6,000	5,000	5,000
Other non-occupants	(a)	(a)	(a)	(a)	(a)	(a)

Source: Deaths—National Center for Statistics and Analysis. (2008). *Traffic Safety Facts 2007 Data—School Transportation-Related Crashes (DOT HS 810 997)*. Washington, DC: National Highway Traffic Safety Administration. *Pedalcyclist deaths are National Safety Council tabulations of Fatality Analysis Reporting System (FARS) data. Injuries—National Center for Statistics and Analysis. (2003–2007). Traffic Safety Facts, 2002–2006 editions.* Washington, DC: National Highway Traffic Safety Administration. *Injury data for 2007 are National Safety Council tabulations of General Estimates System (GES) data.*
a *Less than 500.*

AGE OF DRIVER

The table below shows the total number of licensed drivers and drivers involved in accidents by selected ages and age groups. Also shown is the rate of accident involvement on the basis of the number of drivers in each age group. The fatal accident involvement rates per 100,000 drivers in each age group ranged from a low of 21 for drivers 55 to 64 years of age to a high of 56 for drivers aged 18. The all accident involvement rates per 100 drivers in each age group ranged from 4 for drivers aged 75 and over to 28 for drivers aged 16.

On the basis of miles driven by each age group, however, involvement rates (not shown in the table) are highest for young and old drivers. For drivers aged 16 to 19, the fatal involvement rate per 100 million vehicle miles traveled was 9.2 in 1990, about three times the overall rate for all drivers in passenger vehicles, 3.0. The rate for drivers aged 75 and over was 11.5, the highest of all age groups. The same basic "U"-shaped curve is found for injury accident involvement rates.[a]

[a]Massie, D., Campbell, K., & Williams, A. (1995). Traffic accident involvement rates by driver age and gender. Accident Analysis and Prevention, 27 (1), 73-87.

AGE OF DRIVER—TOTAL NUMBER AND NUMBER IN ACCIDENTS, 2007

Age Group	Licensed Drivers		Drivers in ...					
	Number	Percent	Fatal Accidents			All Accidents		
			Number	Percent	Rate[a]	Number	Percent	Rate[b]
Total	205,100,000	100.0%	58,400	100.0%	28	18,100,000	100.0%	9
Under 16	419,000[c]	0.2	300	0.5	[d]	70,000	0.4	[d]
16	1,307,000	0.6	700	1.2	54	360,000	2.0	28
17	2,283,000	1.1	1,100	1.9	48	530,000	2.9	23
18	2,870,000	1.4	1,600	2.7	56	620,000	3.4	22
19	3,155,000	1.5	1,700	2.9	54	570,000	3.1	18
19 and under	10,034,000	4.9	5,400	9.2	54	2,150,000	11.9	21
20	3,291,000	1.6	1,700	2.9	52	690,000	3.8	21
21	3,362,000	1.6	1,800	3.1	54	530,000	2.9	16
22	3,400,000	1.7	1,800	3.1	53	480,000	2.7	14
23	3,517,000	1.7	1,600	2.7	45	470,000	2.6	13
24	3,603,000	1.8	1,800	3.1	50	450,000	2.5	12
20–24	17,173,000	8.4	8,700	14.9	51	2,620,000	14.5	15
25–34	35,712,000	17.4	10,700	18.3	30	3,740,000	20.7	10
35–44	40,322,000	19.7	9,600	16.4	24	3,220,000	17.8	8
45–54	40,937,000	20.0	9,400	16.1	23	3,030,000	16.7	7
55–64	30,355,000	14.8	6,500	11.1	21	1,990,000	11.0	7
65–74	17,246,000	8.4	3,800	6.5	22	790,000	4.4	5
75 and over	13,321,000	6.5	4,300	7.4	32	560,000	3.1	4

Source: National Safety Council estimates. Drivers in accidents based on data from the National Highway Traffic Safety Administration's Fatality Analysis Reporting System and General Estimates System. Total licensed drivers from the Federal Highway Administration; age distribution by National Safety Council.
Note: Percents may not add to total due to rounding.
[a]Drivers in fatal accidents per 100,000 licensed drivers in each age group.
[b]Drivers in all accidents per 100 licensed drivers in each age group.
[c]Number of licensed drivers under 16 higher than in previous editions due to better reporting to the Federal Highway Administration.
[d]Rates for drivers under age 16 are substantially overstated due to the high proportion of unlicensed drivers involved.

YOUNG DRIVERS

Motor-vehicle crashes are the leading cause of death for young people 15-20 years old. In 2005 (the latest year available), according to a National Safety Council analysis of National Center for Health Statistics mortality data, 6,230 young people died in crashes.

In 2007, there were 6,552 fatal crashes involving young drivers (age 16-20). Young drivers killed in crashes decreased nearly 9%, from 3,407 in 2006 down to 3,108 in 2007. In addition, passenger fatalities in vehicles with young drivers decreased nearly 6% from

2,086 to 1,967. Seventeen percent of young drivers involved in fatal crashes had blood alcohol concentrations of 0.08 or greater.

As shown in the table below, both crashes and fatalities involving young drivers have decreased from 2006. The only crash type showing an increase from 2006 is property damage only crashes with a 4% increase. Although young driver fatalities among males are decreasing faster than females, males still represent nearly 74% of the fatalities.

NUMBER OF CRASHES AND FATALITIES IN CRASHES INVOLVING YOUNG DRIVERS, 2006–2007

	Year		Percent Change
	2006	2007	
Crashes			
Fatal	7,012	6,552	−6.6
Injury	461,000	430,000	−6.7
Property Damage Only	993,000	1,037,000	+4.4
Fatalities			
Young Drivers	3,407	3,108	−8.8
Male	2,513	2,284	−9.1
Female	894	824	−7.8
Passengers[a]	2,086	1,967	−5.7
All Others	2,516	2,437	−3.1

Source: National Center for Statistics and Analysis. (2008). Motor Vehicle Traffic Crash Fatality Counts And Estimates of People Injured for 2007 presentation (DOT HS 811 034). Washington, DC: National Highway Traffic Safety Administration. Accessed on 12/02/08: http://www-nrd.nhtsa.dot.gov/Pubs/811034.PDF. National Center for Statistics and Analysis. (2008). Traffic Safety Facts 2007 Traffic Safety Annual Assessment—Alcohol-Impaired Driving Fatalities (DOT HS 811 016). Washington, DC: National Highway Traffic Safety Administration.
[a] In vehicles with young drivers.

Graduated driver licensing (GDL) is an effective way to reduce the impact of motor-vehicle crashes on the lives of young drivers.

A national evaluation of graduated driver licensing programs sponsored by the National Highway Traffic Safety Administration found that the most comprehensive GDL programs are associated with crash

involvement rates about 20% lower for 16-year-olds than comparable crash involvement rates without GDL programs. The greatest benefit appears to be in programs that include age requirements plus three or more months of waiting before the intermediate stage, nighttime driving restrictions, and either supervised driving of at least 30 hours or a passenger restriction.

COMPARISON OF 16-YEAR-OLD DRIVERS FATALITY RATES BY PRESENCE OF GDL RESTRICTION, UNITED STATES, 1994–2004

GDL Component	Level of Restriction	Number of States Compared[a]	Driver Fatal Crash Involvement Rate[b]
Minimum Age For Learner Permit	15½ years	13	22
	<15½ years	30	35
Mandatory Waiting Period	3 + months	37	27
	None or <3 months	6	31
Minimum Of Supervised Driving	30 + hours	29	23
	None or <30 hours	14	35
Minimum Age Intermediate Stage	16 + years	29	23
	None or <16 years	14	35
Minimum Age Full Licensing	17 + years	23	22
	<17 years	20	37
Nighttime Restriction	Any	31	23
	None	12	36
Passenger Restriction	Any	21	21
	None	22	31

Source: Baker, S., Chen, L., & Li, G. (2006). National Evaluation of Graduated Driver Licensing Programs. National Highway Traffic Safety Administration (DOT HS 810 614). Washington, DC: National Highway Traffic Safety Administration. Accessed on 12/02/08: http://www.nhtsa.dot.gov/people/injury/NewDriver/GDLReport/images/GDLReport.pdf
[a] As of 2004, for the 43 states studied.
[b] Driver fatal crash involvement rate: the number of crashes per 100,000 person-years for relevant states. Because more than one GDL component is applied at a time, rates may reflect the impact of multiple GDL components.

In 2007, there were an estimated 5,900 pedestrian deaths and 85,000 injuries in motor-vehicle accidents. About 61% of these deaths and injuries occur when pedestrians improperly cross roadways or intersections or dart/run into streets. Playing, working, standing, etc. in the roadway accounted for about 11% of pedestrian deaths and injuries, while walking with traffic accounted for over 6%.

The distribution of pedestrian deaths and injuries by action varies for persons of different ages.

Darting/running into the road was the leading type for the three youngest age groups, varying from 36% for those aged 10 to 14 years to 68% for those aged 0 to 4 years. Improper crossing of the roadway or intersection was the leading type for the 15 to 19, 20 to 24, 25 to 44, 45 to 64, and 65 and over age groups, ranging from 29% for those aged 25 to 44 years to about 48% for those aged 20 to 24.

DEATHS AND INJURIES OF PEDESTRIANS BY AGE AND ACTION, 2007

		Age of Persons Killed or Injured							
	Total[a]	0–4	5–9	10–14	15–19	20–24	25–44	45–64	65 & Over
All Actions	100.0%	4.0%	8.9%	11.2%	13.4%	8.9%	24.4%	20.3%	8.9%
Totals	100.0%	100.0%	100.0%	100.0%	100.0%	100.0%	100.0%	100.0%	100.0%
Improper crossing of roadway or intersection	37.5%	17.9%	16.9%	32.3%	38.0%	47.5%	28.9%	46.6%	65.0%
Darting or running into road	23.8%	68.2%	59.8%	35.7%	22.8%	23.2%	14.1%	10.5%	12.0%
Walking with traffic	6.5%	0.0%	0.0%	7.9%	11.8%	2.7%	11.8%	4.1%	0.6%
Walking against traffic	1.4%	0.0%	0.0%	0.4%	2.1%	1.9%	3.0%	0.7%	0.6%
Playing/working/standing, etc. in roadway	10.6%	7.7%	1.9%	1.3%	5.5%	6.4%	18.0%	16.6%	9.8%
Nonmotorist pushing a vehicle in roadway	0.2%	0.0%	0.0%	0.0%	0.0%	0.0%	0.0%	1.0%	0.0%
Inattentive--talking, eating, etc.	1.2%	0.0%	0.0%	3.5%	3.3%	0.7%	0.5%	0.4%	0.7%
Other action	9.4%	3.3%	14.6%	2.4%	5.0%	13.5%	13.3%	8.9%	8.2%
Not stated	9.5%	2.9%	6.8%	16.5%	11.5%	4.0%	10.2%	11.1%	3.0%

Source: NSC analysis of NHTSA, General Estimates System data.
[a] Total includes "Age Unknown."

PEDESTRIAN DEATHS AND DEATH RATES BY SEX AND AGE GROUP, UNITED STATES, 2005

Source: National Safety Council based on National Center for Health Statistics data.

DEATHS AND MILEAGE DEATH RATES BY MONTH

Motor-vehicle deaths in 2007 were at their lowest level in February and increased to their highest level in July. In 2007, the highest monthly mileage death rate of 1.53 deaths per 100,000,000 vehicle miles occurred in September. The overall rate for the year was 1.44.

Source: Deaths—National Safety Council estimates. Mileage—Federal Highway Administration, Traffic Volume Trends.

MOTOR-VEHICLE DEATHS AND MILEAGE DEATH RATES BY MONTH, 2007

HOLIDAYS

Holidays are traditionally a time of travel for families across the United States and many choose the automobile — with the highest fatality rate of any of the major forms of transportation based on fatalities per passenger mile (see page 136) — as their mode of travel and therefore increase their risk of dying in a motor-vehicle crash. In addition, holidays are often the cause for celebrations that include the drinking of alcohol, which is a major contributing factor to motor-vehicle crashes. Alcohol-impaired (BAC of .08 g/dL or above) fatalities in 2007 represented 32% of the total traffic fatalities for the year. The table below shows the number of fatalities for each major holiday period and the percent of those fatalities that were alcohol-related (BAC of .01 g/dL or greater).

MOTOR-VEHICLE DEATHS AND PERCENT ALCOHOL-RELATED DURING HOLIDAY PERIODS, 2003–2007

	Holiday Period[a]											
	New Year's Day		Memorial Day		Independence Day		Labor Day		Thanksgiving		Christmas	
Year	Deaths[b]	Alcohol-Related[c] %	Deaths[b]	Alcohol-Related[c] %	Deaths[b]	Alcohol-Related[c] %	Deaths[b]	Alcohol-Related[c] %	Deaths[b]	Alcohol-Related[c] %	Deaths[b]	Alcohol-Related[c] %
2003	203 (1)	63	472 (3)	48	500 (3)	55	490 (3)	51	544 (4)	45	488 (4)	46
2004	549 (4)	50	496 (3)	49	502 (3)	49	480 (3)	49	556 (4)	42	370 (3)	49
2005	449 (3)	52	512 (3)	50	565 (3)	53	500 (3)	53	605 (4)	47	383 (3)	50
2006	432 (3)	55	493 (3)	52	629 (4)	49	487 (3)	48	623 (4)	47	379 (3)	51
2007	387 (3)	—	475 (3)	—	184 (1)	—	508 (3)	—	542 (4)	—	454 (4)	—

Source: National Highway Traffic Safety Administration (NHTSA), Fatality Analysis Reporting System and NHTSA, Traffic Safety Facts, 2006 *edition.*
Note: Dashes indicate data not available.
[a] The length of the holiday period depends on the day of the week on which the holiday falls. Memorial Day and Labor Day are always 3.25 days, Thanksgiving is always 4.25 days, and New Year's, Independence Day, and Christmas are 3.25 days if the holiday falls on Friday through Monday, 4.25 days if on Tuesday or Thursday, and 1.25 days if on Wednesday.
[b] Number in parentheses refers to the number of whole days in the holiday period.
[c] Blood alcohol concentration (BAC) of .01 grams per deciliter (g/dl) or greater. The holiday periods used to calculate the percentages conform to the NHTSA holiday period definitions that add another quarter day to the periods noted in footnote (a).

WORK ZONE DEATHS AND INJURIES

In 2007 there were 835 people killed and 41,475 people injured in work zone crashes (see table below). Compared to 2006, work zone fatalities decreased 17% and injuries were up 10%. Of the 835 people killed in work zones, 644 were in construction zones, 88 were in maintenance zones, 11 were in utility zones, and 92 were in an unknown type of work zone.

Over the 10 years from 1998 through 2007, work zone deaths have ranged from 772 to 1,181 and averaged 1,001 per year.

Based on a National Safety Council survey in August 2008, 35 states reported having work zone speed laws and 49 states had special penalties for traffic violations in work zones, such as increased or doubled fines. Hawaii and District of Columbia were the only jurisdictions with neither.

PERSONS KILLED AND INJURED IN WORK ZONES, UNITED STATES, 2007

	Total	Vehicle Occupants	Pedestrians	Pedalcyclists	Other Nonmotorists
Killed	835	712	110	8	5
Injured	41,475	39,895	994	540	46

Source: National Safety Council analysis of data from National Highway Traffic Safety Administration Fatality Analysis Reporting System (FARS) and General Estimates Systems (GES).

EMERGENCY VEHICLES

CRASHES INVOLVING EMERGENCY VEHICLES, UNITED STATES, 2007

	Ambulance		Fire Truck/Car		Police Car	
	Total	Emergency Use[a]	Total	Emergency Use[a]	Total	Emergency Use[a]
Emergency vehicles in fatal crashes	29	18	18	17	123	57
Emergency vehicles in injury crashes	730	394	481	358	8,120	4,517
Emergency vehicles in all crashes	4,051	2,152	3,622	1,632	24,632	11,999
Emergency vehicle drivers killed	1	1	4	4	37	20
Emergency vehicle passengers killed	14	12	3	3	5	1
Other vehicle occupants killed	20	11	15	14	73	37
Nonmotorists killed	2	1	1	1	20	6
Total killed in crashes	37	25	23	22	135	64
Total injured in crashes	1,464	659	687	522	14,824	8,756

Source: National Safety Council analysis of data from National Highway Traffic Safety Administration Fatality Analysis Reporting System (FARS) and General Estimates Systems (GES).
[a]Emergency lights and/or sirens in use.

The National Safety Council and the National Highway Traffic Safety Administration (NHTSA) count motor-vehicle crash deaths using somewhat different criteria. The Council counts total motor-vehicle-related fatalities—both traffic and nontraffic—that occur within one year of the crash. This is consistent with the data compiled from death certificates by the National Center for Health Statistics (NCHS). The Council uses the NCHS death certificate data as the final count of deaths from all causes.

NHTSA counts only traffic fatalities that occur within 30 days of the crash in its Fatality Analysis Reporting System (FARS). This means that the FARS count omits about 800 to 1,000 motor-vehicle-related deaths each year that occur more than 30 days after the crash. Nontraffic fatalities (those that do not occur on public highways; e.g., parking lots, private roads and driveways), which account for 900 to 1,400 deaths annually, are also omitted. By using a 30-day cut off, NHTSA can issue a "final" count about eight months after the reference year.

Because of the time it takes to process 2.4 million death certificates, the NCHS data are not available until about 22 months after the reference year. This means, for example, that this edition of Injury Facts includes the 2005 NCHS final counts by cause of death including motor-vehicle crashes and estimates of the totals for 2006 and 2007. For motor-vehicle deaths, these estimates are based on data supplied by traffic authorities in 49 states and the District of Columbia. For other causes of death, the estimates are based on data supplied by state vital statistics authorities. See the Technical Appendix for more information on estimation procedures.

The graph below shows the NCHS death certificate counts of total motor-vehicle deaths through 2005 and the NSC estimates for 2006 and 2007 compared to the NHTSA FARS counts of traffic deaths.

MOTOR-VEHICLE DEATHS: NSC AND NHTSA, 1992–2007

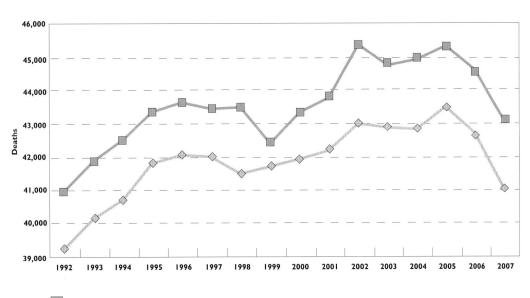

■ NATIONAL SAFETY COUNCIL

◆ NATIONAL HIGHWAY TRAFFIC SAFETY ADMINISTRATION

MOTOR-VEHICLE DEATHS AND RATES

MOTOR-VEHICLE DEATHS AND RATES, UNITED STATES, 1913–2007

Year	No. of Deaths	Estimated No. of Vehicles (Millions)	Estimated Vehicle Miles (Billions)	Estimated No. of Drivers (Millions)	Death Rates		
					Per 10,000 Motor Vehicles	Per 100,000,000 Vehicle Miles	Per 100,000 Population
1913	4,200	1.3	(a)	2.0	33.38	(a)	4.4
1914	4,700	1.8	(a)	3.0	26.65	(a)	4.8
1915	6,600	2.5	(a)	3.0	26.49	(a)	6.6
1916	8,200	3.6	(a)	5.0	22.66	(a)	8.1
1917	10,200	5.1	(a)	7.0	19.93	(a)	10.0
1918	10,700	6.2	(a)	9.0	17.37	(a)	10.3
1919	11,200	7.6	(a)	12.0	14.78	(a)	10.7
1920	12,500	9.2	(a)	14.0	13.53	(a)	11.7
1921	13,900	10.5	(a)	16.0	13.25	(a)	12.9
1922	15,300	12.3	(a)	19.0	12.47	(a)	13.9
1923	18,400	15.1	85	22.0	12.18	21.65	16.5
1924	19,400	17.6	104	26.0	11.02	18.65	17.1
1925	21,900	20.1	122	30.0	10.89	17.95	19.1
1926	23,400	22.2	141	33.0	10.54	16.59	20.1
1927	25,800	23.3	158	34.0	11.07	16.33	21.8
1928	28,000	24.7	173	37.0	11.34	16.18	23.4
1929	31,200	26.7	197	40.0	11.69	15.84	25.7
1930	32,900	26.7	206	40.0	12.32	15.97	26.7
1931	33,700	26.1	216	39.0	12.91	15.60	27.2
1932	29,500	24.4	200	36.0	12.09	14.75	23.6
1933	31,363	24.2	201	35.0	12.96	15.60	25.0
1934	36,101	25.3	216	37.0	14.27	16.71	28.6
1935	36,369	26.5	229	39.0	13.72	15.88	28.6
1936	38,089	28.5	252	42.0	13.36	15.11	29.7
1937	39,643	30.1	270	44.0	13.19	14.68	30.8
1938	32,582	29.8	271	44.0	10.93	12.02	25.1
1939	32,386	31.0	285	46.0	10.44	11.35	24.7
1940	34,501	32.5	302	48.0	10.63	11.42	26.1
1941	39,969	34.9	334	52.0	11.45	11.98	30.0
1942	28,309	33.0	268	49.0	8.58	10.55	21.1
1943	23,823	30.9	208	46.0	7.71	11.44	17.8
1944	24,282	30.5	213	45.0	7.97	11.42	18.3
1945	28,076	31.0	250	46.0	9.05	11.22	21.2
1946	33,411	34.4	341	50.0	9.72	9.80	23.9
1947	32,697	37.8	371	53.0	8.64	8.82	22.8
1948	32,259	41.1	398	55.0	7.85	8.11	22.1
1949	31,701	44.7	424	59.3	7.09	7.47	21.3
1950	34,763	49.2	458	62.2	7.07	7.59	23.0
1951	36,996	51.9	491	64.4	7.13	7.53	24.1
1952	37,794	53.3	514	66.8	7.10	7.36	24.3
1953	37,956	56.3	544	69.9	6.74	6.97	24.0
1954	35,586	58.6	562	72.2	6.07	6.33	22.1
1955	38,426	62.8	606	74.7	6.12	6.34	23.4
1956	39,628	65.2	631	77.9	6.07	6.28	23.7
1957	38,702	67.6	647	79.6	5.73	5.98	22.7
1958	36,981	68.8	665	81.5	5.37	5.56	21.3
1959	37,910	72.1	700	84.5	5.26	5.41	21.5
1960	38,137	74.5	719	87.4	5.12	5.31	21.2
1961	38,091	76.4	738	88.9	4.98	5.16	20.8
1962	40,804	79.7	767	92.0	5.12	5.32	22.0
1963	43,564	83.5	805	93.7	5.22	5.41	23.1
1964	47,700	87.3	847	95.6	5.46	5.63	25.0
1965	49,163	91.8	888	99.0	5.36	5.54	25.4
1966	53,041	95.9	930	101.0	5.53	5.70	27.1
1967	52,924	98.9	962	103.2	5.35	5.50	26.8
1968	54,862	103.1	1,016	105.4	5.32	5.40	27.5
1969	55,791	107.4	1,071	108.3	5.19	5.21	27.7
1970	54,633	111.2	1,120	111.5	4.92	4.88	26.8
1971	54,381	116.3	1,186	114.4	4.68	4.57	26.3
1972	56,278	122.3	1,268	118.4	4.60	4.43	26.9
1973	55,511	129.8	1,309	121.6	4.28	4.24	26.3
1974	46,402	134.9	1,290	125.6	3.44	3.59	21.8
1975	45,853	137.9	1,330	129.8	3.33	3.45	21.3
1976	47,038	143.5	1,412	133.9	3.28	3.33	21.6

See source and footnotes on page 111.

MOTOR-VEHICLE DEATHS AND RATES
(CONT.)

MOTOR-VEHICLE DEATHS AND RATES, UNITED STATES, 1913–2007, Cont.

Year	No. of Deaths	Estimated No. of Vehicles (Millions)	Estimated Vehicle Miles (Billions)	Estimated No. of Drivers (Millions)	Death Rates		
					Per 10,000 Motor Vehicles	Per 100,000,000 Vehicle Miles	Per 100,000 Population
1977	49,510	148.8	1,477	138.1	3.33	3.35	22.5
1978	52,411	153.6	1,548	140.8	3.41	3.39	23.6
1979	53,524	159.6	1,529	143.3	3.35	3.50	23.8
1980	53,172	161.6	1,521	145.3	3.29	3.50	23.4
1981	51,385	164.1	1,556	147.1	3.13	3.30	22.4
1982	45,779	165.2	1,592	150.3	2.77	2.88	19.8
1983	44,452	169.4	1,657	154.2	2.62	2.68	19.0
1984	46,263	171.8	1,718	155.4	2.69	2.69	19.6
1985	45,901	177.1	1,774	156.9	2.59	2.59	19.3
1986	47,865	181.4	1,835	159.5	2.63	2.60	19.9
1987	48,290	183.9	1,924	161.8	2.63	2.51	19.9
1988	49,078	189.0	2,026	162.9	2.60	2.42	20.1
1989	47,575	191.7	2,107	165.6	2.48	2.26	19.3
1990	46,814	192.9	2,148	167.0	2.43	2.18	18.8
1991	43,536	192.5	2,172	169.0	2.26	2.00	17.3
1992	40,982	194.4	2,240	173.1	2.11	1.83	16.1
1993	41,893	198.0	2,297	173.1	2.12	1.82	16.3
1994	42,524	201.8	2,360	175.4	2.11	1.80	16.3
1995	43,363	205.3	2,423	176.6	2.11	1.79	16.5
1996	43,649	210.4	2,486	179.5	2.07	1.76	16.5
1997	43,458	211.5	2,562	182.7	2.05	1.70	16.2
1998	43,501	215.0	2,632	185.2	2.02	1.65	16.1
1999	42,401	220.5	2,691	187.2	1.92	1.58	15.5
2000	43,354	225.8	2,747	190.6	1.92	1.58	15.8
2001	43,788	235.3	2,797	191.3	1.86	1.57	15.4
2002	45,380	234.6	2,856	194.3	1.93	1.59	15.8
2003	44,757	236.8	2,890	196.2	1.89	1.55	15.4
2004	44,933	243.0	2,965	199.0	1.85	1.52	15.3
2005[b]	45,343	247.4	2,989	200.5	1.83	1.52	15.3
2006[b]	44,600	250.8	3,014	202.8	1.78	1.48	14.9
2007[c]	43,100	255.7	2,996	205.1	1.69	1.44	14.3
Changes							
1997 to 2007	−1%	+21%	+17%	+12%	−18%	−15%	−12%
2006 to 2007	−3%	+2%	−1%	+1%	−5%	−3%	−4%

Source: Deaths from National Center for Health Statistics except 1964, 2006, and 2007, which are National Safety Council estimates based on data from the National Highway Traffic Safety Administration's Fatality Analysis Reporting System. See Technical Appendix for comparability. Motor-vehicle registrations, mileage and drivers estimated by Federal Highway Administration except 2007 registrations and drivers which are National Safety Council estimates.
[a] Mileage data inadequate prior to 1923.
[b] Revised.
[c] Preliminary.

MOTOR-VEHICLE DEATHS BY TYPE OF ACCIDENT

MOTOR-VEHICLE DEATHS BY TYPE OF ACCIDENT, UNITED STATES, 1913–2007

| Year | Total Deaths | | Deaths from Collision with — | | | | | | Deaths from Noncollision Accidents | Nontraffic Deaths[a] |
		Pedestrians	Other Motor Vehicles	Railroad Trains	Streetcars	Pedal-cycles	Animal-Drawn Vehicle or Animal	Fixed Objects		
1913	4,200	(b)	(b)	(b)	(b)	(b)	(b)	(b)	(b)	(c)
1914	4,700	(b)	(b)	(b)	(b)	(b)	(b)	(b)	(b)	(c)
1915	6,600	(b)	(b)	(b)	(b)	(b)	(b)	(b)	(b)	(c)
1916	8,200	(b)	(b)	(b)	(b)	(b)	(b)	(b)	(b)	(c)
1917	10,200	(b)	(b)	(b)	(b)	(b)	(b)	(b)	(b)	(c)
1918	10,700	(b)	(b)	(b)	(b)	(b)	(b)	(b)	(b)	(c)
1919	11,200	(b)	(b)	(b)	(b)	(b)	(b)	(b)	(b)	(c)
1920	12,500	(b)	(b)	(b)	(b)	(b)	(b)	(b)	(b)	(c)
1921	13,900	(b)	(b)	(b)	(b)	(b)	(b)	(b)	(b)	(c)
1922	15,300	(b)	(b)	(b)	(b)	(b)	(b)	(b)	(b)	(c)
1923	18,400	(b)	(b)	(b)	(b)	(b)	(b)	(b)	(b)	(c)
1924	19,400	(b)	(b)	1,130	410	(b)	(b)	(b)	(b)	(c)
1925	21,900	(b)	(b)	1,410	560	(b)	(b)	(b)	(b)	(c)
1926	23,400	(b)	(b)	1,730	520	(b)	(b)	(b)	(b)	(c)
1927	25,800	10,820	3,430	1,830	520	(b)	(b)	(b)	(b)	(c)
1928	28,000	11,420	4,310	2,140	570	(b)	(b)	540	8,070	(c)
1929	31,200	12,250	5,400	2,050	530	(b)	(b)	620	9,380	(c)
1930	32,900	12,900	5,880	1,830	480	(b)	(b)	720	9,970	(c)
1931	33,700	13,370	6,820	1,710	440	(b)	(b)	870	9,570	(c)
1932	29,500	11,490	6,070	1,520	320	350	400	800	8,500	(c)
1933	31,363	12,840	6,470	1,437	318	400	310	900	8,680	(c)
1934	36,101	14,480	8,110	1,457	332	500	360	1,040	9,820	(c)
1935	36,369	14,350	8,750	1,587	253	450	250	1,010	9,720	(c)
1936	38,089	15,250	9,500	1,697	269	650	250	1,060	9,410	(c)
1937	39,643	15,500	10,320	1,810	264	700	200	1,160	9,690	(c)
1938	32,582	12,850	8,900	1,490	165	720	170	940	7,350	(c)
1939	32,386	12,400	8,700	1,330	150	710	200	1,000	7,900	(c)
1940	34,501	12,700	10,100	1,707	132	750	210	1,100	7,800	(c)
1941	39,969	13,550	12,500	1,840	118	910	250	1,350	9,450	(c)
1942	28,309	10,650	7,300	1,754	124	650	240	850	6,740	(c)
1943	23,823	9,900	5,300	1,448	171	450	160	700	5,690	(c)
1944	24,282	9,900	5,700	1,663	175	400	140	700	5,600	(c)
1945	28,076	11,000	7,150	1,703	163	500	130	800	6,600	(c)
1946	33,411	11,600	9,400	1,703	174	450	130	950	8,900	(c)
1947	32,697	10,450	9,900	1,736	102	550	150	1,000	8,800	(c)
1948	32,259	9,950	10,200	1,474	83	500	100	1,000	8,950	(c)
1949	31,701	8,800	10,500	1,452	56	550	140	1,100	9,100	838
1950	34,763	9,000	11,650	1,541	89	440	120	1,300	10,600	900
1951	36,996	9,150	13,100	1,573	46	390	100	1,400	11,200	966
1952	37,794	8,900	13,500	1,429	32	430	130	1,450	11,900	970
1953	37,956	8,750	13,400	1,506	26	420	120	1,500	12,200	1,026
1954	35,586	8,000	12,800	1,289	28	380	90	1,500	11,500	1,004
1955	38,426	8,200	14,500	1,490	15	410	90	1,600	12,100	989
1956	39,628	7,900	15,200	1,377	11	440	100	1,600	13,000	888
1957	38,702	7,850	15,400	1,376	13	460	80	1,700	11,800	1,016
1958	36,981	7,650	14,200	1,316	9	450	80	1,650	11,600	929
1959	37,910	7,850	14,900	1,202	6	480	70	1,600	11,800	948
1960	38,137	7,850	14,800	1,368	5	460	80	1,700	11,900	995
1961	38,091	7,650	14,700	1,267	5	490	80	1,700	12,200	1,065
1962	40,804	7,900	16,400	1,245	3	500	90	1,750	12,900	1,029
1963	43,564	8,200	17,600	1,385	10	580	80	1,900	13,800	990
1964	47,700	9,000	19,600	1,580	5	710	100	2,100	14,600	1,123
1965	49,163	8,900	20,800	1,556	5	680	120	2,200	14,900	1,113
1966	53,041	9,400	22,200	1,800	2	740	100	2,500	16,300	1,108
1967	52,924	9,400	22,000	1,620	3	750	100	2,350	16,700	1,165
1968	54,862	9,900	22,400	1,570	4	790	100	2,700	17,400	1,061
1969	55,791	10,100	23,700	1,495	2	800	100	3,900d	15,700d	1,155
1970	54,633	9,900	23,200	1,459	3	780	100	3,800	15,400	1,140
1971	54,381	9,900	23,100	1,378	2	800	100	3,800	15,300	1,015
1972	56,278	10,300	23,900	1,260	2	1,000	100	3,900	15,800	1,064
1973	55,511	10,200	23,600	1,194	2	1,000	100	3,800	15,600	1,164
1974	46,402	8,500	19,700	1,209	1	1,000	100	3,100	12,800	1,088
1975	45,853	8,400	19,550	979	1	1,000	100	3,130	12,700	1,033
1976	47,038	8,600	20,100	1,033	2	1,000	100	3,200	13,000	1,026

See source and footnotes on page 113.

MOTOR-VEHICLE DEATHS BY TYPE OF ACCIDENT, UNITED STATES, 1913–2007, Cont.

Year	Total Deaths	Deaths from Collision with —							Deaths from Noncollision Accidents	Nontraffic Deaths[a]
		Pedestrians	Other Motor Vehicles	Railroad Trains	Streetcars	Pedal-cycles	Animal-Drawn Vehicle or Animal	Fixed Objects		
1977	49,510	9,100	21,200	902	3	1,100	100	3,400	13,700	1,053
1978	52,411	9,600	22,400	986	1	1,200	100	3,600	14,500	1,074
1979	53,524	9,800	23,100	826	1	1,200	100	3,700	14,800	1,271
1980	53,172	9,700	23,000	739	1	1,200	100	3,700	14,700	1,242
1981	51,385	9,400	22,200	668	1	1,200	100	3,600	14,200	1,189
1982	45,779	8,400	19,800	554	1	1,100	100	3,200	12,600	1,066
1983	44,452	8,200	19,200	520	1	1,100	100	3,100	12,200	1,024
1984	46,263	8,500	20,000	630	0	1,100	100	3,200	12,700	1,055
1985	45,901	8,500	19,900	538	2	1,100	100	3,200	12,600	1,079
1986	47,865	8,900	20,800	574	2	1,100	100	3,300	13,100	998
1987	48,290	7,500[e]	20,700	554	1	1,000[e]	100	13,200[e]	5,200[e]	993
1988	49,078	7,700	20,900	638	2	1,000	100	13,400	5,300	1,054
1989	47,575	7,800	20,300	720	2	900	100	12,900	4,900	989
1990	46,814	7,300	19,900	623	2	900	100	13,100	4,900	987
1991	43,536	6,600	18,200	541	1	800	100	12,600	4,700	915
1992	40,982	6,300	17,600	521	2	700	100	11,700	4,100	997
1993	41,893	6,400	18,300	553	3	800	100	11,500	4,200	994
1994	42,524	6,300	18,900	549	1	800	100	11,500	4,400	1,017
1995	43,363	6,400	19,000	514	(c)	800	100	12,100	4,400	1,032
1996	43,649	6,100	19,600	373	(c)	800	100	12,100	4,600	1,127
1997	43,458	5,900	19,900	371	(c)	800	100	12,000	4,400	1,118
1998	43,501	5,900	19,700	309	(c)	700	100	12,200	4,600	1,310
1999	42,401	6,100	18,600	314	1	800	100	11,800	4,700	1,436
2000	43,354	5,900	19,100	321	(c)	800	100	12,300	4,800	1,360
2001	43,788	6,100	18,800	324	3	800	100	12,800	4,900	1,345
2002	45,380	6,100	19,200	283	(c)	800	100	13,600	5,300	1,315
2003	44,757	6,000	19,300	245	(c)	800	100	13,100	5,200	1,417
2004	44,933	6,000	19,600	253	(c)	900	100	13,000	5,100	1,501
2005[f]	45,343	6,100	19,000	250	(c)	1,000	100	13,600	5,300	1,853
2006[f]	44,600	6,000	18,100	300	(c)	1,100	100	13,700	5,300	—
2007[g]	43,100	5,900	17,200	200	(c)	1,000	100	13,500	5,200	—
Changes in Deaths										
1997 to 2007	−1%	0%	−14%	−46%	—	+25%	0%	+12%	+18%	—
2006 to 2007	−3%	−2%	−5%	−33%	—	−9%	0%	−1%	−2%	—

Source: Total deaths from National Center for Health Statistics except 1964 and 2005-2006, which are National Safety Council estimates based on data from the National Highway Traffic Safety Administration's Fatality Analysis Reporting System. Most totals by type are estimated and may not add to the total deaths. See Technical Appendix for comparability.
[a] See definition, page 199. Nontraffic deaths are included in appropriate accident type totals in table; in 2005, 28% of the nontraffic deaths were pedestrians.
[b] Insufficient data for approximations.
[c] Data not available.
[d] 1969 through 1986 totals are not comparable to previous years.
[e] Procedures and benchmarks for estimating deaths for certain types of accidents were changed for the 1990 edition. Estimates for 1987 and later years are not comparable to earlier years.
[f] Revised.
[g] Preliminary.

MOTOR-VEHICLE DEATHS BY AGE

MOTOR-VEHICLE DEATHS BY AGE, UNITED STATES, 1913–2007

Year	All Ages	Under 5 Years	5–14 Years	15–24 Years	25–44 Years	45–64 Years	65–74 Years	75 & Over[a]
1913	4,200	300	1,100	600	1,100	800	300	
1914	4,700	300	1,200	700	1,200	900	400	
1915	6,600	400	1,500	1,000	1,700	1,400	600	
1916	8,200	600	1,800	1,300	2,100	1,700	700	
1917	10,200	700	2,400	1,400	2,700	2,100	900	
1918	10,700	800	2,700	1,400	2,500	2,300	1,000	
1919	11,200	900	3,000	1,400	2,500	2,100	1,300	
1920	12,500	1,000	3,300	1,700	2,800	2,300	1,400	
1921	13,900	1,100	3,400	1,800	3,300	2,700	1,600	
1922	15,300	1,100	3,500	2,100	3,700	3,100	1,800	
1923	18,400	1,200	3,700	2,800	4,600	3,900	2,200	
1924	19,400	1,400	3,800	2,900	4,700	4,100	2,500	
1925	21,900	1,400	3,900	3,600	5,400	4,800	2,800	
1926	23,400	1,400	3,900	3,900	5,900	5,200	3,100	
1927	25,800	1,600	4,000	4,300	6,600	5,800	3,500	
1928	28,000	1,600	3,800	4,900	7,200	6,600	3,900	
1929	31,200	1,600	3,900	5,700	8,000	7,500	4,500	
1930	32,900	1,500	3,600	6,200	8,700	8,000	4,900	
1931	33,700	1,500	3,600	6,300	9,100	8,200	5,000	
1932	29,500	1,200	2,900	5,100	8,100	7,400	4,800	
1933	31,363	1,274	3,121	5,649	8,730	7,947	4,642	
1934	36,101	1,210	3,182	6,561	10,232	9,530	5,386	
1935	36,369	1,253	2,951	6,755	10,474	9,562	5,374	
1936	38,089	1,324	3,026	7,184	10,807	10,089	5,659	
1937	39,643	1,303	2,991	7,800	10,877	10,475	6,197	
1938	32,582	1,122	2,511	6,016	8,772	8,711	5,450	
1939	32,386	1,192	2,339	6,318	8,917	8,292	5,328	
1940	34,501	1,176	2,584	6,846	9,362	8,882	5,651	
1941	39,969	1,378	2,838	8,414	11,069	9,829	6,441	
1942	28,309	1,069	1,991	5,932	7,747	7,254	4,316	
1943	23,823	1,132	1,959	4,522	6,454	5,996	3,760	
1944	24,282	1,203	2,093	4,561	6,514	5,982	3,929	
1945	28,076	1,290	2,386	5,358	7,578	6,794	4,670	
1946	33,411	1,568	2,508	7,445	8,955	7,532	5,403	
1947	32,697	1,502	2,275	7,251	8,775	7,468	5,426	
1948	32,259	1,635	2,337	7,218	8,702	7,190	3,173	2,004
1949	31,701	1,667	2,158	6,772	8,892	7,073	3,116	2,023
1950	34,763	1,767	2,152	7,600	10,214	7,728	3,264	2,038
1951	36,996	1,875	2,300	7,713	11,253	8,276	3,444	2,135
1952	37,794	1,951	2,295	8,115	11,380	8,463	3,472	2,118
1953	37,956	2,019	2,368	8,169	11,302	8,318	3,508	2,271
1954	35,586	1,864	2,332	7,571	10,521	7,848	3,247	2,203
1955	38,426	1,875	2,406	8,656	11,448	8,372	3,455	2,214
1956	39,628	1,770	2,640	9,169	11,551	8,573	3,657	2,268
1957	38,702	1,785	2,604	8,667	11,230	8,545	3,560	2,311
1958	36,981	1,791	2,710	8,388	10,414	7,922	3,535	2,221
1959	37,910	1,842	2,719	8,969	10,358	8,263	3,487	2,272
1960	38,137	1,953	2,814	9,117	10,189	8,294	3,457	2,313
1961	38,091	1,891	2,802	9,088	10,212	8,267	3,467	2,364
1962	40,804	1,903	3,028	10,157	10,701	8,812	3,696	2,507
1963	43,564	1,991	3,063	11,123	11,356	9,506	3,786	2,739
1964	47,700	2,120	3,430	12,400	12,500	10,200	4,150	2,900
1965	49,163	2,059	3,526	13,395	12,595	10,509	4,077	3,002
1966	53,041	2,182	3,869	15,298	13,282	11,051	4,217	3,142
1967	52,924	2,067	3,845	15,646	12,987	10,902	4,285	3,192
1968	54,862	1,987	4,105	16,543	13,602	11,031	4,261	3,333
1969	55,791	2,077	4,045	17,443	13,868	11,012	4,210	3,136
1970	54,633	1,915	4,159	16,720	13,446	11,099	4,084	3,210
1971	54,381	1,885	4,256	17,103	13,307	10,471	4,108	3,251
1972	56,278	1,896	4,258	17,942	13,758	10,836	4,138	3,450
1973	55,511	1,998	4,124	18,032	14,013	10,216	3,892	3,236
1974	46,402	1,546	3,332	15,905	11,834	8,159	3,071	2,555
1975	45,853	1,576	3,286	15,672	11,969	7,663	3,047	2,640
1976	47,038	1,532	3,175	16,650	12,112	7,770	3,082	2,717

See source and footnotes on page 115.

MOTOR-VEHICLE DEATHS BY AGE, UNITED STATES, 1913–2007, Cont.

Year	All Ages	Under 5 Years	5–14 Years	15–24 Years	25–44 Years	45–64 Years	65–74 Years	75 & Over[a]
1977	49,510	1,472	3,142	18,092	13,031	8,000	3,060	2,713
1978	52,411	1,551	3,130	19,164	14,574	8,048	3,217	2,727
1979	53,524	1,461	2,952	19,369	15,658	8,162	3,171	2,751
1980	53,172	1,426	2,747	19,040	16,133	8,022	2,991	2,813
1981	51,385	1,256	2,575	17,363	16,447	7,818	3,090	2,836
1982	45,779	1,300	2,301	15,324	14,469	6,879	2,825	2,681
1983	44,452	1,233	2,241	14,289	14,323	6,690	2,827	2,849
1984	46,263	1,138	2,263	14,738	15,036	6,954	3,020	3,114
1985	45,901	1,195	2,319	14,277	15,034	6,885	3,014	3,177
1986	47,865	1,188	2,350	15,227	15,844	6,799	3,096	3,361
1987	48,290	1,190	2,397	14,447	16,405	7,021	3,277	3,553
1988	49,078	1,220	2,423	14,406	16,580	7,245	3,429	3,775
1989	47,575	1,221	2,266	12,941	16,571	7,287	3,465	3,824
1990	46,814	1,123	2,059	12,607	16,488	7,282	3,350	3,905
1991	43,536	1,076	2,011	11,664	15,082	6,616	3,193	3,894
1992	40,982	1,020	1,904	10,305	14,071	6,597	3,247	3,838
1993	41,893	1,081	1,963	10,500	14,283	6,711	3,116	4,239
1994	42,524	1,139	2,026	10,660	13,966	7,097	3,385	4,251
1995	43,363	1,004	2,055	10,600	14,618	7,428	3,300	4,358
1996	43,649	1,035	1,980	10,576	14,482	7,749	3,419	4,408
1997	43,458	933	1,967	10,208	14,167	8,134	3,370	4,679
1998	43,501	921	1,868	10,026	14,095	8,416	3,410	4,765
1999	42,401	834	1,771	10,128	13,516	8,342	3,276	4,534
2000	43,354	819	1,772	10,560	13,811	8,867	3,038	4,487
2001	43,788	770	1,686	10,725	14,020	9,029	2,990	4,568
2002	45,380	733	1,614	11,459	14,169	9,701	3,113	4,591
2003	44,757	766	1,642	10,972	13,794	10,032	2,967	4,584
2004	44,933	778	1,653	10,987	13,699	10,369	2,974	4,473
2005[b]	44,343	763	1,447	10,908	13,987	10,851	3,110	4,277
2006[b]	44,600	700	1,300	11,000	13,900	10,900	2,900	3,900
2007[c]	43,100	600	1,200	10,500	13,300	10,800	2,900	3,800
Changes in Deaths								
1997 to 2007	−1%	−36%	−40%	+3%	−6%	+33%	−14%	−19%
2006 to 2007	−3%	−14%	−8%	−5%	−4%	−1%	0%	−3%

Source: 1913 to 1932 calculated from National Center for Health Statistics data for registration states; 1933 to 1963, 1965 to 2005 are NCHS totals. All other figures are National Safety Council estimates. See Technical Appendix for comparability.
[a]Includes "age unknown." In 2005 these deaths numbered 6.
[b]Revised.
[c]Preliminary.

MOTOR-VEHICLE DEATH RATES BY AGE

MOTOR-VEHICLE DEATH RATES[a] BY AGE, UNITED STATES, 1913–2007

Year	All Ages	Under 5 Years	5–14 Years	15–24 Years	25–44 Years	45–64 Years	65–74 Years	75 & Over
1913	4.4	2.3	5.5	3.1	3.8	5.3	8.5	
1914	4.8	2.5	5.7	3.5	4.1	6.2	9.3	
1915	6.6	3.5	7.3	5.0	5.6	8.8	13.5	
1916	8.1	4.7	8.6	6.0	7.0	10.7	15.8	
1917	10.0	5.6	10.6	7.4	8.6	12.6	18.6	
1918	10.3	6.9	12.3	7.7	8.3	13.7	21.2	
1919	10.7	7.5	13.9	7.5	8.1	12.4	24.1	
1920	11.7	8.6	14.6	8.7	8.8	13.5	27.0	
1921	12.9	9.0	14.5	9.2	10.2	15.4	31.0	
1922	13.9	9.2	15.0	10.8	11.1	17.2	34.9	
1923	16.5	9.7	15.6	13.4	13.6	21.0	40.5	
1924	17.1	11.1	16.1	14.3	13.7	21.8	43.7	
1925	19.1	11.0	15.6	17.2	15.8	25.0	48.9	
1926	20.1	11.0	15.9	18.6	17.1	26.3	51.4	
1927	21.8	12.8	16.0	20.0	18.8	28.9	56.9	
1928	23.4	12.7	15.5	21.9	20.2	32.4	62.2	
1929	25.7	13.4	15.6	25.6	22.3	35.6	68.6	
1930	26.7	13.0	14.7	27.4	23.9	37.0	72.5	
1931	27.2	13.3	14.5	27.9	24.8	37.4	70.6	
1932	23.6	11.3	12.0	22.6	22.0	32.9	63.6	
1933	25.0	12.0	12.7	24.8	23.4	34.7	63.1	
1934	28.6	11.7	13.0	28.6	27.2	40.7	71.0	
1935	28.6	12.3	12.2	29.2	27.6	39.9	68.9	
1936	29.7	13.2	12.6	30.8	28.2	41.3	70.5	
1937	30.8	13.0	12.7	33.2	28.2	42.0	75.1	
1938	25.1	11.0	10.8	25.4	22.5	34.3	64.1	
1939	24.7	11.2	10.4	26.5	22.6	32.2	60.2	
1940	26.1	11.1	11.5	28.7	23.5	33.9	62.1	
1941	30.0	12.7	12.6	35.7	27.5	37.0	68.6	
1942	21.1	9.5	8.8	25.8	19.2	26.9	44.5	
1943	17.8	9.4	8.6	20.6	16.1	21.9	37.6	
1944	18.3	9.6	9.1	22.5	16.6	21.6	38.2	
1945	21.2	10.0	10.3	27.8	19.7	24.2	44.1	
1946	23.9	11.9	10.8	34.4	21.1	26.4	49.6	
1947	22.8	10.5	9.7	32.8	20.3	25.7	48.2	
1948	22.1	11.0	9.8	32.5	19.8	24.3	39.6	55.4
1949	21.3	10.7	9.0	30.7	19.9	23.4	37.8	53.9
1950	23.0	10.8	8.8	34.5	22.5	25.1	38.8	52.4
1951	24.1	10.9	9.2	36.0	24.7	26.5	39.5	53.0
1952	24.3	11.3	8.7	38.6	24.7	26.7	38.5	50.8
1953	24.0	11.5	8.5	39.1	24.5	25.8	37.7	52.6
1954	22.1	10.4	8.1	36.2	22.6	24.0	33.9	49.0
1955	23.4	10.2	8.0	40.9	24.5	25.2	35.1	47.1
1956	23.7	9.4	8.4	42.9	24.6	25.3	36.2	46.4
1957	22.7	9.2	8.0	39.7	23.9	24.8	34.4	45.5
1958	21.3	9.1	8.1	37.0	22.3	22.6	33.5	42.3
1959	21.5	9.1	7.9	38.2	22.2	23.2	32.3	41.8
1960	21.2	9.6	7.9	37.7	21.7	22.9	31.3	41.1
1961	20.8	9.2	7.6	36.5	21.8	22.5	30.7	40.5
1962	22.0	9.3	8.1	38.4	22.9	23.7	32.2	41.7
1963	23.1	9.8	8.0	40.0	24.3	25.2	32.6	44.3
1964	25.0	10.5	8.8	42.6	26.8	26.6	35.5	45.2
1965	25.4	10.4	8.9	44.2	27.0	27.0	34.6	45.4
1966	27.1	11.4	9.7	48.7	28.5	27.9	35.4	46.2
1967	26.8	11.2	9.5	48.4	27.8	27.1	35.6	45.4
1968	27.5	11.1	10.1	49.8	28.8	27.0	35.1	46.0
1969	27.7	12.0	9.9	50.7	29.1	26.6	34.3	42.0
1970	26.8	11.2	10.2	46.7	27.9	26.4	32.7	42.2
1971	26.3	10.9	10.5	45.7	27.4	24.7	32.4	41.3
1972	26.9	11.1	10.7	47.1	27.4	25.3	32.0	42.6
1973	26.3	11.9	10.5	46.3	27.2	23.6	29.4	39.1
1974	21.8	9.4	8.6	40.0	22.4	18.8	22.6	30.1
1975	21.3	9.8	8.6	38.7	22.1	17.5	21.9	30.1
1976	21.6	9.8	8.4	40.3	21.8	17.6	21.6	30.1

See source and footnotes on page 117.

MOTOR-VEHICLE DEATH RATES[a] BY AGE, UNITED STATES, 1913–2007, Cont.

Year	All Ages	Under 5 Years	5–14 Years	15–24 Years	25–44 Years	45–64 Years	65–74 Years	75 & Over
1977	22.5	9.5	8.5	43.3	22.7	18.1	20.9	29.3
1978	23.6	9.9	8.6	45.4	24.6	18.2	21.5	28.7
1979	23.8	9.1	8.3	45.6	25.6	18.4	20.7	28.1
1980	23.4	8.7	7.9	44.8	25.5	18.0	19.1	28.0
1981	22.4	7.4	7.5	41.1	25.2	17.6	19.4	27.5
1982	19.8	7.5	6.7	36.8	21.5	15.5	17.5	25.2
1983	19.0	7.0	6.6	34.8	20.6	15.0	17.2	26.0
1984	19.6	6.4	6.7	36.4	21.0	15.6	18.2	27.7
1985	19.3	6.7	6.9	35.7	20.5	15.4	17.9	27.5
1986	19.9	6.6	7.0	38.5	21.0	15.2	18.1	28.3
1987	19.9	6.6	7.1	37.1	21.3	15.7	18.8	29.1
1988	20.1	6.7	7.1	37.8	21.2	15.9	19.5	30.2
1989	19.3	6.6	6.5	34.6	20.8	15.9	19.4	29.8
1990	18.8	6.0	5.8	34.2	20.4	15.7	18.5	29.7
1991	17.3	5.6	5.6	32.1	18.3	14.2	17.5	28.9
1992	16.1	5.2	5.2	28.5	17.1	13.6	17.6	27.8
1993	16.3	5.5	5.3	29.1	17.3	13.5	16.7	30.0
1994	16.3	5.8	5.4	29.5	16.8	13.9	18.1	29.4
1995	16.5	5.1	5.4	29.3	17.5	14.2	17.6	29.4
1996	16.5	5.4	5.2	29.2	17.3	14.4	18.3	29.0
1997	16.2	4.9	5.1	27.9	17.0	14.7	18.2	29.9
1998	16.1	4.9	4.8	26.9	16.9	14.7	18.5	29.8
1999	15.5	4.4	4.5	26.8	16.3	14.1	18.0	27.8
2000	15.7	4.3	4.5	27.5	16.8	14.5	16.7	27.0
2001	15.4	4.0	4.1	26.8	16.5	14.0	16.3	26.8
2002	15.8	3.7	3.9	28.2	16.8	14.6	17.0	26.5
2003	15.4	3.9	4.0	26.6	16.4	14.6	16.2	26.0
2004	15.3	3.9	4.1	26.4	16.3	14.7	16.1	25.1
2005[b]	15.3	3.8	3.6	25.9	16.6	14.9	16.7	23.6
2006[b]	14.9	3.4	3.2	26.0	16.6	14.6	15.5	21.3
2007[c]	14.3	2.9	3.0	24.7	15.9	14.1	15.0	20.5
Changes in Rates								
1997 to 2007	−12%	−41%	−41%	−11%	−6%	−4%	−18%	−31%
2006 to 2007	−4%	−15%	−6%	−5%	−4%	−3%	−3%	−4%

Source: 1913 to 1932 calculated from National Center for Health Statistics data for registration states; 1933 to 1963, 1965 to 2004 are NCHS totals. All other figures are National Safety Council estimates. See Technical Appendix for comparability.
[a] *Death rates are deaths per 100,000 population in each age group.*
[b] *Revised.*
[c] *Preliminary.*

FLEET ACCIDENT RATES BENCHMARKING

For the first time since 2001, the National Safety Council (NSC) is collecting motor vehicle fleet accident data from U.S. organizations as part of a new benchmarking program. This new benchmarking program was developed by the National Safety Council's Transportation Safety Division, the NSC's Research and Statistics department, NSC member companies, and various transportation organizations with fleets throughout the country. This program intends to provide a source that organizations can use to compare their fleet's safety performance with other organizations operating similar vehicles.

The 59 participating fleets in this year's benchmarking program responded to a national email campaign targeted to National Safety Council Transportation Division members as well as other non-member organizations with commercial fleets. The availability and quality of this information is determined by the organizations participating in this confidential program. It is critical for the ongoing success of this program that every organization that finds value in this data participate by providing their own data. Organizations operating commercial fleets are invited to contribute to this program by contributing data. To learn more about the program and to complete the on-line data collection form, please go to www.survey.nsc.org/fleetsurvey2009.

The tables provided on this page and the next report the benchmarking findings by both industry type and vehicle type. For the purposes of this program, a motor vehicle accident is defined as, "an unstabilized situation that includes at least one harmful event (injury or property damage) involving a motor vehicle (in motion, in readiness for motion, or on a roadway, but not parked in a designated parking area) that does not result from discharge of a firearm or explosive device and does not directly result from a cataclysm."

In order to protect the anonymity of participating organizations, data are only reported if it represents the responses of three or more organizations. Increased participation in this program in future years will allow the reporting of more vehicle types and industries.

The pie chart on the next page illustrates the reported proportion of preventable to non-preventable motor vehicle fleet accidents. The National Safety Council defines a preventable accident as, "any motor vehicle accident involving a fleet vehicle which results in property damage and/or personal injury, regardless of who was injured, what property was damaged, to what extent, or where it occurred, in which the driver in question failed to exercise every reasonable precaution to prevent the accident." Interestingly, the reported split between preventable and non-preventable accidents is nearly equal.

Source: Committee on Motor Vehicle Traffic Accident Classification. (1997). Manual on Classification of Motor Vehicle Traffic Accidents, ANSI D16.1-1996, Itasca, IL: National Safety Council. Natonal Safety Council. (2004). A Guide to Determine Motor Vehicle Accident Preventability 2004 Edition. Itasca, IL: Author.

FLEET ACCIDENT RATES BY INDUSTRY, 2007

Industry[a]	NAICS Code[b]	Number of Organizations Reporting	Number of Vehicles	Vehicle Miles	Non-Preventable	Preventable	Total	Accidents per 1,000,000 Vehicle Miles		
								Non-Preventable	Preventable	Total
Truck Transportation	484	15	2,790	203,746,917	328	275	603	1.61	1.35	2.96
Postal Service	491	8	84	286,228	4	6	10	13.97	20.96	39.94
Ambulatory Health Care Services	621	8	154	4,503,056	10	28	38	2.22	6.22	8.44

[a] Only vehicle types represented by three or more organizations are reported.
[b] North American Industry Classification System, 2007 Edition, for industries.

FLEET ACCIDENT RATES BY TYPE OF VEHICLES, 2007

Vehicle Type	Number of Fleets	Number of Vehicles	Vehicle Miles	Non-Preventable	Preventable	Total	Accidents per 1,000,000 Vehicle Miles		
							Non-Preventable	Preventable	Total
All Vehicle Types[a]	**59**	**7,248**	**266,166,001**	**649**	**680**	**1,329**	**243.83**	**255.48**	**499.31**
Automobiles	**9**	**495**	**9,348,811**	**70**	**56**	**126**	**7.49**	**5.99**	**13.48**
Passenger cars	9	495	9,348,811	70	56	126	7.49	5.99	13.48
Light Trucks (<10,000 lb GVWR)	**15**	**721**	**8,034,146**	**41**	**34**	**75**	**5.10**	**4.23**	**9.34**
Pickup trucks	5	454	4,588,853	9	11	20	1.96	2.40	4.36
Utility vehicles (including SUVs)	5	46	635,485	3	2	5	4.72	3.15	7.87
Other light truck	5	221	2,809,808	29	21	50	10.32	7.47	17.79
All Medium/Heavy Trucks (>=10,000 lb GVWR)	**26**	**5,850**	**244,377,644**	**531**	**567**	**1,098**	**2.17**	**2.32**	**4.49**
Medium/Heavy Trucks (>=10,000lb GVWR) - City Operations	**7**	**1,822**	**76,470,713**	**167**	**234**	**401**	**2.18**	**3.06**	**5.24**
Truck tractors with one van or tanker trailer	3	704	61,028,939	76	120	196	1.25	1.97	3.21
Medium/heavy pickup, utility, van, and other	4	1,118	15,441,774	91	114	205	5.89	7.38	13.28
Medium/Heavy Trucks (>= 10,000 lb GVWR) - Inter-City Operations	**19**	**4,028**	**167,906,931**	**364**	**333**	**697**	**2.17**	**1.98**	**4.15**
Medium/heavy single-unit trucks	5	2,252	51,211,338	145	213	358	2.83	4.16	6.99
Truck tractor with one tanker trailer	4	436	33,218,307	27	17	44	0.81	0.51	1.32
Other medium/heavy truck	10	1,340	83,477,286	192	103	295	2.30	1.23	3.53
Specialty Vehicles	**9**	**182**	**4,405,400**	**7**	**23**	**30**	**1.59**	**5.22**	**6.81**
Ambulances	5	133	3,867,554	2	23	25	0.52	5.95	6.46
Other specialty vehicles	3	26	343,000	2	0	2	5.83	0.00	5.83

Source: Summarized from the National Safety Council's Fleet Benchmarking Program.
[a] Only vehicle types represented by three or more organizations are reported.

PROPORTION OF PREVENTABLE TO NON-PREVENTABLE MOTOR FLEET ACCIDENTS

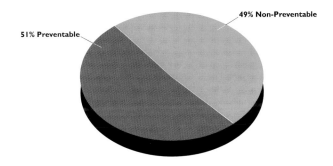

49% Non-Preventable

51% Preventable

NATIONAL SAFETY COUNCIL

INJURY FACTS®

122

The Home and Community venue is the combination of the Home class and the Public class. Home and Community together with the Occupational and Transportation venues make up the totality of unintentional injuries. Home and Community includes all unintentional injuries that are not work related and do not involve motor vehicles on streets and highways.

In 2007, an estimated 74,000 unintentional-injury deaths occurred in the Home and Community venue, or 62% of all unintentional-injury deaths that year. The number of deaths was up about 1% from the revised 2006 total of 73,100. Another 20,600,000 people suffered nonfatal disabling injuries. The death rate per 100,000 population was 24.5, the same as the revised 2006 rate.

About 1 out of 15 people experienced an unintentional injury in the Home and Community venue and about 1 out of 4,100 people died from such an injury. About 40% of the deaths and disabling injuries involved workers while they were away from work (off the job).

The graph on the next page shows the five leading causes of unintentional-injury deaths in the Home and Community venue and the broad age groups (children, youths and adults, and the elderly) affected by them. This is one way to prioritize issues in this venue. Below is a graph of the trend in deaths and death rates from 1997 to the present. Similar graphs for the Public and Home classes are on pages 124 and 128.

The National Safety Council adopted the Bureau of Labor Statistics' Census of Fatal Occupational Injuries count for work-related unintentional injuries beginning with 1992 data. Because of the lower Work class total resulting from this change, adjustments had to be made to the Home and Public classes. Long-term historical comparisons for these three classes should be made with caution. Also, beginning with 1999 data, deaths are now classified according to the 10th revision of the *International Classification of Diseases*. Caution should be used in comparing data classified under the 10th revision with prior revisions. See the Technical Appendix for more information about both changes.

Deaths **74,000**
Disabling injuries **20,600,000**
Deaths rate per 100,000 population **24.5**
Costs . . . . **$273 billion**

HOME AND COMMUNITY DEATHS AND DEATH RATES, UNITED STATES, 1997–2007

LEADING CAUSES OF UNINTENTIONAL-INJURY DEATHS IN HOME AND COMMUNITY, UNITED STATES, 2007

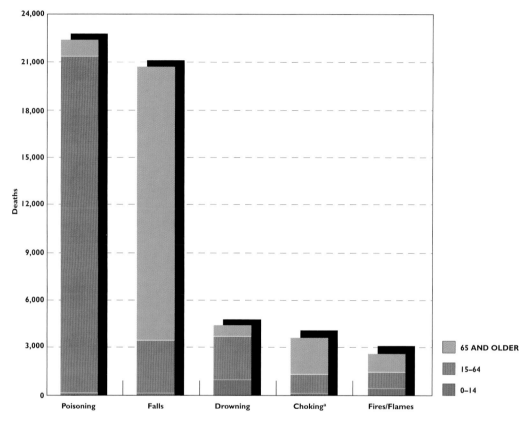

ᵃInhalation and ingestion of food or other object that obstructs breathing.

CAUSES OF UNINTENTIONAL-INJURY DEATHS IN HOME AND COMMUNITY, UNITED STATES, 2007

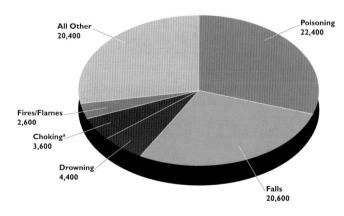

ᵃInhalation and ingestion of food or other object that obstructs breathing.

Between 1912 and 2007, public unintentional-injury deaths per 100,000 population were reduced 64% from 30 to 10.1 (after adjusting for the 1948 change in classification). In 1912, an estimated 28,000 to 30,000 persons died from public nonmotor-vehicle injuries. In 2007, with a population tripled, and travel and recreational activity greatly increased, 30,500 persons died of public unintentional injuries and 10,200,000 suffered disabling injuries. The public class excludes deaths and injuries involving motor vehicles and persons at work or at home.

The number of public unintentional-injury deaths was up 25% from the revised 2006 figure of 24,300. The death rate per 100,000 population increased from 8.1 to 10.1, or 25%.

With an estimated 10,200,000 disabling unintentional injuries occurring in public places and a population of more than 301 million people, on average about one person in 30 experienced such an injury.

The Council adopted the Bureau of Labor Statistics' Census of Fatal Occupational Injuries count for work-related unintentional injuries beginning with 1992 data. This affected long-term historical comparisons for the Work, Home, and Public classes. Beginning with 1999 data, deaths are classified according to the 10th revision of the International Classification of Diseases. Caution should be used in comparing current data with data classified under prior revisions. See the Technical Appendix for more information.

Deaths **30,500**
Disabling injuries **10,200,000**
Death rate per 100,000 population **10.1**
Costs . . . . **$108.3 billion**

PUBLIC DEATHS AND DEATH RATES, UNITED STATES, 1997–2007

PRINCIPAL TYPES OF PUBLIC UNINTENTIONAL-INJURY DEATHS, UNITED STATES, 1987–2007

Year	Total Public[a]	Falls	Drowning	Poisoning	Choking[g]	Fires/ Burns	Firearms	Mechanical Suffocation	Air Transport	Water Transport	Rail Transport[b]
1987	18,400	4,000	3,200	800	1,100	500	600	[c]	900	800	400
1988	18,400	4,100	3,100	900	1,100	500	600	[c]	700	800	400
1989	18,200	4,200	3,000	900	1,000	500	600	[c]	800	700	400
1990	17,400	4,300	2,800	900	1,000	400	500	[c]	700	800	400
1991	17,600	4,500	2,800	1,000	900	400	600	[c]	700	700	500
1992	19,000	4,400	2,500	1,700	1,600	200	400	[c]	700	700	600
1993	19,700	4,600	2,800	1,900	1,500	200	400	[c]	600	700	600
1994	19,600	4,700	2,400	2,100	1,500	200	400	[c]	600	600	600
1995	20,100	5,000	2,800	2,000	1,600	200	300	[c]	600	700	500
1996	21,000	5,300	2,500	2,100	1,700	200	300	[c]	700	600	500
1997	21,700	5,600	2,600	2,300	1,700	200	300	[c]	500	600	400
1998	22,600	6,000	2,900	2,300	1,700	200	300	[c]	500	600	500
1999[d]	22,200	4,800	2,600	2,800	2,000	200	300	500	500	600	400
2000	22,700	5,500	2,400	2,900	2,200	200	200	300	500	500	400
2001	21,800	5,600	2,400	2,700	2,100	200	200	300	700	500	400
2002	22,500	5,900	2,500	3,600	2,200	300	200	300	500	500	400
2003	23,200	6,300	2,400	3,400	2,200	300	200	300	600	500	400
2004	22,700	6,700	2,400	3,400	2,200	200	200	200	400	500	400
2005[e]	23,400	6,800	2,600	3,500	2,100	[c]	[c]	200	400	500	400
2006[e]	24,300	6,700	2,300	3,600	1,700	[c]	[c]	100	500	500	600
2007[f]	30,500	9,000	3,400	5,500	2,200	[c]	[c]	200	500	600	600

Source: National Safety Council estimates based on data from the National Center for Health Statistics and state vital statistics departments. The Council adopted the Bureau of Labor Statistics' Census of Fatal Occupational Injuries count for work-related unintentional injuries retroactive to 1992 data. Because of the lower Work class total resulting from this change, several thousand unintentional-injury deaths that had been classified by the Council as work-related, had to be reassigned to the Home and Public classes. For this reason long-term historical comparisons for these three classes should be made with caution. See the Technical Appendix for an explanation of the methodological changes.
[a] *Includes some deaths not shown separately.*
[b] *Includes subways and elevateds.*
[c] *Estimates not available.*
[d] *In 1999, a revision was made in the International Classification of Diseases. See the Technical Appendix for comparability with earlier years.*
[e] *Revised.*
[f] *Preliminary.*
[g] *Inhalation and ingestion of food or other object that obstructs breathing.*

PRINCIPAL TYPES OF PUBLIC UNINTENTIONAL-INJURY DEATHS, UNITED STATES, 2007

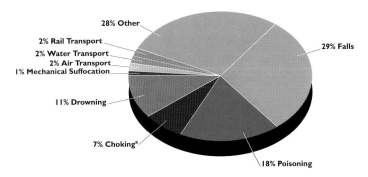

28% Other
2% Rail Transport
2% Water Transport
2% Air Transport
1% Mechanical Suffocation
11% Drowning
7% Choking[a]
18% Poisoning
29% Falls

[a] *Inhalation and ingestion of food object that obstructs breathing.*

DEATHS DUE TO UNINTENTIONAL PUBLIC INJURIES, 2007

TYPE OF EVENT AND AGE OF VICTIM

All Public

Includes deaths in public places or places used in a public way and not involving motor vehicles. Most sports, recreation, and transportation deaths are included. Excludes deaths in the course of employment.

	Total	Change from 2006	Death Rate[a]
Deaths	30,500	+25%	10.1

Age	0–4	5–14	15–24	25–44	45–64	65–74	75+
Deaths	400	400	2,600	6,400	7,700	2,300	10,700

Falls

Includes deaths from falls from one level to another or on the same level in public places. Excludes deaths from falls in moving vehicles.

	Total	Change from 2006	Death Rate[a]
Deaths	9,000	+34%	3.0

Age	0–4	5–14	15–24	25–44	45–64	65–74	75+
Deaths	10	10	180	350	1,000	950	6,500

Poisoning

Includes deaths from drugs, medicines, other solid and liquid substances, and gases and vapors. Excludes poisonings from spoiled foods, salmonella, etc., which are classified as disease deaths.

	Total	Change from 2006	Death Rate[a]
Deaths	5,500	+53%	1.8

Age	0–4	5–14	15–24	25–44	45–64	65–74	75+
Deaths	0	0	700	2,500	2,100	80	120

Choking

Includes deaths from unintentional ingestion or inhalation of food or other objects resulting in the obstruction of respiratory passages.

	Total	Change from 2006	Death Rate[a]
Deaths	2,200	+29%	0.7

Age	0–4	5–14	15–24	25–44	45–64	65–74	75+
Deaths	10	0	60	180	450	300	1,200

See footnotes on page 127.

TYPE OF EVENT AND AGE OF VICTIM

Drowning

Includes drownings of person swimming or playing in water, or falling into water, except on home premises or at work. Excludes drownings involving boats, which are in water transportation.

	Total	Change from 2006	Death Rate[a]
Deaths	3,400	+48%	1.1

Age	0–4	5–14	15–24	25–44	45–64	65–74	75+
Deaths	270	230	750	900	850	130	270

Water transport

Includes deaths in water transport accidents from falls, burns, etc., as well as drownings. Excludes crews and persons traveling in the course of employment.

	Total	Change from 2006	Death Rate[a]
Deaths	600	+20%	0.2

Age	0–4	5–14	15–24	25–44	45–64	65–74	75+
Deaths	0	10	120	190	180	50	50

Air transport

Includes deaths in private flying, passengers in commercial aviation, and deaths of military personnel in the U.S. Excludes crews and persons traveling in the course of employment.

	Total	Change from 2006	Death Rate[a]
Deaths	500	0%	0.2

Age	0–4	5–14	15–24	25–44	45–64	65–74	75+
Deaths	0	10	30	130	250	60	20

Railroad

Includes deaths arising from railroad vehicles in motion (except involving motor vehicles), subway and elevated trains, and persons boarding or alighting from standing trains. Excludes crews and persons traveling in the course of employment.

	Total	Change from 2006	Death Rate[a]
Deaths	600	0%	0.2

Age	0–4	5–14	15–24	25–44	45–64	65–74	75+
Deaths	10	10	120	200	210	30	20

All Other Public

Most important types included are: mechanical suffocation, excessive natural heat or cold, firearms, fires and flames, and machinery.

	Total	Change from 2006	Death Rate[a]
Deaths	8,700	(d)%	2.9

Age	0–4	5–14	15–24	25–44	45–64	65–74	75+
Deaths	100	150	650	1,900	2,700	700	2,500

[a] Deaths per 100,000 population.
[b] Deaths per 100,000 population in each age group.
[c] Death rate less than 0.05.
[d] Direct comparison is not possible. Starting in 2007 all other public includes mechanical suffocation.

Between 1912 and 2007, unintentional-home-injury deaths per 100,000 population were reduced 42% from 28 to 14.4 (after adjusting for the 1948 classification change). In 1912, when there were 21 million households, an estimated 26,000 to 28,000 persons were killed by unintentional home injuries. In 2006, with more than 116 million households and the population tripled, home deaths numbered 43,500.

The injury total of 10,400,000 means that 1 person in 29 in the United States was disabled one full day or more by unintentional injuries received in the home in 2007. Disabling injuries are more numerous in the home than in the workplace and in motor-vehicle crashes combined.

The National Health Interview Survey indicates that about 16,769,000 episodes of medically-attended home injuries occurred in 2006 (the latest year available). This means that about 1 person in 18 incurred a home injury requiring medical attention. About 46% of all medically attended injuries occurred at home.

The National Safety Council adopted the Bureau of Labor Statistics' Census of Fatal Occupational Injuries count for work-related unintentional injuries beginning with 1992 data. This affected long-term historical comparisons for the Work, Home, and Public classes. Beginning with 1999 data, deaths are classified according to the 10th revision of the *International Classification of Diseases*. Caution should be used in comparing current data with data classified under prior revisions. See the Technical Appendix for more information.

Deaths **43,500**
Disabling Injuries **10,400,000**
Death rate per 100,000 population **14.4**
Costs .... **$164.7 billion**

HOME DEATHS AND DEATH RATES, UNITED STATES, 1997–2007

PRINCIPAL TYPES OF HOME UNINTENTIONAL-INJURY DEATHS, UNITED STATES, 1987–2007

Year	Total Home	Falls	Fires/ Burns[a]	Choking[f]	Mechanical Suffocation	Drowning	Poisoning	Natural Heat/Cold	Firearms	Other
1987	21,400	6,300	3,900	2,500	600	700	4,100	(b)	800	2,500
1988	22,700	6,600	4,100	2,600	600	700	4,800	(b)	800	2,500
1989	22,500	6,600	3,900	2,500	600	700	5,000	(b)	800	2,400
1990	21,500	6,700	3,400	2,300	600	900	4,500	(b)	800	2,300
1991	22,100	6,900	3,400	2,200	700	900	5,000	(b)	800	2,200
1992	24,000	7,700	3,700	1,500	700	900	5,200	(b)	1,000	3,300
1993	26,100	7,900	3,700	1,700	700	900	6,500	(b)	1,100	3,600
1994	26,300	8,100	3,700	1,600	800	900	6,800	(b)	900	3,500
1995	27,200	8,400	3,500	1,500	800	900	7,000	(b)	900	4,200
1996	27,500	9,000	3,500	1,500	800	900	7,300	(b)	800	3,700
1997	27,700	9,100	3,200	1,500	800	900	7,800	(b)	700	3,500
1998	29,000	9,500	2,900	1,800	800	1,000	8,400	(b)	600	4,000
1999[c]	30,500	7,600	3,000	1,900	1,100	900	9,300	700	600	5,400
2000	29,200	7,100	2,700	2,100	1,000	1,000	9,800	400	500	4,600
2001	33,200	8,600	3,000	2,000	1,100	900	11,300	400	600	5,300
2002	36,200	9,700	2,800	1,900	1,100	900	13,900	400	500	5,000
2003	38,600	10,300	2,900	2,100	1,000	800	15,900	400	500	4,700
2004	41,500	11,300	2,900	2,200	1,200	900	17,500	400	400	4,700
2005[d]	46,200	12,000	2,900	2,300	1,300	900	20,000	500	500	5,800
2006[d]	48,800	12,100	3,000	1,800	1,100	1,100	21,600	600	500	7,000
2007[e]	43,500	11,600	2,400	1,400	900	1,000	16,900	500	400	8,400

Source: National Safety Council estimates based on data from National Center for Health Statistics and state vital statistics departments. The Council adopted the Bureau of Labor Statistics' Census of Fatal Occupational Injuries count for work-related unintentional injuries retroactive to 1992 data. Because of the lower Work class total resulting from this change, several thousand unintentional-injury deaths that had been classified by the Council as work-related, had to be reassigned to the Home and Public classes. For this reason long-term historical comparisons for these three classes should be made with caution. See the Technical Appendix for an explanation of the methodological changes.
[a] Includes deaths resulting from conflagration, regardless of nature of injury.
[b] Included in Other.
[c] In 1999, a revision was made in the International Classification of Diseases. See the Technical Appendix for comparability with earlier years.
[d] Revised.
[e] Preliminary.
[f] Inhalation and ingestion of food or other object that obstructs breathing.

PRINCIPAL TYPES OF HOME UNINTENTIONAL-INJURY DEATHS, UNITED STATES, 2007

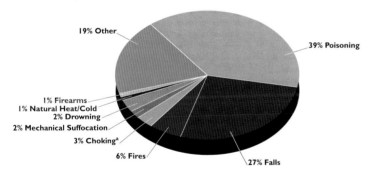

19% Other
39% Poisoning
1% Firearms
1% Natural Heat/Cold
2% Drowning
2% Mechanical Suffocation
3% Choking[a]
6% Fires
27% Falls

[a] Inhalation and ingestion of food or other object that obstructs breathing.

DEATHS DUE TO UNINTENTIONAL HOME INJURIES, 2007

TYPE OF EVENT AND AGE OF VICTIM

All Home

Includes deaths in the home and on home premises to occupants, guests, and trespassers. Also includes hired household workers but excludes other persons working on home premises.

	Total	Change from 2006	Death Rate[a]
Deaths	43,500	−11%	14.4

Poisoning

Includes deaths from drugs, medicines, other solid and liquid substances, and gases and vapors. Excludes poisonings from spoiled foods, salmonella, etc., which are classified as disease deaths.

	Total	Change from 2006	Death Rate[a]
Deaths	16,900	−22%	5.6

Falls

Includes deaths from falls from one level to another or on the same level in the home or on home premises.

	Total	Change from 2006	Death Rate[a]
Deaths	11,600	−4%	3.8

Fires, Flames, and Smoke

Includes deaths from fires, burns, and injuries in conflagrations in the home--such as asphyxiation, falls, and struck by falling objects. Excludes burns from hot objects or liquids.

	Total	Change from 2006	Death Rate[a]
Deaths	2,400	−20%	0.8

See footnotes on page 131.

TYPE OF EVENT AND AGE OF VICTIM

Choking

Includes deaths from unintentional ingestion or inhalation of objects or food resulting in the obstruction of respiratory passages.

	Total	Change from 2006	Death Rate[a]
Deaths	1,400	−22%	0.5

Age	0–4	5–14	15–24	25–44	45–64	65–74	75+
Deaths	80	10	40	80	400	190	600

Mechanical suffocation

Includes deaths from smothering by bed clothes, thin plastic materials, etc.; suffocation by cave-ins or confinement in closed spaces; and mechanical strangulation and hanging.

	Total	Change from 2006	Death Rate[a]
Deaths	900	−18%	0.3

Age	0–4	5–14	15–24	25–44	45–64	65–74	75+
Deaths	450	90	60	110	100	60	30

Drowning

Includes drownings of persons in or on home premises—such as in swimming pools and bathtubs. Excludes drowning in floods and other cataclysms.

	Total	Change from 2006	Death Rate[a]
Deaths	1,000	−9%	0.3

Age	0–4	5–14	15–24	25–44	45–64	65–74	75+
Deaths	400	90	30	110	120	100	150

Firearms

Includes firearms injuries in or on home premises—such as while cleaning or playing with guns. Excludes deaths from explosive materials.

	Total	Change from 2006	Death Rate[a]
Deaths	400	−20%	0.1

Age	0–4	5–14	15–24	25–44	45–64	65–74	75+
Deaths	20	60	140	120	30	20	10

All Other Home

Most important types included are: natural heat and cold, struck by or against objects, machinery, and electric current.

	Total	Change from 2006	Death Rate[a]
Deaths	8,900	(d)%	3.0

Age	0–4	5–14	15–24	25–44	45–64	65–74	75+
Deaths	450	150	100	700	1,500	900	5,100

[a] Deaths per 100,000 population.
[b] Deaths per 100,000 population in each age group.
[c] Death rate less than 0.05.
[d] Direct comparison is not possible. Starting in 2007 all other home includes natural heat and cold.

SPORTS AND RECREATION INJURIES

In the U.S. in 2007, bicycle riding injuries resulted in over half a million emergency department visits.

The table below shows estimates of injuries treated in hospital emergency departments and participants associated with various sports and recreational activities. Differences between the two sources in methods, coverage, classification systems, and definitions can affect comparisons among sports. Because this list of sports is not complete, because the frequency and

duration of participation is not known, and because the number of participants varies greatly, no inference should be made concerning the relative hazard of these sports or rank with respect to risk of injury. In particular, it is *not* appropriate to calculate injury rates from these data.

SPORTS PARTICIPATION AND INJURIES, UNITED STATES, 2007

Sport or Activity	Participants	Injuries	\multicolumn{5}{c}{Percent of Injuries by Age}
			0–4	5–14	15–24	25–64	65 & Over
Archery	6,600,000	4,393	2.5	14.1	14.4	58.5	10.5
Baseball	14,000,000	167,661	2.4	48.8	28.7	19.5	0.6
Softball	10,000,000	110,086	0.4	24.9	29.8	43.9	1.0
Basketball	24,100,000	481,011	0.3	32.5	47.7	19.3	0.2
Bicycle riding[a]	37,400,000	505,413	5.5	43.5	17.8	29.8	3.3
Billiards, pool	29,500,000	5,045	8.2	26.3	18.1	44.5	3.0
Bowling	43,500,000	21,819	6.7	18.7	16.7	47.4	10.6
Boxing	794,000[b]	14,884	0.4	8.5	54.3	36.7	0.1
Cheerleading	3,800,000[c]	26,786	0.4	47.4	50.5	1.4	0.3
Exercise	(d)	194,431[e]	3.2	15.0	19.6	51.7	10.5
Fishing	35,300,000	71,615	2.9	19.4	15.5	52.4	9.9
Football	17,800,000[b, f]	455,193	0.3	47.1	42.4	10.1	0.1
Golf	22,700,000	36,886[g]	4.3	22.7	10.1	41.3	21.6
Gymnastics	(d)	29,373[h]	3.3	68.8	22.0	5.6	0.3
Hockey, street, roller & field	(d)	6,081[i]	0.0	25.9	65.5	8.6	0.0
Horseback riding	(d)	78,527	1.4	19.2	18.9	56.7	3.7
Horseshoe pitching	(d)	2,300	6.6	22.2	16.3	51.8	3.0
Ice hockey	2,100,000	18,679	0.5	30.4	49.0	20.2	0.0
Ice skating	(d)	23,375[j]	1.0	53.4	18.6	25.9	1.1
Martial arts	4,700,000[b]	26,655	1.4	24.3	27.8	45.8	0.7
Mountain biking	7,400,000	10,458	0.0	8.1	19.4	72.3	0.2
Mountain climbing	4,600,000	3,875[c]	1.5	9.0	43.4	43.7	1.9
Racquetball, squash & paddleball	(d)	6,642	0.0	4.2	31.8	56.4	7.6
Roller skating	(d)	67,734[k]	0.8	58.9	13.6	25.8	0.9
Rugby	(d)	11,458	0.0	4.0	75.1	20.9	0.0
Scuba diving	(d)	1,963[c]	0.0	4.1	6.9	89.0	0.0
Skateboarding	10,100,000	143,682	1.5	49.0	39.3	10.0	0.1
Snowboarding	5,100,000	57,792	0.1	29.0	50.4	20.2	0.3
Snowmobiling	2,724,000[b]	12,735	1.1	10.9	33.7	51.5	2.8
Soccer	13,800,000	198,679	0.5	41.6	40.5	17.1	0.2
Swimming	52,300,000	171,704[l]	9.6	41.4	18.6	27.6	2.7
Tennis	12,300,000	21,775	0.2	18.8	18.1	46.0	16.9
Track & field	(d)	19,853	0.1	43.6	48.8	7.5	0.3
Volleyball	12,000,000	57,039	0.1	29.4	41.7	28.5	0.3
Water skiing	5,300,000	9,652	0.7	5.0	45.2	49.1	0.0
Weight lifting	33,200,000	72,369	4.2	10.7	36.1	47.0	2.0
Wrestling	2,100,000	37,320	0.0	36.4	58.6	5.0	0.0

Source: Participants — National Sporting Goods Association; figures include those seven years of age or older who participated more than once per year except for bicycle riding, swimming, and weightlifting, which include those who participated six or more times per year. Injuries — Consumer Product Safety Commission; figures include only injuries treated in hospital emergency departments.

[a] *Excludes mountain biking.*
[b] *Data for 2004.*
[c] *Data for 2006.*
[d] *Data not available.*
[e] *Includes exercise equipment (45,351 injuries) and exercise activity (149,080 injuries).*
[f] *Includes 9,600,000 in touch football and 8,200,000 in tackle football.*
[g] *Excludes golf carts (17,284 injuries).*
[h] *Excludes trampolines (107,435 injuries).*
[i] *Includes field hockey (4,819 injuries) and roller hockey (1,262 injuries[c]). Excludes 34,165 injuries in hockey, unspecified.*
[j] *Excludes 10,564 injuries in skating, unspecified.*
[k] *Includes roller skating (43,146 injuries) and in-line skating (24,588 injuries).*
[l] *Includes injuries associated with swimming, swimming pools, pool slides, diving or diving boards, and swimming pool equipment.*

A recent study examined National Electronic Injury Surveillance System-All Injury Program (NEISS-AIP) data to develop and characterize national estimates of nonfatal outdoor recreational injuries. Cases were selected for injuries that occurred in natural or environmental settings and that were associated with 1 of 21 outdoor products used or for activities participated in during outdoor recreation in natural or environmental settings.

An estimated total of 212,708 persons were treated annually in U.S. emergency departments for injuries sustained while participating in outdoor recreational activities during the period from 2004–2005. The overall injury rate was 72.1 per 100,000 population, with the injury rate for males over two times higher than that for females. The injury rate was highest in the 15– to 19–year age group and lowest in the 45 years and older age group.

The most common body parts injured during outdoor recreational activities were the extremities, including the lower limbs (27%) and upper limbs (25%), followed by the head and neck region (23.3%). Fracture (27.4%) and strain or sprain (23.9%) injuries were the most

common primary diagnoses, with traumatic brain injury (TBI) diagnosed in 6.5% of injuries. The leading causes of outdoor recreational injuries were falls (48%), being struck by or against an object (18%), and overexertion (10%). Snowboarding (26%), sledding (11%), and hiking (6%) were the leading activities associated with outdoor recreational injuries.

The authors indicate that an understanding of the frequency of the most common injuries and their causes may help to reduce misperceptions that lead to overconfidence or misjudging an activity's level of risk. The prevalence of TBI among participants in outdoor recreational activities indicates that following helmet use recommendations for a number of activities, such as skiing, snowboarding, downhill mountain biking, rock climbing, snowmobiling, and sledding, offers a means to reduce the frequency of head injuries. Lastly, the 3 principles of wilderness injury prevention—planning, preparation, and problem anticipation—should be followed to reduce both the number and severity of injuries.

Source: Flores, A. H., Haileyesus, T., & Greenspan, A. I. (Summer, 2008). National Estimates of Outdoor Recreational Injuries Treated in Emergency Departments, United States, 2004–2005. Wilderness and Environmental Medicine, 19(2), 91–98.

NATIONAL ESTIMATES OF OUTDOOR RECREATIONAL INJURIES BY AGE GROUP AND ACTIVITY AT TIME OF INJURY, UNITED STATES, 2006

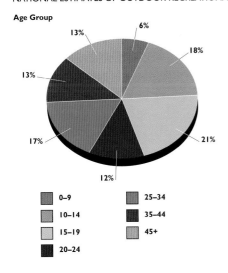

Age Group

0–9	25–34
10–14	35–44
15–19	45+
20–24	

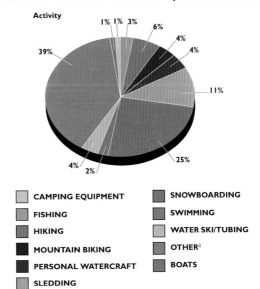

Activity

CAMPING EQUIPMENT	SNOWBOARDING
FISHING	SWIMMING
HIKING	WATER SKI/TUBING
MOUNTAIN BIKING	OTHER[a]
PERSONAL WATERCRAFT	BOATS
SLEDDING	

[a]*Includes snowskiing, surfing, snowmobiles, mountain climbing, scuba diving, horseback riding, ice/snow boating, and other activities.*

WEATHER

Floods caused 21% of weather-related deaths in 2007.

A variety of weather events resulted in 414 deaths in the 50 United States and District of Columbia in 2007. Floods accounted for 21% of the deaths and tornadoes caused 20%. Temperature extremes (mostly extreme heat) accounted for 17% of the deaths.

The data on weather-related deaths was compiled by the National Climatic Data Center (NCDC), which is part of the National Oceanic and Atmospheric Administration. NCDC data may differ from data based on death certificates that appears elsewhere in *Injury Facts®*.

WEATHER-RELATED DEATHS, UNITED STATES, 2007

Event	Total	Jan	Feb	Mar	Apr	May	Jun	Jul	Aug	Sep	Oct	Nov	Dec
Total	**414**	**18**	**52**	**48**	**27**	**48**	**51**	**41**	**65**	**19**	**19**	**1**	**25**
Flood	87	7	0	8	6	14	15	6	24	3	0	0	4
Tornado	81	2	22	27	9	14	0	0	1	0	5	0	1
Temperature Extremes	71	4	19	2	0	0	7	10	21	6	0	1	1
Ocean/Lake Surf	52	1	1	4	5	13	7	10	2	3	2	0	4
Lightning	45	0	0	1	1	5	12	10	9	5	2	0	0
Thunderstorm/High Winds	31	1	1	3	6	1	4	2	8	1	2	0	2
Snow/Ice	27	2	9	3	0	0	0	0	0	0	0	0	13
Wild/Forest Fire	17	0	0	0	0	0	6	3	0	0	8	0	0
Precipitation	2	1	0	0	0	1	0	0	0	0	0	0	0
Hurricane/Tropical Storm	1	0	0	0	0	0	0	0	0	1	0	0	0
Drought	0	0	0	0	0	0	0	0	0	0	0	0	0
Dust Storm	0	0	0	0	0	0	0	0	0	0	0	0	0
Fog	0	0	0	0	0	0	0	0	0	0	0	0	0
Funnel Cloud	0	0	0	0	0	0	0	0	0	0	0	0	0
Hail	0	0	0	0	0	0	0	0	0	0	0	0	0
Waterspout	0	0	0	0	0	0	0	0	0	0	0	0	0

Source: National Safety Council analysis of National Climatic Data Center data.

WEATHER-RELATED FATALITIES BY MONTH, UNITED STATES, 2007

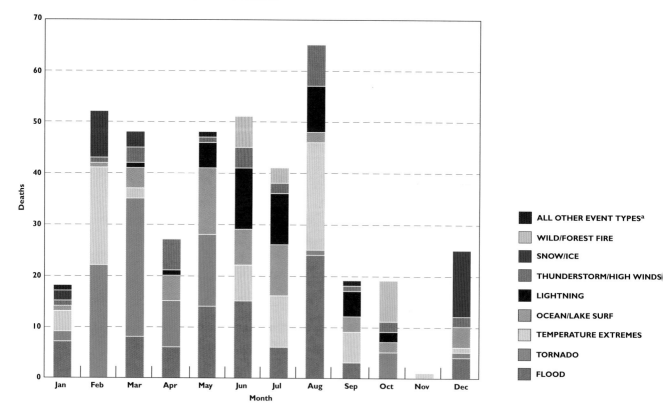

*Includes precipitation and hurricane/tropical storm.

FIREARMS

Unintentional firearms-related deaths up 21% in 2005.

Firearm-related deaths from unintentional, intentional, and undetermined causes totaled 30,694 in 2005, an increase of 4% from 2004. Suicides accounted for 55.4% of firearms deaths, 40.2% were homicides, and 2.6% were unintentional deaths. Males dominate all categories of firearms deaths and accounted for 86.8% of the total.

The number of homicide deaths by firearms increased in 2005 after decreasing for the first time in four years in 2004. Suicide and unintentional firearms deaths each

increased in 2005 following annual declines over the previous two and three year periods, respectively.

Hospital emergency department surveillance data indicate an estimated 15,388 nonfatal unintentional firearm-related injuries in 2005. For assault there were an estimated 50,320 nonfatal injuries, while the estimated total for intentionally self-inflicted nonfatal injuries was 3,082

Source: National Safety Council analysis of National Center for Health Statistics mortality data and National Center for Injury Prevention and Control injury surveillance data using WISQARS™ (http://www.cdc.gov/ncipc/wisqars/).

DEATHS INVOLVING FIREARMS BY AGE AND SEX, UNITED STATES, 2005

Type & Sex	All Ages	Under 5 Years	5–14 Years	15–19 Years	20–24 Years	25–44 Years	45–64 Years	65–74 Years	75 & Over
Total Firearms Deaths	**30,694**	**69**	**335**	**2,623**	**4,198**	**11,403**	**7,731**	**1,929**	**2,406**
Male	26,657	49	252	2,374	3,830	9,780	6,495	1,679	2,198
Female	4,037	20	83	249	368	1,623	1,236	250	208
Unintentional	**789**	**23**	**52**	**98**	**105**	**244**	**175**	**44**	**48**
Male	683	19	39	88	102	212	146	37	40
Female	106	4	13	10	3	32	29	7	8
Suicide	**17,002**	**—**	**84**	**738**	**1,224**	**5,124**	**5,942**	**1,669**	**2,221**
Male	14,916	—	72	658	1,113	4,397	5,085	1,501	2,090
Female	2,086	—	12	80	111	727	857	168	131
Homicide	**12,352**	**43**	**187**	**1,742**	**2,757**	**5,790**	**1,502**	**201**	**130**
Male	10,561	28	131	1,584	2,512	4,943	1,171	131	61
Female	1,791	15	56	158	245	847	331	70	69
Legal Intervention	**330**	**0**	**0**	**21**	**59**	**182**	**61**	**5**	**2**
Male	319	0	0	21	58	178	57	3	2
Female	11	0	0	0	1	4	4	2	0
Undetermined[a]	**221**	**3**	**12**	**24**	**53**	**63**	**51**	**10**	**5**
Male	178	2	10	23	45	50	36	7	5
Female	43	1	2	1	8	13	15	3	0

Source: National Safety Council tabulation of National Center for Health Statistics mortality data.
Note: Dashes (—) indicate category not applicable.
[a]Undetermined means the intentionality of the deaths (unintentional, homicide, suicide) was not determined.

FIREARMS DEATHS BY INTENTIONALITY AND YEAR, UNITED STATES, 1996–2005

Passenger transportation incidents account for about three out of ten unintentional-injury deaths. But the risk of death to the passenger, expressed on a per mile basis, varies greatly by transportation mode. Highway travel by personal vehicle presents the greatest risk; air, rail, and bus travel have much lower death rates. The tables below show the latest information on passenger transportation deaths and death rates.

The statistics for automobiles, vans, sport utility vehicles (SUVs), pickups, and other light trucks shown in the tables below represent all passenger vehicle usage, both intercity and local. The bus data also include intercity and local (transit) bus travel. Railroad includes both intercity (Amtrak) and local commuting travel. Scheduled airlines includes both large airlines and commuter airlines, but excludes on-demand air taxis and charter operations. In comparing the four modes, drivers of automobiles (except taxis), vans, SUVs, and pickup trucks are considered passengers. Bus drivers and airline or railroad crews are not considered passengers.

Other comparisons are possible based on passenger-trips, vehicle-miles, or vehicle-trips, but passenger-miles is the most commonly used basis for comparing the safety of various modes of travel.

TRANSPORTATION ACCIDENT DEATH RATES, 2004–2006

Mode of Transportation	2006			2004–2006 Average Death Rate
	Passenger Deaths	Passenger Miles (billions)	Deaths per 100,000,000 Passenger Miles	
Passenger automobiles[a]	17,792	2,675.4	0.67	0.69
Vans, SUVs, pickup trucks[b]	12,723	1,785.4	0.71	0.74
Buses[c]	15	60.4	0.02	0.05
Transit buses	0	23.0	0.00	0.00
Intercity buses	7	37.4	0.02	0.05
Railroad passenger trains[d]	2	16.2	0.01	0.04
Scheduled airlines[e]	50	574.5	0.01	0.005

Source: Highway passenger deaths — Fatality Analysis Reporting System data. Railroad passenger deaths and miles — Federal Railroad Administration. Airline passenger deaths — National Transportation Safety Board. Airline passenger miles — Bureau of Transportation Statistics. Passenger miles for transit buses — American Public Transit Association. All other figures — National Safety Council estimates.
[a]Includes taxi passengers. Drivers of passenger automobiles are considered passengers.
[b]Includes 2-axle, 4-tire vehicles under 10,000 lbs GVWR other than automobiles.
[c]Figures exclude school buses but include "other" and "unknown" bus types.
[d]Includes Amtrak and commuter rail service.
[e]Includes large airlines and scheduled commuter airlines; excludes charter, cargo, and on-demand service and suicide/sabotage.

PASSENGER DEATHS AND DEATH RATES, UNITED STATES, 1997–2006

Year	Passenger Automobiles		Vans, SUVs, Pickup Trucks		Buses		Railroad Passenger Trains		Scheduled Airlines	
	Deaths	Rate[a]	Deaths	Rate[a]	Deaths	Rate[a]	Deaths	Rate[a]	Deaths	Rate[a]
1997	22,196	0.93	—	—	5	0.01	6	0.05	49	0.01
1998	21,180	0.86	—	—	26	0.05	4	0.03	1	0.00
1999	20,851	0.84	11,295	0.76	40	0.07	14	0.10	24	0.005
2000	20,689	0.81	11,545	0.76	3	0.01	4	0.03	94	0.02
2001	20,310	0.78	11,736	0.76	11	0.02	3	0.02	279	0.06
2002	20,564	0.78	12,278	0.78	36	0.06	7	0.05	0	0.00
2003	19,723	0.74	12,551	0.78	30	0.05	3	0.02	24	0.005
2004	19,183	0.71	12,678	0.75	27	0.05	3	0.02	13	0.002
2005	18,509	0.68	13,043	0.76	43	0.07	16	0.10	22	0.004
2006	17,792	0.67	12,723	0.71	15	0.02	2	0.01	52	0.01
10-year average	20,100	0.78	—	—	24	0.04	6	0.04	56	0.01

Source: See table above. Note: Dashes (—) indicate data not available.
[a]Deaths per 100,000,000 passenger miles.

PASSENGER DEATH RATES, UNITED STATES, 2004–2006

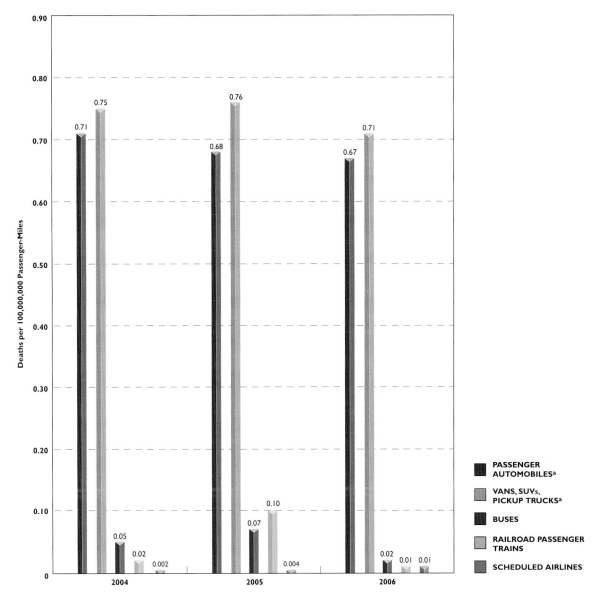

Deaths per 100,000,000 Passenger-Miles

	2004	2005	2006
PASSENGER AUTOMOBILES[a]	0.71	0.68	0.67
VANS, SUVs, PICKUP TRUCKS[a]	0.75	0.76	0.71
BUSES	0.05	0.07	0.02
RAILROAD PASSENGER TRAINS	0.02	0.10	0.01
SCHEDULED AIRLINES	0.002	0.004	0.01

PASSENGER AUTOMOBILES[a]

VANS, SUVs, PICKUP TRUCKS[a]

BUSES

RAILROAD PASSENGER TRAINS

SCHEDULED AIRLINES

[a]Drivers of these vehicles are considered passengers.

AVIATION

In 2007, there were 11 aircraft accidents that resulted in 587 fatalities to passengers according to preliminary full-year data reported by the International Civil Aviation Organization (ICAO). Compared to 2006, the 2007 data show a 22% decline in the number of passenger deaths. The 587 deaths resulted in a preliminary fatality rate of 0.014 per 100 million passenger-kilometers—representing a 26% decrease from the 2006 rate of 0.019.

WORLDWIDE SCHEDULED AIR SERVICE ACCIDENTS, DEATHS, AND DEATH RATES, 1992–2007

Year	Fatal Accidents[a]	Passenger Deaths	Death Rate[b]	Year	Fatal Accidents[a]	Passenger Deaths	Death Rate[b]
1992	28	1,070	0.06	2000	18	757	0.03
1993	33	864	0.04	2001	13	577	0.02
1994	27	1,170	0.05	2002	13	791	0.025
1995	25	711	0.03	2003	7	466	0.015
1996	24	1,146	0.05	2004	9	203	0.01
1997	25	921	0.04	2005	17	712	0.0191
1998	20	904	0.03	2006	12	751	0.019
1999	21	499	0.02	2007[c]	11	587	0.014

Source: International Civil Aviation Organization. Figures include the USSR up to 1992 and the Commonwealth of Independent States thereafter.
[a] Involving a passenger fatality and an aircraft with maximum take-off mass >2,250 kg.
[b] Passenger deaths per 100 million passenger-kilometers.
[c] Preliminary data.

U.S. CIVIL AVIATION ACCIDENTS, DEATHS, AND DEATH RATES, 2002–2007

| | | | | Accident Rates | | | |
| | Accidents | | Total Deaths[a] | Per 100,000 Flight-Hours | | Per Million Aircraft-Miles | |
Year	Total	Fatal		Total	Fatal	Total	Fatal
Large Airlines[b]							
2002	34	0	0	0.203	0	0.0049	0
2003	51	2	22	0.302	0.012	0.0073	0.0003
2004	23	1	13	0.126	0.005	0.0030	0.0001
2005	33	3	22	0.176	0.016	0.0042	0.0004
2006	26	2	50	0.139	0.011	0.0033	0.0003
2007	24	0	0	0.128	0	0.0031	0
Commuter Airlines[b]							
2002	7	0	0	2.559	0	0.1681	0
2003	2	1	2	0.627	0.313	0.0422	0.0211
2004	4	0	0	1.324	0	0.0855	0
2005	6	0	0	2.002	0	0.1312	0
2006	3	1	2	0.995	0.332	0.0645	0.0215
2007	3	0	0	0.993	0	0.0644	0
On-Demand Air Taxis[b]							
2002	60	18	35	2.06	0.62	—	—
2003	73	18	42	2.49	0.61	—	—
2004	66	23	64	2.04	0.71	—	—
2005	65	11	18	1.70	0.29	—	—
2006	53	10	16	1.42	0.27	—	—
2007	62	14	43	1.69	0.38	—	—
General Aviation[b]							
2002[c]	1,715	345	581	6.69	1.33	—	—
2003[c]	1,740	352	633	6.68	1.34	—	—
2004[c]	1,617	314	559	6.49	1.26	—	—
2005[c]	1,670	321	563	7.20	1.38	—	—
2006[c]	1,518	306	703	6.33	1.27	—	—
2007[c]	1,631	284	491	6.84	1.19	—	—

Source: National Transportation Safety Board: 2007 preliminary, 2002–2006 revised; exposure data for rates from Federal Aviation Administration.
Note: Dash (—) indicates data not available.
[a] Includes passengers, crew members, and others such as persons on the ground.
[b] Civil aviation accident statistics collected by the National Transportation Safety Board are classified according to the Federal air regulations under which the flights were made. The classifications are (1) large airlines operating scheduled service under Title 14, Code of Federal Regulations, part 121 (14 CFR 121); (2) commuter carriers operating scheduled service under 14 CFR 135; (3) unscheduled, "on-demand" air taxis under 14 CFR 135; and (4) "general aviation," which includes accidents involving aircraft flown under rules other than 14 CFR 121 and 14 CFR 135. Not shown in the table is nonscheduled air carrier operations under 14 CFR 121, which experienced 2 accidents and 1 fatality in 2007. Since 1997, Large Airlines includes aircraft with 10 or more seats, formerly operated as commuter carriers under 14 CFR 135.
[c] Suicide/sabotage/terrorism and stolen/unauthorized cases are included in "accident" and fatality totals but excluded from rates — General Aviation, 2002 (7 crashes/6 deaths), 2003 (4/3), 2004 (3/0), 2005 (2/1), 2006 (2/1), 2007 (0/0).

RAILROAD

Railroad deaths totaled 846 in 2007, a 6% decrease from the 2006 total of 902 and a 9% decrease from the 1998–2006 average of 927. In 2007, there was an 8% decrease in fatalities at highway-rail crossings and a 5% decrease in fatalities that occurred in other types of incidents. The latter included 468 deaths, or 92%, to trespassers. Seventeen employees were killed while on duty, a 6% increase compared to the 2006 death toll and a 26% decrease from the 1998–2006 average of 23. Deaths to passengers on trains totaled 5, up from 2 deaths in 2006 and equivalent to the nine-year average.

The ratio of railroad-related deaths to nonfatal injuries and illnesses is approximately 1:11. In 2007, railroad accidents resulted in 9,010 cases of nonfatal conditions, compared to 8,637 in 2006 and the 1998–2006 average of 10,384. Twelve percent of the total was attributed to highway-rail crossing incidents, which decreased by 2% from the 2006 total of 1,067 and by 9% from the 1998–2006 average of 1,147. Of the 5,276 nonfatal occupational injuries and illnesses reported in 2007, less than 2% were attributed to highway-rail crossing incidents.

DEATHS AND NONFATAL CASES IN RAILROAD ACCIDENTS AND INCIDENTS, UNITED STATES, 1998–2007

Year	Total	Highway-Rail Crossing Incident?		Occurring in Other Than Highway-Rail Crossing Incident		Employees On Duty At Highway-Rail Crossing?		Passengers on Trains[a] At Highway-Rail Crossing?	
		Yes	No	Trespassers	Others	Yes	No	Yes	No
Deaths									
1998	1,008	431	577	536	41	4	23	2	2
1999	932	402	530	479	51	2	29	11	3
2000	937	425	512	463	49	2	22	0	4
2001	971	421	550	511	39	1	21	0	3
2002	951	357	594	540	54	1	19	0	7
2003	865	334	531	498	33	1	18	1	2
2004	891	371	520	472	48	2	23	0	3
2005	883	358	525	458	67	2	23	0	16
2006	902	368	534	511	23	4	12	0	2
2007	846	337	509	468	41	1	16	0	5
Nonfatal conditions									
1998	11,459	1,303	10,156	513	9,643	122	8,276	19	516
1999	11,700	1,396	10,304	445	9,859	140	8,482	43	438
2000	11,643	1,219	10,424	414	10,010	100	8,323	10	648
2001	10,985	1,157	9,828	404	9,424	97	7,718	20	726
2002	11,103	999	10,104	395	9,709	110	6,534	26	851
2003	9,254	1,034	8,220	398	7,822	75	6,173	74	653
2004	9,187	1,094	8,093	404	7,689	116	5,904	27	672
2005	9,491	1,050	8,441	419	8,022	110	5,705	33	909
2006	8,637	1,067	7,570	478	7,092	95	5,132	95	786
2007	9,010	1,043	7,967	398	7,569	102	5,174	66	1,111

Source: Federal Railroad Administration.
[a] Passenger cases include all circumstances, including getting on/off standing trains, stumbling aboard trains, assaults, train accidents, crossing incidents, etc.

CASUALTIES AT PUBLIC AND PRIVATE HIGHWAY-RAIL CROSSINGS, UNITED STATES, 1998–2007

Year	Deaths				Nonfatal Conditions			
	Total	Motor-Vehicle Related	Pedestrians	Others	Total	Motor-Vehicle Related	Pedestrians	Others
1998	431	369	50	12	1,303	1,257	33	13
1999	402	345	45	12	1,396	1,338	35	23
2000	425	361	51	13	1,219	1,169	34	16
2001	421	345	67	9	1,157	1,110	31	16
2002	357	310	35	12	999	939	29	31
2003	334	281	50	3	1,035	1,000	28	7
2004	371	289	73	9	1,094	1,058	30	6
2005	358	283	58	17	1,052	1,007	37	8
2006	368	304	53	11	1,069	1,035	29	5
2007	337	262	59	16	1,046	1,004	30	12

Source: Federal Railroad Administration.

UNINTENTIONAL FATAL POISONINGS

Poisoning deaths up 13% from 2004 to 2005.

Deaths from unintentional poisoning numbered 23,618 in 2005, the latest year for which data are available. The death rate per 100,000 population was 8.0—10.9 for males and 5.1 for females. Total poisoning deaths increased 13% from 20,950 in 2004 and are 2.5 times the 1996 total. See pages 42–45 for long-term trends.

Almost half of the poisoning deaths (47%) were classified in the "narcotics and psychodysleptics (hallucinogens), not elsewhere classified," category, which includes prescription narcotic analgesics and

illegal drugs such as cocaine, heroin, cannabinol, and LSD.

Carbon monoxide poisoning is included in the category of "other gases and vapors." Deaths due to alcohol poisoning numbered 346 in 2005, but alcohol may also be present in combination with other drugs.

Additional information on human poisoning exposure cases may be found on pages 142 and 185.

UNINTENTIONAL POISONING DEATHS BY TYPE, AGE, AND SEX, UNITED STATES, 2005

Type of Poison	All Ages	0–4 Years	5–14 Years	15–19 Years	20–24 Years	25–44 Years	45–64 Years	65 Years & Over
Both Sexes								
Total Poisoning Deaths	**23,618**	**41**	**51**	**637**	**1,847**	**11,115**	**8,990**	**937**
Deaths per 100,000 population	*8.0*	*0.2*	*0.1*	*3.0*	*8.8*	*13.2*	*12.3*	*2.5*
Nonopioid analgesics, antipyretics and antirheumatics (X40)[a]	226	1	1	3	6	83	97	35
Antiepileptic, sedative-hypnotic, antiparkinsonism and psychotropic drugs, n.e.c. (X41)	1,496	1	0	42	83	716	616	38
Narcotics and psychodysleptics (hallucinogens), n.e.c. (X42)	11,050	5	18	282	905	5,431	4,211	198
Other drugs acting on the autonomic nervous system (X43)	23	3	1	0	1	9	7	2
Other and unspecified drugs, medicaments and biological substances (X44)	9,653	15	9	259	774	4,511	3,620	465
Alcohol (X45)	346	0	0	11	28	137	159	11
Organic solvents and halogenated hydrocarbons and their vapors (X46)	61	2	3	5	5	31	12	3
Other gases and vapors (X47)	642	10	18	30	39	173	224	148
Pesticides (X48)	7	0	0	0	2	2	2	1
Other and unspecified chemical and noxious substances (X49)	114	4	1	5	4	22	42	36
Males								
Total Poisoning Deaths	15,884	23	31	488	1,452	7,616	5,806	468
Deaths per 100,000 population	*10.9*	*0.2*	*0.1*	*4.5*	*13.4*	*18.0*	*16.3*	*3.0*
Nonopioid analgesics, antipyretics and antirheumatics (X40)	103	0	0	1	4	34	49	15
Antiepileptic, sedative-hypnotic, antiparkinsonism and psychotropic drugs, n.e.c. (X41)	996	1	0	27	57	510	382	19
Narcotics and psychodysleptics (hallucinogens), n.e.c. (X42)	7,989	4	11	224	739	3,924	2,981	106
Other drugs acting on the autonomic nervous system (X43)	8	2	0	0	0	3	2	1
Other and unspecified drugs, medicaments and biological substances (X44)	5,916	8	5	199	589	2,860	2,042	213
Alcohol (X45)	278	0	0	10	25	110	125	8
Organic solvents and halogenated hydrocarbons and their vapors (X46)	52	1	3	5	5	27	10	1
Other gases and vapors (X47)	472	6	11	18	29	134	182	92
Pesticides (X48)	5	0	0	0	1	1	2	1
Other and unspecified chemical and noxious substances (X49)	65	1	1	4	3	13	31	12
Females								
Total Poisoning Deaths	7,734	18	20	149	395	3,499	3,184	469
Deaths per 100,000 population	*5.1*	*0.2*	*0.1*	*1.5*	*3.9*	*8.4*	*8.5*	*2.2*
Nonopioid analgesics, antipyretics and antirheumatics (X40)	123	1	1	2	2	49	48	20
Antiepileptic, sedative-hypnotic, antiparkinsonism and psychotropic drugs, n.e.c. (X41)	500	0	0	15	26	206	234	19
Narcotics and psychodysleptics (hallucinogens), n.e.c. (X42)	3,061	1	7	58	166	1,507	1,230	92
Other drugs acting on the autonomic nervous system (X43)	15	1	1	0	1	6	5	1
Other and unspecified drugs, medicaments and biological substances (X44)	3,737	7	4	60	185	1,651	1,578	252
Alcohol (X45)	68	0	0	1	3	27	34	3
Organic solvents and halogenated hydrocarbons and their vapors (X46)	9	1	0	0	0	4	2	2
Other gases and vapors (X47)	170	4	7	12	10	39	42	56
Pesticides (X48)	2	0	0	0	1	1	0	0
Other and unspecified chemical and noxious substances (X49)	49	3	0	1	1	9	11	24

Source: National Safety Council tabulations of National Center for Health Statistics mortality data.
Note: n.e.c. means not elsewhere classified.
[a] *Numbers following titles refer to external cause of injury and poisoning classifications in ICD-10.*

UNINTENTIONAL POISONING DEATHS, UNITED STATES, 1996–2005

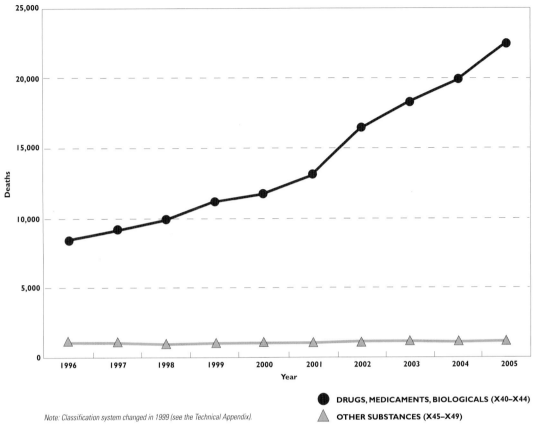

Note: Classification system changed in 1999 (see the Technical Appendix).

● DRUGS, MEDICAMENTS, BIOLOGICALS (X40–X44)

▲ OTHER SUBSTANCES (X45–X49)

FATAL VS. NONFATAL UNINTENTIONAL POISONING

Most people think of poisoning as a childhood issue. That is true for nonfatal poisonings, but not for fatal poisonings. The pie charts below show the distribution of fatal and nonfatal poisonings by age groups. The poisoning exposure data is from the American Association of Poison Control Centers and represents the calls received by poison control centers. The fatality data is from death certificates.

Nonfatal exposures occur predominantly among young children whereas fatal poisonings are overwhelmingly among adults. However, compared to previous years, the proportion of adult exposures is increasing. In 2005, 16% of exposures were among adults compared to fully 28% in 2006. The distribution of poisoning deaths among children and adults is largely unchanged.

POISONING EXPOSURES AND DEATHS BY AGE GROUP, UNITED STATES, SELECTED YEARS

POISONING EXPOSURES, 2006

POISONING DEATHS, 2005

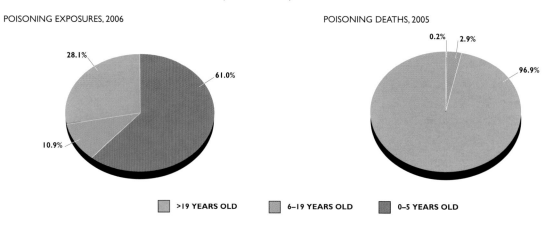

■ >19 YEARS OLD   ■ 6–19 YEARS OLD   ■ 0–5 YEARS OLD

Overall, both fatal and nonfatal unintentional poisonings are on the rise. The charts below illustrate that both categories of poisonings have increased steadily since 2001.

NON-FATAL UNINTENTIONAL POISONING TREND

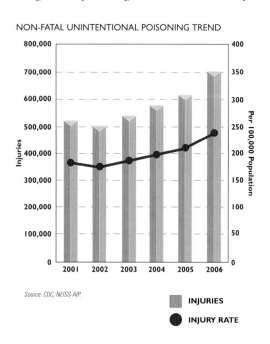

Source: CDC, NEISS-AIP.

■ INJURIES
● INJURY RATE

FATAL UNINTENTIONAL POISONING TREND

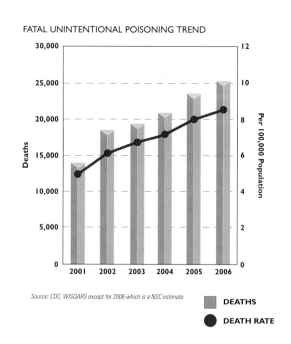

Source: CDC, WISQARS except for 2006 which is a NSC estimate.

■ DEATHS
● DEATH RATE

LADDERS

Use of ladders was associated with an estimated 161,940 injuries treated in hospital emergency departments (ED) in 2005, an increase of 51% from 107,477 in 1990, according to recent research. The rate of such injuries increased 27% from 43.06 per 100,000 population in 1990 to 54.63 in 2005. The estimates were based on data collected through the U.S. Consumer Product Safety Commission's National Electronic Injury Surveillance System and include injuries resulting from climbing on, slipping on, jumping off, stepping off, or falling off a ladder. Excluded were cases described as carrying, hitting, bumping, tripping over, or being hit by a ladder.

Eighty nine percent of patients were treated in the ED and released and 10% were admitted or transferred to another hospital. Hospitalization rates increased with increasing age.

The location where the injury occurred was recorded in 67% of the cases. Where recorded, 97% of the ladder incidents occurred at home. Males were involved in 77% of the cases.

The legs and feet were injured most often (30% of cases) and the most common injury to them was strains and sprains (38% of leg/foot injuries).

Fractures were the most common injury type (32% of cases), usually involving the arms and hands (37% of fractures).

Sprains and strains were the most common injury to the lower trunk; contusions and abrasions for the upper trunk including shoulders and neck; lacerations and avulsions for the head and face.

Source: D'Souza, A.L., Smith, G. A., & Trifiletti, L.B. (2007). Ladder-related injuries treated in emergency departments in the United States, 1990–2005. American Journal of Preventive Medicine, 32(5), 413–418.

NONFATAL UNINTENTIONAL LADDER-RELATED INJURIES TREATED IN HOSPITAL EMERGENCY DEPARTMENTS, UNITED STATES, 1990–2005

Civilian fire deaths in home fires numbered 2,860 in 2005, down 7% from 2004. The total for 2005 was down 46% from the 25-year high of 5,330 deaths in 1981 and was down 25% from the 25-year average of 3,824. Likewise, civilian injuries in home fires in 2005 were down 4% from 2004 and totaled 13,070. This figure was down 40% from the 25-year high of 21,910 in 1988 and 1993, and down 28% from the 25-year average of 18,158.

Smoking materials and heating equipment each accounted for 24% of the fatalities in 2002–2005, followed by cooking equipment (15%), and electrical distribution and lighting equipment and intentional causes (11% each). Cooking equipment was the leading cause for just over a third of home fire injuries, followed by heating equipment and candles at 13% and 11%, respectively. Heating equipment was the leading fire cause resulting in civilian fire deaths for those in age groups less than 5 years of age, 5–9 (along with cooking equipment), 10–14, 20–34, and 85 and over (along with electrical distribution and lighting equipment).

Intentional causes along with electrical distribution and lighting equipment were the leading causes of fire deaths for the 15–17 and 18–19 year old age groups, while smoking was the leading cause for the 35–49, 50–64, 65–74, and 75–84 year old age groups. Cooking equipment was the leading fire cause resulting in civilian fire injuries for all age groups except for those under 5 years of age and those aged 5–9, for which playing with heat source was the leading cause.

As measured by fire death rates per million population, the very old and the very young are at highest risk of death in home structure fires. In 2002–2005, children under age 5 were one and a half times as likely to die in a home fire as the general public. The relative risk of fire death decreases throughout childhood until the late teenage years, where it begins increasing to its peak of nearly four times that of the general public for adults age 85 and over. Adults aged 20–49 have the highest risk of reported nonfatal injury from home fires.

Source: Flynn, J.D. (2008, July). Characteristics of home fire victims. Quincy, MA: National Fire Protection Association.

RISK INDEX OF U.S. CIVILIAN FIRE DEATHS AND INJURIES IN HOMES BY AGE GROUP, 2002–2005

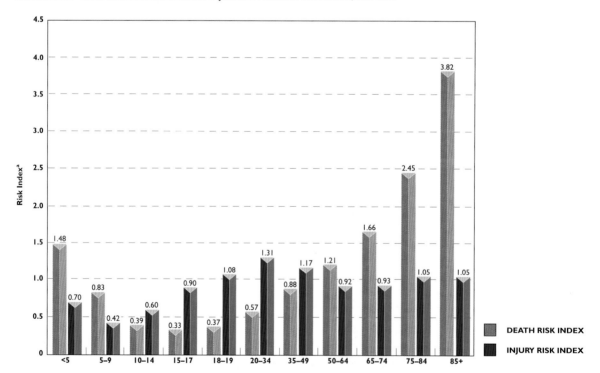

[a] *The risk index for an age group is the ratio of that age group's civilian fire deaths per million population to the civilian fire death rate per million population for all age groups combined. A risk index higher than 1.00 for specific age group means that age group is at higher risk of death than the general public.*

PEDALCYCLES

The estimated number of deaths from collisions between pedalcycles and motor vehicles increased from about 750 in 1940 to 1,200 in 1980, and then declined to about 1,000 in 2007. Nonfatal disabling injuries were estimated to number 59,000 in 2007.

In 2005, 700 pedalcyclists died in motor-vehicle crashes and 227 in other accidents according to National Center for Health Statistics mortality data. Males accounted for 88% of all pedalcycle deaths, more than seven times the female fatalities.

Emergency-room-treated injuries associated with bicycles and bicycle accessories were estimated to total 490,434 in 2006 and 515,871 in 2007, according to the U.S. Consumer Product Safety Commission (see also page 148).

Thompson, Rivara, and Thompson (1989) estimated that bicycle helmets reduce the risk of all head injuries by up to 85% and reduce the risk of brain injuries by as much as 88%. In 2008, 21 states, the District of Columbia, and at least 192 localities had bicycle helmet-use laws according to the Bicycle Helmet Safety Institute.

Source: National Safety Council estimates and tabulations of National Center for Health Statistics mortality data. Data from Bicycle Helmet Safety Institute retrieved 10/29/08 from www.bhsi.org.
Thompson, R.S., Rivara, F.P., & Thompson, D.C. (1989). A case-control study of the effectiveness of bicycle safety helmets. New England Journal of Medicine, 320(21), 1361–1367.

PEDALCYCLE DEATHS AND DEATH RATES BY SEX AND AGE GROUP, UNITED STATES, 2005

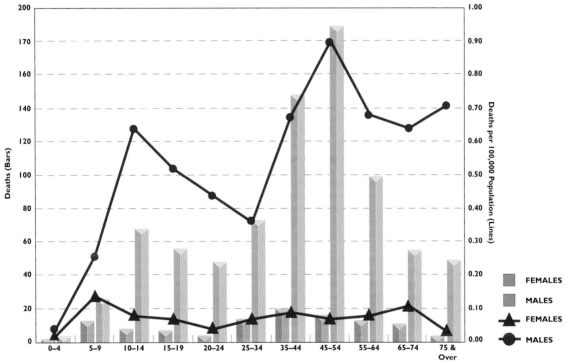

Source: National Safety Council based on National Center for Health Statistics data.

PEDALCYCLE FATALITIES BY MONTH, UNITED STATES, 2005

The leading risks for unintentional-injury (U-I) vary with age and are different for deaths and for nonfatal injuries. The tables here and on the next page list, for eight age groups, the five leading causes of unintentional-injury death and the five leading causes of hospital emergency department (ED) visits, which is one measure of nonfatal injuries.

For all ages, the five leading causes account for 81.9% of all U-I deaths and 76.0% of U-I ED visits. Only motor-vehicle crashes and falls are common to both lists. Motor-vehicle crashes rank first for U-I deaths and fourth for U-I ED visits. Falls rank third for U-I deaths and first for ED U-I visits.

The five leading causes of U-I deaths account for between 76.6% and 92.0% of such deaths depending on the age group. The leading causes of unintentional-injury ED visits account for between 74.7% and 89.4% of such hospital visits.

For deaths, motor-vehicle crashes, poisoning, falls, fires, flames, and smoke, and drowning are most often among the top five with choking, firearms, and mechanical suffocation sometimes included. For ED visits, falls, struck by or against, overexertion, motor-vehicle occupant injuries, and cut or pierce injuries are most often in the top five. In the younger age groups, bites and stings (except dog bites), foreign body injuries, and pedal cycle injuries sometimes are among the leading risks.

LEADING UNINTENTIONAL INJURY RISKS, ALL AGES, UNITED STATES, 2005

Rank	Unintentional-Injury Deaths				Emergency Department U-I Visits			
	Event	Number	Percent	Rate[a]	Event	Number	Percent	Rate[a]
—	Total	117,809	100.0%	39.7	Total	27,156,734	100.0%	9,159
1	Motor-vehicle crashes	45,343	38.5%	15.3	Falls	7,938,467	29.2%	2,677
2	Poisoning	23,618	20.0%	8.0	Struck by or against	4,336,688	16.0%	1,463
3	Falls	19,656	16.7%	6.6	Overexertion	3,284,022	12.1%	1,108
4	Choking[b]	4,386	3.7%	1.5	Motor-vehicle occupant	2,857,722	10.5%	964
5	Drowning	3,582	3.0%	1.2	Cut or pierce	2,236,861	8.2%	754

LEADING UNINTENTIONAL INJURY RISKS, YOUNG CHILDREN (AGES 0–4), UNITED STATES, 2005

Rank	Unintentional-Injury Deaths				Emergency Department U-I Visits			
	Event	Number	Percent	Rate[a]	Event	Number	Percent	Rate[a]
—	Total	2,747	100.0%	13.5	Total	2,229,165	100.0%	10,973
1	Mechanical suffocation	764	27.8%	3.8	Falls	981,285	44.0%	4,830
2	Motor-vehicle crashes	763	27.8%	3.8	Struck by or against	396,912	17.8%	1,954
3	Drowning	557	20.3%	2.7	Bite or sting (except dog)	152,503	6.8%	751
4	Fires, flames, and smoke	238	8.7%	1.2	Foreign body	127,541	5.7%	628
5	Choking[b]	110	4.0%	0.5	Cut or pierce	94,912	4.3%	467

LEADING UNINTENTIONAL INJURY RISKS, CHILDREN AND YOUNG ADOLESCENTS (AGES 5–14), UNITED STATES, 2005

Rank	Unintentional-Injury Deaths				Emergency Department U-I Visits			
	Event	Number	Percent	Rate[a]	Event	Number	Percent	Rate[a]
—	Total	2,415	100.0%	6.0	Total	3,967,069	100.0%	9,811
1	Motor-vehicle crashes	1,447	59.9%	3.6	Falls	1,267,158	31.9%	3,134
2	Drowning	253	10.5%	0.6	Struck by or against	945,870	23.8%	2,339
3	Fires, flames, and smoke	222	9.2%	0.5	Overexertion	344,318	8.7%	852
4	Mechanical suffocation	69	2.9%	0.2	Cut or pierce	261,227	6.6%	646
5	Firearms	52	2.2%	0.1	Pedalcyclist	226,671	5.7%	561

LEADING UNINTENTIONAL INJURY RISKS, TEENS (AGES 15–19), UNITED STATES, 2005

Rank	Unintentional-Injury Deaths				Emergency Department U-I Visits			
	Event	Number	Percent	Rate[a]	Event	Number	Percent	Rate[a]
—	Total	6,616	100.0%	31.4	Total	2,739,663	100.0%	13,007
1	Motor-vehicle crashes	4,967	75.1%	23.6	Struck by or against	567,118	20.7%	2,692
2	Poisoning	637	9.6%	3.0	Falls	462,422	16.9%	2,195
3	Drowning	310	4.7%	1.5	Motor-vehicle occupant	430,787	15.7%	2,045
4	Firearms	98	1.5%	0.5	Overexertion	379,907	13.9%	1,804
5	Falls	77	1.2%	0.4	Cut or pierce	226,905	8.3%	1,077

See footnotes on page 147.

LEADING UNINTENTIONAL INJURY RISKS, YOUNG ADULTS (AGES 20–24), UNITED STATES, 2005

Rank	Unintentional-Injury Deaths				Emergency Department U-I Visits			
	Event	Number	Percent	Rate[a]	Event	Number	Percent	Rate[a]
—	Total	9,137	100.0%	43.4	Total	2,588,770	100.0%	12,297
1	Motor-vehicle crashes	5,941	65.0%	28.2	Motor-vehicle occupant	438,920	17.0%	2,085
2	Poisoning	1,847	20.2%	8.8	Falls	427,299	16.5%	2,030
3	Drowning	339	3.7%	1.6	Struck by or against	417,405	16.1%	1,983
4	Falls	159	1.7%	0.8	Overexertion	367,173	14.2%	1,744
5	Fires, flames, and smoke	106	1.2%	0.5	Cut or pierce	283,969	11.0%	1,349

LEADING UNINTENTIONAL INJURY RISKS, ADULTS (AGES 25–44), UNITED STATES, 2005

Rank	Unintentional-Injury Deaths				Emergency Department U-I Visits			
	Event	Number	Percent	Rate[a]	Event	Number	Percent	Rate[a]
—	Total	30,916	100.0%	36.8	Total	7,950,780	100.0%	9,464
1	Motor-vehicle crashes	13,987	45.2%	16.6	Falls	1,570,193	19.7%	1,869
2	Poisoning	11,115	36.0%	13.2	Overexertion	1,314,831	16.5%	1,565
3	Falls	902	2.9%	1.1	Struck by or against	1,188,483	14.9%	1,415
4	Drowning	882	2.9%	1.0	Motor-vehicle occupant	1,061,565	13.4%	1,264
5	Fires, flames, and smoke	558	1.8%	0.7	Cut or pierce	821,673	10.3%	978

LEADING UNINTENTIONAL INJURY RISKS, ADULTS (AGES 45–64), UNITED STATES, 2005

Rank	Unintentional-Injury Deaths				Emergency Department U-I Visits			
	Event	Number	Percent	Rate[a]	Event	Number	Percent	Rate[a]
—	Total	29,192	100.0%	40.1	Total	4,817,533	100.0%	6,614
1	Motor-vehicle crashes	10,851	37.2%	14.9	Falls	1,428,839	29.7%	1,962
2	Poisoning	8,990	30.8%	12.3	Overexertion	628,802	13.1%	863
3	Falls	2,632	9.0%	3.6	Struck by or against	615,387	12.8%	845
4	Fires, flames, and smoke	895	3.1%	1.2	Motor-vehicle occupant	542,854	11.3%	745
5	Drowning	758	2.6%	1.0	Cut or pierce	433,434	9.0%	595

LEADING UNINTENTIONAL INJURY RISKS, OLDER ADULTS (AGES 65–74), UNITED STATES, 2005

Rank	Unintentional-Injury Deaths				Emergency Department U-I Visits			
	Event	Number	Percent	Rate[a]	Event	Number	Percent	Rate[a]
—	Total	8,632	100.0%	46.3	Total	1,071,191	100.0%	5,744
1	Motor-vehicle crashes	3,110	36.0%	16.7	Falls	519,042	48.5%	2,783
2	Falls	2,319	26.9%	12.4	Motor-vehicle occupant	96,429	9.0%	517
3	Choking[b]	566	6.6%	3.0	Struck by or against	95,870	8.9%	514
4	Poisoning	435	5.0%	2.3	Overexertion	88,972	8.3%	477
5	Fires, flames, and smoke	390	4.5%	2.1	Cut or pierce	69,893	6.5%	375

LEADING UNINTENTIONAL INJURY RISKS, ELDERLY (AGES 75 AND OLDER), UNITED STATES, 2005

Rank	Unintentional-Injury Deaths				Emergency Department U-I Visits			
	Event	Number	Percent	Rate[a]	Event	Number	Percent	Rate[a]
—	Total	28,154	100.0%	155.2	Total	1,786,175	100.0%	9,848
1	Falls	13,485	47.9%	74.4	Falls	1,281,721	71.8%	7,067
2	Motor-vehicle crashes	4,277	15.2%	23.6	Struck by or against	109,597	6.1%	604
3	Choking[b]	2,581	9.2%	14.2	Motor-vehicle occupant	81,087	4.5%	447
4	Fires, flames, and smoke	726	2.6%	4.0	Overexertion	78,970	4.4%	435
5	Poisoning	502	1.8%	2.8	Cut or pierce	44,598	2.5%	246

Source: National Safety Council analysis of NCHS mortality data and CDC, NCIPC, NEISS-AIP data.
[a] *Deaths or emergency department visits per 100,000 population.*
[b] *Inhalation and ingestion of food or other object obstructing breathing.*

INJURIES ASSOCIATED WITH CONSUMER PRODUCTS

Over 2 million injury-related emergency department visits each year are associated with stairs, steps, floors, and flooring materials.

The following list of items found in and around the home was selected from the U.S. Consumer Product Safety Commission's National Electronic Injury Surveillance System (NEISS) for 2007. The NEISS estimates are calculated from a statistically representative sample of hospitals in the United States. Injury totals represent estimates of the number of hospital emergency department-treated cases nationwide associated with various products. However, product involvement may or may not be the cause of the injury.

CONSUMER PRODUCT–RELATED INJURIES TREATED IN HOSPITAL EMERGENCY DEPARTMENTS, 2007
(excluding most sports or sports equipment; see also page 132)

Description	Injuries
Home Workshop Equipment	
Saws (hand or power)	87,725
Hammers	35,037
Drills	21,532
Packaging & Containers, Household	
Household containers & packaging	205,324
Bottles and jars	72,485
Bags	38,538
Paper products	23,043
Cardboard products	20,291
Housewares	
Knives	429,368
Tableware and flatware (excl. knives)	99,010
Drinking glasses	74,004
Waste containers, trash baskets, etc.	35,344
Cookware, bowls and canisters	29,754
Scissors	29,693
Manual cleaning equipment (excl. buckets)	24,227
Other kitchen gadgets	21,779
Home Furnishing, Fixtures, and Accessories	
Beds	532,061
Chairs	318,994
Tables, n.e.c.[a]	309,252
Household cabinets, racks, & shelves	269,617
Bathtubs and showers	238,847
Ladders	175,915
Sofas, couches, davenports, divans, etc.	149,806
Rugs and carpets	128,361
Other furniture[b]	118,146
Toilets	71,464
Misc. decorating items	60,869
Stools	51,869
Benches	30,115
Mirrors or mirror glass	24,121
Sinks	23,343
Home Structures and Construction Materials	
Floors or flooring materials	1,166,310
Stairs or steps	1,161,945
Other door[c]	304,556
Ceilings and walls	296,908
Porches, balconies, open-side floors	147,520
Nails, screws, tacks or bolts	146,595
Windows	120,897
Fences or fence posts	109,181
House repair and construction materials	78,391
Door sills or frames	55,390
Poles	44,375
Counters or countertops	43,459
Handrails, railings or banisters	41,912
Glass Doors	32,725

Description	Injuries
General Household Appliances	
Refrigerators	34,201
Ranges or ovens, not specified	29,913
Heating, Cooling, and Ventilating Equipment	
Pipes (excluding smoking pipes)	31,927
Home Communication and Entertainment Equipment	
Televisions	59,844
Personal-Use Items	
Footwear	155,224
Wheelchairs	118,901
Crutches, canes, walkers	91,849
Jewelry	80,171
Daywear	45,165
First aid equipment	42,060
Razors and shavers	38,656
Other clothing[d]	36,908
Desk supplies	34,604
Coins	32,078
Luggage	23,184
Hair grooming equipment & accessories	20,683
Yard and Garden Equipment	
Lawn mowers	78,773
Pruning, trimming & edging equipment	46,515
Other unpowered garden tools[e]	27,316
Chainsaws	26,669
Manual snow or ice removal tools	26,117
Sports and Recreation	
Bicycles	515,871
Skateboards	143,682
Trampolines	107,435
Toys, n.e.c.	106,568
Swimming pools	86,822
Minibikes or trailbikes	83,158
Monkey bars or other playground climbing	77,845
Swings or swing sets	59,144
Scooters (unpowered)	49,821
Dancing	46,441
Slides or sliding boards	45,465
Aquariums and other pet supplies	44,835
Sleds	42,345
Other playground equipment[f]	28,873
Miscellaneous Products	
Carts	51,427
Hot water	37,694

Source: U.S. Consumer Product Safety Commission, National Electronic Injury Surveillance System, Product Summary Report, All Products, CY2006.
Note: Products are listed above if the estimate was greater than 20,000 cases.
n.e.c. = not elsewhere classified.
[a] Excludes baby changing and television tables or stands.

[b] Excludes cabinets, racks shelves, desks, bureaus, chests, buffets, etc.
[c] Excludes glass doors and garage doors.
[d] Excludes costumes, masks, daywear, footwear, nightwear, and outerwear.
[e] Includes cultivators, hoes, pitchforks, rakes, shovels, spades, and trowels.
[f] Excludes monkey bars, seesaws, slides, and swings.

PRINCIPAL TYPES OF HOME AND COMMUNITY UNINTENTIONAL-INJURY DEATHS, UNITED STATES, 1987–2007

Year	Total Home and Community[a]	Falls	Drowning	Poisoning	Choking[g]	Fires, Burns	Firearms	Mechanical Suffocation	Air Transport	Water Transport	Rail Transport[b]	Other
1987	39,800	10,300	3,900	4,900	3,600	4,400	1,400	([c])	900	800	400	9,200
1988	41,100	10,700	3,800	5,700	3,700	4,600	1,400	([c])	700	800	400	9,300
1989	40,700	10,800	3,700	5,900	3,500	4,400	1,400	([c])	800	700	400	9,100
1990	38,900	11,000	3,700	5,400	3,300	3,800	1,300	([c])	700	800	400	8,500
1991	39,700	11,400	3,700	6,000	3,100	3,800	1,400	([c])	700	700	500	8,400
1992	43,000	12,100	3,400	6,900	3,100	3,900	1,400	([c])	700	700	600	10,200
1993	45,800	12,500	3,700	8,400	3,200	3,900	1,500	([c])	600	700	600	10,700
1994	45,900	12,800	3,300	8,900	3,100	3,900	1,300	([c])	600	600	600	10,800
1995	47,300	13,400	3,700	9,000	3,100	3,700	1,200	([c])	600	700	500	11,400
1996	48,500	14,300	3,400	9,400	3,200	3,700	1,100	([c])	700	600	500	11,600
1997	49,400	14,700	3,500	10,100	3,200	3,400	1,000	([c])	500	600	400	12,000
1998	51,600	15,500	3,900	10,700	3,500	3,100	900	([c])	500	600	500	12,400
1999[d]	52,700	12,400	3,500	12,100	3,900	3,200	900	1,600	500	600	400	13,600
2000	51,900	12,600	3,400	12,700	4,300	2,900	800	1,300	500	500	400	12,500
2001	55,000	14,200	3,300	14,000	4,100	3,200	800	1,400	700	500	400	12,400
2002	58,700	15,600	3,400	17,500	4,100	3,100	700	1,400	500	500	400	11,500
2003	61,800	16,600	3,200	19,300	4,300	3,200	700	1,300	600	500	400	11,700
2004	64,200	18,000	3,300	20,900	4,400	3,100	600	1,400	400	500	400	11,200
2005[e]	69,600	18,800	3,500	23,500	4,400	([c])	([c])	1,500	400	500	400	16,600
2006[e]	73,100	18,800	3,400	25,200	3,500	([c])	([c])	1,200	500	500	600	19,400
2007[f]	74,000	20,600	4,400	22,400	3,600	([c])	([c])	1,100	500	600	600	20,200

Source: National Safety Council estimates based on data from National Center for Health Statistics and state vital statistics departments. The Council adopted the Bureau of Labor Statistics' Census of Fatal Occupational Injuries count for work-related unintentional injuries retroactive to 1992 data. Because of the lower Work class total resulting from this change, several thousand unintentional-injury deaths that had been classified by the Council as work-related, had to be reassigned to the Home and Public classes. For this reason long-term historical comparisons for these three classes should be made with caution. See the Technical Appendix for an explanation of the methodological changes.
[a] Includes some deaths not shown separately.
[b] Includes subways and elevateds.
[c] Estimates for both home and community are not available.
[d] In 1999, a revision was made in the International Classification of Diseases. See the Technical Appendix for comparability with earlier years.
[e] Revised.
[f] Preliminary.
[g] Inhalation and ingestion of food or other object that obstructs breathing.

PRINCIPAL TYPES OF HOME AND COMMUNITY UNINTENTIONAL-INJURY DEATHS, UNITED STATES, 2007

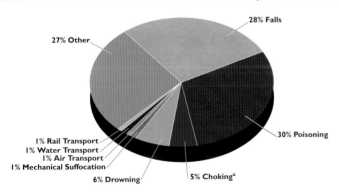

[a]Inhalation and ingestion of food or other object that obstructs breathing.

NATIONAL SAFETY COUNCIL

INJURY FACTS®

Injuries may be divided into three broad groups—unintentional, intentional, and undetermined intent. Most of *Injury Facts* presents data on unintentional (accidental) injuries. This section presents data on intentional injuries.

Under the World Health Organization's Safe Communities initiative, for which the National Safety Council is the affiliate support center in the United States, injury prevention is not limited to unintentional injuries. Data on intentional injuries is presented here to support Safety Communities and complement the unintentional-injury data shown in other sections of *Injury Facts*.

Intentional injuries may be divided into four subgroups—intentional self-harm (suicide), assault (homicide), legal intervention, and operations of war. The diagram below illustrates the injury groupings and shows the death totals for 2005.

INJURY DEATHS BY INTENT, UNITED STATES, 2005

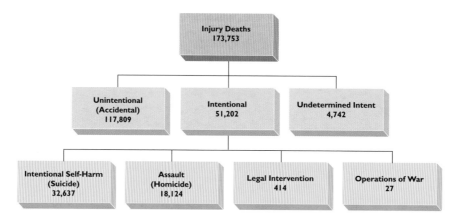

Intentional self-harm includes suicide and attempted suicide by purposely self-inflicted poisoning or injury. The most common methods of intentional self-harm that result in death are firearms; hanging, strangulation, and suffocation; and poisoning.

Assault includes homicide and injuries inflicted by another person with intent to injure or kill (excluding legal intervention and operations of war). The most common means of homicide are firearms, sharp objects, and hanging, strangulation, and suffocation.

Legal intervention includes legal execution. Operations of war include injuries to military personnel and civilians caused by war and civil insurrection. The death must have occurred in the United States. In the vital statistics system, war deaths (and other deaths) occurring outside the United States are counted by the country in which they occurred.

Each of the three broad groups of injuries were among the 15 leading causes of deaths in the United States in 2005. Unintentional (accidental) injuries ranked 5th, intentional self-harm (suicide) ranked 11th, and assault (homicide) ranked 15th.

Intentional self-harm ranked as high as second (after unintentional injuries) for persons aged 15 and 30–33 and ranked third for those aged 12–14, 16–29, and 34. Suicide deaths were highest at age 44 (799) and ranked

fourth at this age after cancer, heart disease, and unintentional injuries. Assault ranked as high as second (after unintentional injuries) for persons aged 16–29. It ranked third among people aged 1, 2, 11, 15, 30, and 31. Homicide deaths were highest at age 21 (705). **For people ages 15–31, accidents, suicide, and homicide are the three leading causes of death.** The graph below shows the number of deaths due to injuries by single year of age from 0 to 99.

INJURY DEATHS BY AGE, UNITED STATES, 2005

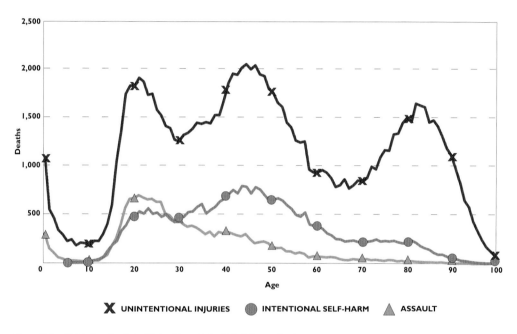

Source: National Safety Council analysis of National Center for Health Statistics mortality data.

Males have higher death rates than females for injuries of all intents. Males also have higher nonfatal injury rates than females for unintentional injuries and assault.

Females, however, have a higher injury rate than males for intentional self-harm.

DEATH AND NONFATAL INJURY RATES BY INTENT AND SEX, UNITED STATES, 2005

Sex	Deaths per 100,000 Population			Nonfatal Injuries per 100,000 Population		
	Unintentional	Homicide	Suicide	Unintentional	Assault	Self-Harm
Both Sexes	39.7	6.1	11.0	9,159	560	126
Males	52.3	9.9	17.8	10,198	692	109
Females	27.5	2.5	4.5	8,148	432	142
Ratio of Male to Female	1.9	4.0	4.0	1.3	1.6	0.8

Source: CDC, NCIPC, WISQARS.

The graph below shows the trends from 1992 to the present in injury deaths and death rates. Unintentional-injury deaths and death rates have increased by 40.3% and 21.4%, respectively. Suicide deaths increased 7.1% but the death rate declined 7.3%. Homicide deaths and death rates decreased 27.9% and 37.7%, respectively, over the 1992–2005 period. Age-adjusted death rates, which remove the effects of the changing age distribution of the population, increased 17.7% for unintentional injuries, decreased 8.8% for suicide, and decreased 35.2% for homicide.

INJURY DEATHS AND DEATH RATES, UNITED STATES, 1992–2005

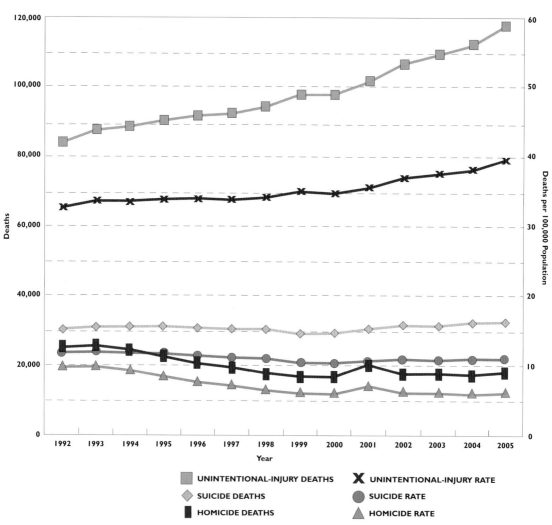

Source: National Safety Council analysis of National Center for Health Statistics mortality data.

Several national surveys provide information on the amount of medical care provided for injuries. The National Electronic Injury Surveillance System All Injuries Program (NEISS-AIP) provides estimates of the number of episodes of injury treated in hospital emergency departments. The most recent estimates (2006) are 27.7 million cases involving unintentional injuries, 1.7 million involving assault, and 0.4 million involving self harm.[a]

The National Hospital Ambulatory Medical Care Survey (NHAMCS) is another survey of emergency department visits with results that are similar to the NEISS-AIP. The latest NHAMCS estimates (2006) are 27.7 million unintentional injury visits, 1.8 million assault visits, and 0.6 million self-harm visits. Another 0.5 million visits were for injuries of undetermined intent.[b]

The NHAMCS also provides estimates of the number of hospital outpatient department visits for injuries. In 2006, about 6.4 million visits were for unintentional injuries and 262,000 were for intentional injuries. An additional 1.7 million visits were for injuries of undetermined intent.[c]

The National Ambulatory Medical Care Survey (NAMCS) gives estimates of the number of physician office visits for injuries. The survey estimated about 49.2 million office visits for unintentional injuries and 18.9 million visits for injuries of undetermined intent. (The estimate of visits for intentional injuries was not published because it did not meet standards of reliability or precision.)[d]

According to the National Hospital Discharge Survey, about 2.1 million people were hospitalized for intentional and unintentional injuries in 2006.[e]

Apart from surveys of medical care utilization for intentional injuries, there are estimates of the general incidence of self-harm and violent behavior within the population. Overall, there is one suicide for every 25 attempts. For youth between 15 and 24, the ratio is one suicide for every 100-200 attempts. And for adults 65 and older there is one suicide for every 4 attempts.[f]

The National Crime Victimization Survey for 2006 reported a total of 25.1 million victimizations (involving either a person or household as the victim) of which 6.3 million were personal crimes and 18.8 million were property crimes. Of the personal crimes, 6.1 million were crimes of violence, which include rape and sexual assault (0.3 million), robbery (0.7 million), and assault (5.1 million). Personal theft accounted for 0.2 million victimizations. A weapon was present in 25.2% of violent incidents.[g]

[a] CDC, NCIPC, WISQARS. Retrieved July 30, 2008, from http://webappa.cdc.gov/sasweb/ncipc/nfirates2001.html.

[b] Pitts, S.R., Niska, R.W., Xu, J., & Burt, C.W. (2008). National hospital ambulatory medical care survey: 2006 emergency department summary. National Health Statistics Report, No. 7. Hyattsville, MD: National Center for Health Statistics.

[c] Hing, E., Hall, M.J., & Xu, J. (2008). National hospital ambulatory medical care survey: 2006 outpatient department summary. National Health Statistics Report, No. 4. Hyattsville, MD: National Center for Health Statistics.

[d] Cherry, D.K., Hing, E., Woodwell, D.A., & Rechtsteiner, E.A. (2008). National ambulatory medical care survey: 2006 summary. National Health Statistics Report, No. 3. Hyattsville, MD: National Center for Health Statistics.

[e] DeFrances, C.J., Lucas, C.A., Buie, V.C., & Golosinskiy, A. (2008). 2006 national hospital discharge survey. National Health Statistics Report, No. 5. Hyattsville, MD: National Center for Health Statistics.

[f] Goldsmith, S.K., Pellmar, T.C., Kleinman, A.M., & Bunney, W.E. (Eds.). (2002). Reducing Suicide: A National Imperative. Washington, DC: National Academy Press.

[g] Rand, M, & Catalano, S. (2007). Criminal Victimization, 2006. NCJ 219413. Washington, DC: U.S. Department of Justice, Bureau of Justice Statistics.

ASSAULT/HOMICIDE

Assault includes homicide and injuries inflicted by another person with intent to injure or kill (excluding legal intervention and operations of war). The four leading forms of fatal assault injuries account for 84% of the total—firearms (68%), sharp objects (12%),

hanging, strangulation, and suffocation (3%), and other maltreatment syndromes (1%) (maltreatment other than neglect and abandonment, and sexual assault by bodily force).

ASSAULT/HOMICIDE DEATHS AND DEATH RATES BY AGE GROUP, UNITED STATES, 2005

	Total	0–4	5–14	15–24	25–44	45–64	65–74	75+
Total	**18,124**	**681**	**341**	**5,466**	**7,861**	**2,922**	**440**	**413**
Rate[a]	6.1	3.4	0.8	13.0	9.4	4.0	2.4	2.3
Firearms	12,352	43	187	4,499	5,790	1,502	201	130
Rate[a]	4.2	0.2	0.5	10.7	6.9	2.1	1.1	0.7
Sharp objects	2,097	13	27	528	900	497	81	51
Rate[a]	0.7	0.1	0.1	1.3	1.1	0.7	0.4	0.3
Hanging, strangulation, and suffocation	633	48	32	110	240	126	30	47
Rate[a]	.02	0.2	0.1	0.3	0.3	0.2	0.2	0.3
Other maltreatment syndromes	168	154	6	1	3	2	1	1
Rate[a]	0.1	0.8	[b]	[b]	[b]	[b]	[b]	[b]
Other means	2,874	423	89	328	928	795	127	184
Rate[a]	1.0	2.1	0.2	0.8	1.1	1.1	0.7	1.0

[a]Deaths per 100,000 population in each age group.
[b]Less than 0.05.

HOMICIDE DEATH RATES BY AGE GROUP, UNITED STATES, 1992–2005

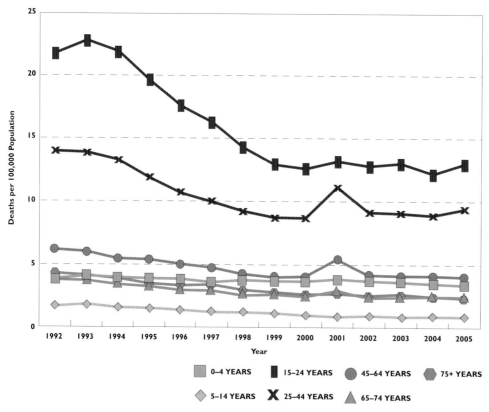

Source: National Safety Council analysis of National Center for Health Statistics mortality data.

INTENTIONAL SELF-HARM/SUICIDE

Intentional self-harm includes suicide and attempted suicide by purposely self-inflicted poisoning or injury. The four leading form of fatal self-harm injuries account for 92% of the total—firearms (52%), hanging, strangulation, and suffocation (23%), self-poisoning by drugs and medicines (13%), and self-poisoning by other chemicals and noxious substances (5%). It is generally accepted that children under 5 years of age cannot commit suicide.

INTENTIONAL SELF-HARM/SUICIDE DEATHS AND DEATH RATES BY AGE GROUP, UNITED STATES, 2005

	Total	0–4	5–14	15–24	25–44	45–64	65–74	75+
Total	**32,637**	—	**272**	**4,212**	**11,540**	**11,201**	**2,344**	**3,068**
Rate[a]	11.0	—	0.7	10.0	13.7	15.4	12.7	16.9
Firearms	17,002	—	84	1,962	5,124	5,942	1,669	2,221
Rate[a]	5.7	—	0.2	4.7	6.1	8.2	8.9	12.2
Hanging, strangulation, and suffocation	7,248	—	174	1,570	3,194	1,772	234	304
Rate[a]	2.4	—	0.4	3.7	3.8	2.4	1.3	1.7
Poisoning by drugs and medicines	4,240	—	7	264	1,633	1,944	199	193
Rate[a]	1.4	—	(b)	0.6	1.9	2.7	1.1	1.1
Poisoning by other substances	1,504	—	1	97	580	615	92	119
Rate[a]	0.5	—	(b)	0.2	0.7	0.8	0.5	0.7
Other means	2,643	—	6	319	1,009	928	150	231
Rate[a]	0.9	—	(b)	0.8	1.2	1.3	0.8	1.3

Note: Dashes (—) indicate not applicable.
[a]Deaths per 100,000 population in each age group.
[b]Less than 0.05.

SUICIDE DEATH RATES BY AGE GROUP, UNITED STATES, 1992–2005

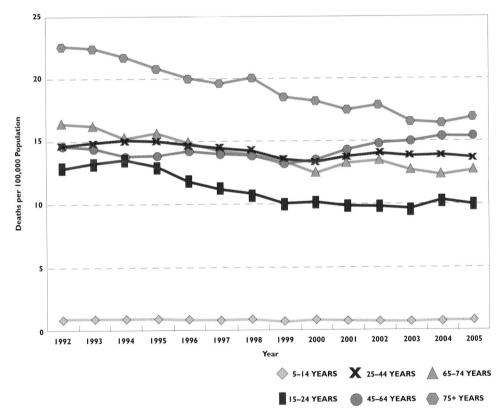

Source: National Safety Council analysis of National Center for Health Statistics mortality data.

NATIONAL SAFETY COUNCIL

INJURY FACTS®

Motor-vehicle crashes are the leading cause of U-I deaths in 47 states.

This section on state-level data includes data for occupational and motor-vehicle injuries as well as general injury mortality.

Death rates for unintentional injuries (U-I) can vary greatly from one type of injury to the next and from state to state. The graph on the next page shows for each state the death rates (per 100,000 population) for total unintentional-injury deaths and the four leading types of unintentional-injury deaths nationally—motor-vehicle crashes, poisonings, falls, and choking (inhalation or ingestion of food or other object that obstructs breathing).

The map on page 162 shows graphically the overall unintentional-injury death rates by state. Rates by region were lowest in Middle Atlantic and highest in the east south central states.

The charts on pages 163 through 165 show (a) total unintentional-injury deaths and where U-I rank as a cause of death in each state, and (b) the five leading causes of U-I deaths in each state.

Unintentional injuries as a whole are the fifth leading cause of death in the United States and in 29 states. U-I are the third leading cause of death in Alaska, Arizona, Colorado, Louisiana, Mississippi, New Mexico, and Wyoming and the fourth leading cause in 11 states and the District of Columbia. U-I rank sixth in three states (Maryland, Massachusetts, and New York).

In 2005, motor-vehicle crashes were the leading cause of U-I deaths in 47 states. Falls were the leading cause in Rhode Island and Vermont. The leading cause in the District of Columbia and Massachusetts was poisoning.

The second leading cause of U-I deaths was poisoning in 29 states and falls in 18 states and the District of Columbia. Motor-vehicle crashes were second in Massachusetts, Rhode Island, and Vermont. Cataclysmic storms were ranked second in Louisiana. (Poisoning and falls were tied for second in Hawaii and it is included in both counts.)

The most common third leading causes of U-I deaths were falls in 28 states, and poisoning in 19 states. Choking ranked third in Nebraska, fire in Maryland, water transportation in Alaska, and motor-vehicle in District of Columbia.

Choking was the fourth leading cause of U-I deaths in 23 states and the District of Columbia, while the fourth ranking cause was drowning in 16 states, and fires, flames, and smoke in six states. Natural heat and cold ranked fourth in Arizona and Nevada, falls in Louisiana, cataclysmic storm in Mississippi and poisoning in Nebraska.

Fires, burns, and smoke was the fifth leading U-I cause of death in 19 states and the District of Columbia. Choking ranked fifth in 16 states, and drowning was fifth in 13 states. The fifth ranking cause was falls in Alaska, and poisoning in Maryland.

The table on pages 166 and 167 shows the number of U-I deaths by state for the 15 most common types of injury events. State populations are also shown to facilitate computation of detailed death rates.

The table on page 168 consists of a 4-year state-by-state comparison of unintentional-injury deaths and death rates for 2002 through 2005.

Page 169 shows fatal occupational injuries by state and counts of deaths for some of the principal types of events—transportation accidents, assaults and violent acts, contacts with objects and equipment, falls, exposure to harmful substances or environments, and fires and explosions.

Nonfatal occupational injury and illness incidence rates for most states are shown in the table on page 170 and graphically in the map on page 171. States not shown do not have state occupational safety and health plans.

Pages 172 and 173 show motor-vehicle-related deaths and death rates by state both in tables and maps. The maps show death rates based on population, vehicle miles traveled, and registered vehicles.

UNINTENTIONAL-INJURY DEATH RATES BY STATE, UNITED STATES, 2005

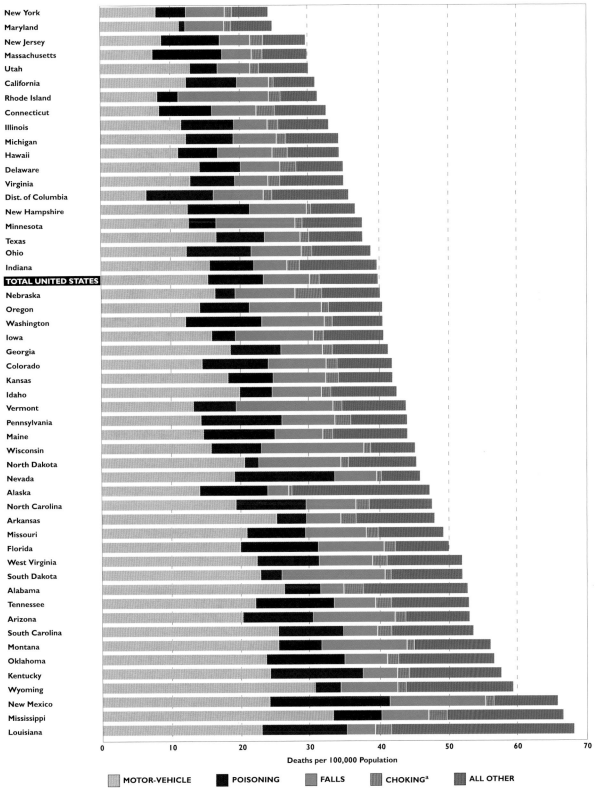

Deaths per 100,000 Population

| | MOTOR-VEHICLE | | POISONING | | FALLS | | CHOKING[a] | | ALL OTHER |

[a]Suffocation by ingestion or inhalation of food or other object.

UNINTENTIONAL-INJURY DEATH RATES BY STATE

UNINTENTIONAL-INJURY DEATHS PER 100,000 POPULATION BY STATE, 2005

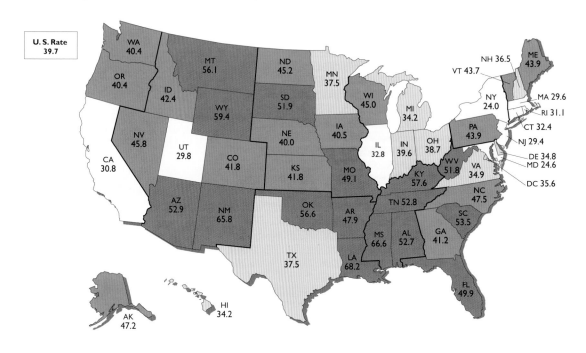

U. S. Rate
39.7

WA 40.4
OR 40.4
ID 42.4
MT 56.1
ND 45.2
MN 37.5
WI 45.0
MI 34.2
NH 36.5
VT 43.7
ME 43.9
NY 24.0
MA 29.6
RI 31.1
CT 32.4
NV 45.8
UT 29.8
WY 59.4
SD 51.9
NE 40.0
IA 40.5
IL 32.8
IN 39.6
OH 38.7
PA 43.9
NJ 29.4
DE 34.8
MD 24.6
DC 35.6
CA 30.8
CO 41.8
KS 41.8
MO 49.1
KY 57.6
WV 51.8
VA 34.9
NC 47.5
AZ 52.9
NM 65.8
OK 56.6
AR 47.9
TN 52.8
SC 53.5
MS 66.6
AL 52.7
GA 41.2
TX 37.5
LA 68.2
FL 49.9
AK 47.2
HI 34.2

REGIONAL RATES

NEW ENGLAND (CT, ME, MA, NH, RI, VT)	33.0
MIDDLE ATLANTIC (NJ, NY, PA)	31.3
EAST NORTH CENTRAL (IL, IN, MI, OH, WI)	36.9
WEST NORTH CENTRAL (IA, KS, MN, MO, NE, ND, SD)	43.0
SOUTH ATLANTIC (DE, DC, FL, GA, MD, NC, SC, VA, WV)	43.5
EAST SOUTH CENTRAL (AL, KY, MS, TN)	56.2
WEST SOUTH CENTRAL (AR, LA, OK, TX)	44.4
MOUNTAIN (AZ, CO, ID, MT, NV, NM, UT, WY)	47.5
PACIFIC (AK, CA, HI, OR, WA)	33.1

BELOW 33.0 — 9 STATES

33.0 TO 39.7 — 9 STATES
AND DISTRICT OF COLUMBIA

39.8 TO 47.5 — 16 STATES

ABOVE 47.5 — 16 STATES

Source: National Center for Health Statistics, and U.S. Census Bureau.

The following series of charts is a state-by-state ranking of the five leading causes of deaths due to unintentional injuries (U-I) based on 2005 data. The first line of each section gives the rank of unintentional-injury deaths among all causes of death, the total number of U-I deaths, and the rate of U-I deaths per 100,000 population in the state. The following lines list the five leading types of unintentional-injury deaths in the state along with the number and rate for each type.

TOTAL UNITED STATES

Rank	Cause	Deaths	Rate
5	All U-I	117,809	39.7
1	Motor-vehicle	45,343	15.3
2	Poisoning[a]	23,618	8.0
3	Falls	19,656	6.6
4	Choking[b]	4,386	1.5
5	Drowning[c]	3,582	1.2

ALABAMA

Rank	Cause	Deaths	Rate
4	All U-I	2,395	52.7
1	Motor-vehicle	1,188	26.1
2	Poisoning[a]	238	5.2
3	Falls	153	3.4
4	Choking[b]	124	2.7
5	Fires, flames, smoke	105	2.3

ALASKA

Rank	Cause	Deaths	Rate
3	All U-I	313	47.2
1	Motor-vehicle	93	14.0
2	Poisoning[a]	65	9.8
3	Water transportation	25	3.8
4	Drowning[c]	24	3.6
5	Falls	20	3.0

ARIZONA

Rank	Cause	Deaths	Rate
3	All U-I	3,150	52.9
1	Motor-vehicle	1,200	20.2
2	Falls	700	11.8
3	Poisoning[a]	603	10.1
4	Natural heat or cold	106	1.8
5	Choking[b]	90	1.5

ARKANSAS

Rank	Cause	Deaths	Rate
5	All U-I	1,329	47.9
1	Motor-vehicle	696	25.1
2	Falls	137	4.9
3	Poisoning[a]	120	4.3
4	Fires, flames, smoke	77	2.8
5	Choking[b]	60	2.2

CALIFORNIA

Rank	Cause	Deaths	Rate
5	All U-I	11,129	30.8
1	Motor-vehicle	4,427	12.2
2	Poisoning[a]	2,642	7.3
3	Falls	1,657	4.6
4	Drowning[c]	457	1.3
5	Choking[b]	243	0.7

COLORADO

Rank	Cause	Deaths	Rate
3	All U-I	1,947	41.8
1	Motor-vehicle	673	14.4
2	Poisoning[a]	445	9.5
3	Falls	390	8.4
4	Choking[b]	73	1.6
5	Drowning[c]	43	0.9

CONNECTICUT

Rank	Cause	Deaths	Rate
5	All U-I	1,134	32.4
1	Motor-vehicle	293	8.4
2	Poisoning[a]	267	7.6
3	Falls	222	6.3
4	Choking[b]	92	2.6
5	Drowning[c]	28	0.8

DELAWARE

Rank	Cause	Deaths	Rate
5	All U-I	293	34.8
1	Motor-vehicle	119	14.1
2	Poisoning[a]	50	5.9
3	Falls	48	5.7
4	Choking[b]	19	2.3
5	Fires, flames, smoke	12	1.4

DISTRICT OF COLUMBIA

Rank	Cause	Deaths	Rate
4	All U-I	207	35.6
1	Poisoning[a]	56	9.6
2	Falls	42	7.2
3	Motor-vehicle	38	6.5
4	Choking[b]	7	1.2
5	Fires, flames, smoke	6	1.0

FLORIDA

Rank	Cause	Deaths	Rate
5	All U-I	8,868	49.9
1	Motor-vehicle	3,526	19.8
2	Poisoning[a]	1,999	11.3
3	Falls	1,678	9.4
4	Drowning[c]	360	2.0
5	Choking[b]	285	1.6

GEORGIA

Rank	Cause	Deaths	Rate
4	All U-I	3,762	41.2
1	Motor-vehicle	1,686	18.5
2	Poisoning[a]	666	7.3
3	Falls	550	6.0
4	Choking[b]	129	1.4
5	Drowning[c]	115	1.3

HAWAII

Rank	Cause	Deaths	Rate
4	All U-I	436	34.2
1	Motor-vehicle	141	11.1
2	Falls	99	7.8
2	Poisoning[a]	73	5.7
4	Drowning[c]	39	3.1
5	Choking[b]	28	2.2

IDAHO

Rank	Cause	Deaths	Rate
5	All U-I	606	42.4
1	Motor-vehicle	283	19.8
2	Falls	102	7.1
3	Poisoning[a]	67	4.7
4	Drowning[c]	23	1.6
5	Choking[b]	19	1.3

ILLINOIS

Rank	Cause	Deaths	Rate
5	All U-I	4,182	32.8
1	Motor-vehicle	1,469	11.5
2	Poisoning[a]	970	7.6
3	Falls	616	4.8
4	Choking[b]	194	1.5
5	Drowning[c]	130	1.0

INDIANA

Rank	Cause	Deaths	Rate
5	All U-I	2,480	39.6
1	Motor-vehicle	975	15.6
2	Poisoning[a]	397	6.3
3	Falls	298	4.8
4	Choking[b]	116	1.9
5	Fires, flames, smoke	81	1.3

IOWA

Rank	Cause	Deaths	Rate
5	All U-I	1,202	40.5
1	Motor-vehicle	468	15.8
2	Falls	334	11.3
3	Poisoning[a]	102	3.4
4	Choking[b]	42	1.4
5	Drowning[c]	37	1.2

KANSAS

Rank	Cause	Deaths	Rate
5	All U-I	1,149	41.8
1	Motor-vehicle	498	18.1
2	Falls	210	7.6
3	Poisoning[a]	179	6.5
4	Choking[b]	52	1.9
5	Drowning[c]	34	1.2

See footnotes on page 165.

KENTUCKY

Rank	Cause	Deaths	Rate
4	All U-I	2,405	57.6
I	Motor-vehicle	1,003	24.0
2	Poisoning[a]	558	13.4
3	Falls	208	5.0
4	Fires, flames, smoke	94	2.3
5	Choking[b]	73	1.7

LOUISIANA

Rank	Cause	Deaths	Rate
3	All U-I	3,072	68.2
I	Motor-vehicle	1,029	22.8
2	Cataclysmic storm	634	14.1
3	Poisoning[a]	556	12.3
4	Falls	181	4.0
5	Fires, flames, smoke	109	2.4

MAINE

Rank	Cause	Deaths	Rate
5	All U-I	579	43.9
I	Motor-vehicle	192	14.6
2	Poisoning[a]	136	10.3
3	Falls	91	6.9
4	Choking[b]	19	1.4
4	Drowning[c]	19	1.4

MARYLAND

Rank	Cause	Deaths	Rate
6	All U-I	1,376	24.6
I	Motor-vehicle	628	11.2
2	Falls	308	5.5
3	Fires, flames, smoke	58	1.0
4	Drowning[c]	54	1.0
4	Poisoning[a]	54	1.0

MASSACHUSETTS

Rank	Cause	Deaths	Rate
6	All U-I	1,907	29.6
I	Poisoning[a]	640	9.9
2	Motor-vehicle	484	7.5
3	Falls	268	4.2
4	Choking[b]	103	1.6
5	Drowning[c]	56	0.9

MICHIGAN

Rank	Cause	Deaths	Rate
5	All U-I	3,451	34.2
I	Motor-vehicle	1,231	12.2
2	Poisoning[a]	685	6.8
3	Falls	632	6.3
4	Choking[b]	129	1.3
5	Fires, flames, smoke	122	1.2

MINNESOTA

Rank	Cause	Deaths	Rate
5	All U-I	1,922	37.5
I	Motor-vehicle	642	12.5
2	Falls	582	11.4
3	Poisoning[a]	205	4.0
4	Drowning[c]	57	1.1
5	Choking[b]	52	1.0

MISSISSIPPI

Rank	Cause	Deaths	Rate
3	All U-I	1,936	66.6
I	Motor-vehicle	965	33.2
2	Poisoning[a]	202	6.9
3	Falls	198	6.8
4	Cataclysmic storm	181	6.2
5	Choking[b]	79	2.7

MISSOURI

Rank	Cause	Deaths	Rate
5	All U-I	2,848	49.1
I	Motor-vehicle	1,203	20.7
2	Falls	503	8.7
3	Poisoning[a]	493	8.5
4	Choking[b]	104	1.8
5	Fires, flames, smoke	67	1.2

MONTANA

Rank	Cause	Deaths	Rate
4	All U-I	524	56.1
I	Motor-vehicle	236	25.2
2	Falls	114	12.2
3	Poisoning[a]	59	6.3
4	Drowning[c]	13	1.4
5	Choking[b]	11	1.2

NEBRASKA

Rank	Cause	Deaths	Rate
5	All U-I	704	40.0
I	Motor-vehicle	287	16.3
2	Falls	151	8.6
3	Choking[b]	68	3.9
4	Poisoning[a]	51	2.9
5	Fires, flames, smoke	26	1.5

NEVADA

Rank	Cause	Deaths	Rate
4	All U-I	1,104	45.8
I	Motor-vehicle	459	19.0
2	Poisoning[a]	348	14.4
3	Falls	145	6.0
4	Natural heat or cold	31	1.3
5	Drowning[c]	28	1.2

NEW HAMPSHIRE

Rank	Cause	Deaths	Rate
5	All U-I	477	36.5
I	Motor-vehicle	162	12.4
2	Poisoning[a]	117	9.0
3	Falls	107	8.2
4	Drowning[c]	13	1.0
5	Fires, flames, smoke	10	0.8

NEW JERSEY

Rank	Cause	Deaths	Rate
5	All U-I	2,561	29.4
I	Motor-vehicle	760	8.7
2	Poisoning[a]	728	8.4
3	Falls	380	4.4
4	Choking[b]	163	1.9
5	Fires, flames, smoke	62	0.7

NEW MEXICO

Rank	Cause	Deaths	Rate
3	All U-I	1,267	65.8
I	Motor-vehicle	461	23.9
2	Poisoning[a]	334	17.3
3	Falls	271	14.1
4	Drowning[c]	32	1.7
5	Fires, flames, smoke	26	1.3

NEW YORK

Rank	Cause	Deaths	Rate
6	All U-I	4,645	24.0
I	Motor-vehicle	1,530	7.9
2	Falls	1,065	5.5
3	Poisoning[a]	846	4.4
4	Choking[b]	202	1.0
5	Fires, flames, smoke	171	0.9

NORTH CAROLINA

Rank	Cause	Deaths	Rate
5	All U-I	4,123	47.5
I	Motor-vehicle	1,666	19.2
2	Poisoning[a]	877	10.1
3	Falls	619	7.1
4	Choking[b]	169	1.9
5	Fires, flames, smoke	111	1.3

NORTH DAKOTA

Rank	Cause	Deaths	Rate
5	All U-I	287	45.2
I	Motor-vehicle	130	20.5
2	Falls	75	11.8
3	Poisoning[a]	13	2.0
4	Fires, flames, smoke	12	1.9
5	Choking[b]	7	1.1

See footnotes on page 165.

OHIO

Rank	Cause	Deaths	Rate
5	All U-I	4,438	38.7
1	Motor-vehicle	1,404	12.2
2	Poisoning[a]	1,063	9.3
3	Falls	839	7.3
4	Choking[b]	171	1.5
5	Fires, flames, smoke	110	1.0

PENNSYLVANIA

Rank	Cause	Deaths	Rate
5	All U-I	5,446	43.9
1	Motor-vehicle	1,771	14.3
2	Poisoning[a]	1,438	11.6
3	Falls	950	7.7
4	Choking[b]	282	2.3
5	Fires, flames, smoke	167	1.3

SOUTH DAKOTA

Rank	Cause	Deaths	Rate
5	All U-I	402	51.9
1	Motor-vehicle	176	22.7
2	Falls	115	14.8
3	Poisoning[a]	24	3.1
4	Fires, flames, smoke	15	1.9
5	Drowning[c]	10	1.3

UTAH

Rank	Cause	Deaths	Rate
4	All U-I	743	29.8
1	Motor-vehicle	319	12.8
2	Falls	116	4.7
3	Poisoning[a]	99	4.0
4	Choking[b]	32	1.3
5	Drowning[c]	28	1.1

WASHINGTON

Rank	Cause	Deaths	Rate
5	All U-I	2,543	40.4
1	Motor-vehicle	762	12.1
2	Poisoning[a]	684	10.9
3	Falls	570	9.1
4	Drowning[c]	87	1.4
5	Choking[b]	75	1.2

WYOMING

Rank	Cause	Deaths	Rate
3	All U-I	302	59.4
1	Motor-vehicle	155	30.5
2	Falls	42	8.3
3	Poisoning[a]	19	3.7
4	Drowning[c]	13	2.6
5	Fires, flames, smoke	7	1.4

OKLAHOMA

Rank	Cause	Deaths	Rate
5	All U-I	2,005	56.6
1	Motor-vehicle	833	23.5
2	Poisoning[a]	400	11.3
3	Falls	219	6.2
4	Fires, flames, smoke	88	2.5
5	Drowning[c]	61	1.7

RHODE ISLAND

Rank	Cause	Deaths	Rate
5	All U-I	334	31.1
1	Falls	139	12.9
2	Motor-vehicle	87	8.1
3	Poisoning[a]	33	3.1
3	Choking[b]	18	1.7
4	Drowning[c]	13	1.2

TENNESSEE

Rank	Cause	Deaths	Rate
5	All U-I	3,147	52.8
1	Motor-vehicle	1,308	22.0
2	Poisoning[a]	676	11.4
3	Falls	353	5.9
4	Fires, flames, smoke	140	2.4
5	Choking[b]	137	2.3

VERMONT

Rank	Cause	Deaths	Rate
4	All U-I	272	43.7
1	Falls	87	14.0
2	Motor-vehicle	82	13.2
3	Poisoning[a]	38	6.1
4	Drowning[c]	9	1.4
5	Fires, flames, smoke	8	1.3

WEST VIRGINIA

Rank	Cause	Deaths	Rate
5	All U-I	940	51.8
1	Motor-vehicle	403	22.2
2	Poisoning[a]	163	9.0
3	Falls	138	7.6
4	Choking[b]	39	2.1
5	Fires, flames, smoke	32	1.8

OREGON

Rank	Cause	Deaths	Rate
5	All U-I	1,469	40.4
1	Motor-vehicle	512	14.1
2	Falls	379	10.4
3	Poisoning[a]	260	7.1
4	Drowning[c]	57	1.6
5	Choking[b]	38	1.0

SOUTH CAROLINA

Rank	Cause	Deaths	Rate
4	All U-I	2,272	53.5
1	Motor-vehicle	1,071	25.2
2	Poisoning[a]	401	9.4
3	Falls	208	4.9
4	Choking[b]	90	2.1
5	Fires, flames, smoke	83	2.0

TEXAS

Rank	Cause	Deaths	Rate
4	All U-I	8,598	37.5
1	Motor-vehicle	3,780	16.5
2	Poisoning[a]	1,595	7.0
3	Falls	1,178	5.1
4	Drowning[c]	312	1.4
5	Choking[b]	288	1.3

VIRGINIA

Rank	Cause	Deaths	Rate
5	All U-I	2,638	34.9
1	Motor-vehicle	969	12.8
2	Poisoning[a]	485	6.4
3	Falls	360	4.8
4	Choking[b]	128	1.7
5	Fires, flames, smoke	81	1.1

WISCONSIN

Rank	Cause	Deaths	Rate
4	All U-I	2,490	45.0
1	Motor-vehicle	870	15.7
2	Falls	809	14.6
3	Poisoning[a]	399	7.2
4	Drowning[c]	54	1.0
5	Choking[b]	53	1.0

Source: National Safety Council tabulations of National Center for Health Statistics mortality data.
[a] *Solid, liquid, gas, and vapor poisoning.*
[b] *Inhalation or ingestion of food or other objects.*
[c] *Excludes transport drownings.*

UNINTENTIONAL-INJURY DEATHS BY STATE AND EVENT

UNINTENTIONAL-INJURY DEATHS BY STATE AND TYPE OF EVENT, UNITED STATES, 2005

State	Population (000)	Total[a]	Motor-vehicle[b]	Poisoning	Falls	Choking[c]	Drowning[d]	Fires Flames, and Smoke	Mechanical Suffocation
Total U.S.	296,507	117,809	45,343	23,618	19,656	4,386	3,582	3,197	1,514
Alabama	4,548	2,395	1,188	238	153	124	75	105	33
Alaska	663	313	93	65	20	3	24	14	16
Arizona	5,953	3,150	1,200	603	700	90	87	57	31
Arkansas	2,776	1,329	696	120	137	60	58	77	21
California	36,154	11,129	4,427	2,642	1,657	243	457	201	133
Colorado	4,663	1,947	673	445	390	73	43	23	21
Connecticut	3,501	1,134	293	267	222	92	28	27	5
Delaware	842	293	119	50	48	19	3	12	4
Dist. of Columbia	582	207	38	56	42	7	3	6	2
Florida	17,768	8,868	3,526	1,999	1,678	285	360	135	124
Georgia	9,133	3,762	1,686	666	550	129	115	109	30
Hawaii	1,273	436	141	73	99	28	39	6	7
Idaho	1,429	606	283	67	102	19	23	18	8
Illinois	12,765	4,182	1,469	970	616	194	130	117	87
Indiana	6,266	2,480	975	397	298	116	63	81	50
Iowa	2,966	1,202	468	102	334	42	37	33	12
Kansas	2,748	1,149	498	179	210	52	34	22	14
Kentucky	4,173	2,405	1,003	558	208	73	67	94	35
Louisiana	4,507	3,072	1,029	556	181	102	89	109	26
Maine	1,318	579	192	136	91	19	19	14	4
Maryland	5,590	1,376	628	54	308	52	54	58	14
Massachusetts	6,433	1,907	484	640	268	103	56	38	15
Michigan	10,101	3,451	1,231	685	632	129	100	122	87
Minnesota	5,127	1,922	642	205	582	52	57	28	42
Mississippi	2,908	1,936	965	202	198	79	44	71	11
Missouri	5,798	2,848	1,203	493	503	104	58	67	51
Montana	935	524	236	59	114	11	13	9	7
Nebraska	1,758	704	287	51	151	68	9	26	9
Nevada	2,412	1,104	459	348	145	18	28	14	11
New Hampshire	1,307	477	162	117	107	8	13	10	5
New Jersey	8,703	2,561	760	728	380	163	51	62	26
New Mexico	1,926	1,267	461	334	271	23	32	26	5
New York	19,316	4,645	1,530	846	1,065	202	119	171	44
North Carolina	8,672	4,123	1,666	877	619	169	87	111	45
North Dakota	635	287	130	13	75	7	6	12	3
Ohio	11,471	4,438	1,404	1,063	839	171	97	110	83
Oklahoma	3,543	2,005	833	400	219	56	61	88	18
Oregon	3,639	1,469	512	260	379	38	57	24	15
Pennsylvania	12,405	5,446	1,771	1,438	950	282	116	167	43
Rhode Island	1,074	334	87	33	139	18	13	7	0
South Carolina	4,247	2,272	1,071	401	208	90	65	83	9
South Dakota	775	402	176	24	115	7	10	15	9
Tennessee	5,956	3,147	1,308	676	353	137	89	140	32
Texas	22,929	8,598	3,780	1,595	1,178	288	312	231	98
Utah	2,490	743	319	99	116	32	28	16	7
Vermont	622	272	82	38	87	8	9	8	2
Virginia	7,564	2,638	969	485	360	128	77	81	33
Washington	6,292	2,543	762	684	570	75	87	52	37
West Virginia	1,814	940	403	163	138	39	13	32	8
Wisconsin	5,528	2,490	870	399	809	53	54	51	45
Wyoming	509	302	155	19	42	6	13	7	5

See source and footnotes on page 167.

UNINTENTIONAL-INJURY DEATHS BY STATE AND TYPE OF EVENT, UNITED STATES, 2005, Cont.

State	Natural Heat or Cold	Struck By/Against Object	Machinery	Firearms	Electric Current	Water Transport	Air Transport	Rail Transport	All Other Accidents
Total U.S.	1,166	880	755	789	398	523	590	446	10,966
Alabama	13	25	13	37	8	8	6	9	360
Alaska	15	2	0	2	3	25	5	2	24
Arizona	106	16	8	15	15	5	14	12	191
Arkansas	11	13	11	14	4	10	11	8	78
California	64	69	38	146	46	37	88	66	815
Colorado	39	15	13	9	4	9	31	6	153
Connecticut	17	15	1	9	1	3	5	2	147
Delaware	1	2	1	0	1	1	4	1	27
Dist. of Columbia	0	0	0	1	1	0	0	0	51
Florida	30	56	43	23	34	44	51	33	447
Georgia	21	30	28	16	18	16	13	16	319
Hawaii	4	4	1	0	2	0	2	0	30
Idaho	6	10	9	5	2	5	9	1	39
Illinois	43	10	16	21	17	10	13	32	437
Indiana	20	16	25	13	12	2	7	12	393
Iowa	10	7	30	5	4	8	10	6	94
Kansas	10	6	15	5	5	4	7	0	88
Kentucky	24	21	23	16	3	9	4	10	257
Louisiana	16	19	13	38	15	35	12	6	826
Maine	16	4	4	1	1	6	4	0	68
Maryland	31	13	11	1	6	6	1	5	134
Massachusetts	16	15	4	4	1	9	3	4	247
Michigan	43	17	19	15	9	37	8	7	310
Minnesota	19	29	18	9	4	17	8	2	208
Mississippi	14	17	7	20	10	9	11	6	272
Missouri	38	27	35	23	11	15	10	5	205
Montana	10	7	7	4	1	6	3	5	32
Nebraska	9	5	6	2	2	1	0	3	75
Nevada	31	1	3	5	1	2	4	2	32
New Hampshire	9	1	2	1	0	1	2	0	39
New Jersey	25	17	4	5	2	3	10	12	313
New Mexico	18	6	7	5	1	1	4	6	67
New York	46	33	23	33	14	16	9	30	464
North Carolina	29	29	24	27	5	11	12	17	395
North Dakota	5	1	4	2	0	1	1	1	26
Ohio	27	18	33	24	14	17	23	11	504
Oklahoma	30	14	18	16	13	5	12	5	217
Oregon	13	10	11	7	1	13	17	5	107
Pennsylvania	42	35	39	32	5	11	15	18	482
Rhode Island	5	0	2	1	0	1	6	0	22
South Carolina	17	17	16	34	11	12	16	12	210
South Dakota	11	2	2	4	0	2	2	2	21
Tennessee	21	27	30	36	1	3	10	8	276
Texas	82	83	53	62	61	26	43	33	673
Utah	5	11	4	1	1	8	5	1	90
Vermont	0	4	1	0	1	0	1	0	31
Virginia	31	31	26	6	9	10	15	7	370
Washington	28	28	17	10	8	24	24	9	128
West Virginia	14	11	12	13	4	3	3	2	82
Wisconsin	26	25	23	7	2	15	11	5	95
Wyoming	5	6	2	4	4	1	5	1	27

Source: National Safety Council analysis of National Center for Health Statistics mortality data.
[a] Deaths are by place of residence and exclude nonresident aliens. See also page 162.
[b] See page 172 for National Safety Council estimates of motor-vehicle deaths by place of accident.
[c] Suffocation by inhalation or ingestion of food or object obstructing breathing.
[d] Excludes water transport drownings.

Nationwide, from 2002 to 2005, unintentional-injury (U-I) deaths increased 10% over the four years and the death rate increased 7%. By state, the greatest decrease in U-I deaths and death rates occurred in the District of Columbia (–27% and –29%) and the greatest increase occurred in Louisiana (+46% and +45%). Louisiana's

large increase in UI deaths in 2005 can be largely attributed to Hurricane Katrina that was responsible for 1,323 deaths across Florida, Louisiana and Mississippi.

The table below shows the trend in unintentional-injury deaths and death rates by state over the most recent four years for which data are available.

UNINTENTIONAL-INJURY DEATHS BY STATE, UNITED STATES, 2002–2005

State	Deaths[a]				Deaths per 100,000 Population			
	2005[b]	2004	2003	2002	2005[b]	2004	2003	2002
Total U.S.	117,809	112,012	109,277	106,742	39.8	38.1	37.6	37.1
Alabama	2,395	2,363	2,194	2,205	52.8	52.3	48.7	49.2
Alaska	313	333	340	350	46.8	50.7	52.4	54.6
Arizona	3,150	2,853	2,812	2,666	52.9	49.7	50.4	49.0
Arkansas	1,329	1,350	1,239	1,273	47.9	49.1	45.4	47.0
California	11,129	10,530	10,348	10,028	30.9	29.4	29.2	28.7
Colorado	1,947	1,843	1,809	1,837	41.7	40.1	39.8	40.8
Connecticut	1,134	1,236	1,111	1,161	32.5	35.4	31.9	33.6
Delaware	293	291	310	312	34.9	35.1	37.9	38.7
Dist. of Columbia	207	327	346	283	35.6	56.4	62.0	50.1
Florida	8,868	8,442	8,081	7,572	50.0	48.6	47.6	45.4
Georgia	3,762	3,732	3,542	3,389	41.3	41.8	40.5	39.7
Hawaii	436	423	451	424	34.4	33.6	36.1	34.3
Idaho	606	623	655	586	42.5	44.7	47.9	43.6
Illinois	4,182	3,858	3,704	3,974	32.9	30.3	29.3	31.6
Indiana	2,480	2,380	2,150	2,099	39.6	38.2	34.7	34.1
Iowa	1,202	1,105	1,143	1,095	40.7	37.4	38.9	37.3
Kansas	1,149	1,103	1,070	1,103	41.9	40.3	39.3	40.7
Kentucky	2,405	2,179	2,228	2,045	57.7	52.6	54.1	50.0
Louisiana	3,072	2,306	2,229	2,102	68.3	51.3	49.6	47.0
Maine	579	479	529	509	44.1	36.5	40.4	39.2
Maryland	1,376	1,334	1,353	1,290	24.7	24.0	24.5	23.7
Massachusetts[c]	1,907	1,281	1,325	1,358	29.7	19.9	20.6	21.2
Michigan	3,451	3,191	3,224	3,212	34.1	31.6	32.0	32.0
Minnesota	1,922	1,817	1,898	1,918	37.6	35.7	37.5	38.2
Mississippi	1,936	1,704	1,624	1,636	66.7	58.9	56.4	57.1
Missouri	2,848	2,923	2,943	2,761	49.2	50.8	51.5	48.6
Montana	524	536	535	555	56.0	57.9	58.3	60.9
Nebraska	704	725	703	756	40.1	41.5	40.4	43.8
Nevada	1,104	1,119	1,028	930	45.8	48.0	45.9	42.9
New Hampshire	477	474	434	402	36.6	36.5	33.7	31.5
New Jersey	2,561	2,203	2,263	2,466	29.6	25.4	26.2	28.8
New Mexico	1,267	1,254	1,231	1,142	66.1	66.0	65.5	61.6
New York	4,645	4,376	4,518	4,552	24.1	22.7	23.5	23.8
North Carolina	4,123	4,069	3,866	3,705	47.5	47.7	45.9	44.6
North Dakota	287	298	290	264	45.1	46.9	45.8	41.7
Ohio	4,438	4,152	3,654	4,047	38.7	36.2	32.0	35.5
Oklahoma	2,005	1,918	1,693	1,537	56.7	54.4	48.3	44.1
Oregon	1,469	1,439	1,416	1,393	40.5	40.1	39.7	39.5
Pennsylvania	5,446	5,196	5,061	4,749	44.0	42.0	40.9	38.5
Rhode Island	334	328	446	292	31.3	30.4	41.5	27.3
South Carolina	2,272	2,084	1,966	1,979	53.4	49.7	47.4	48.2
South Dakota	402	456	431	385	51.5	59.2	56.4	50.6
Tennessee	3,147	3,486	3,227	2,976	52.5	59.2	55.2	51.4
Texas	8,598	8,289	8,417	8,237	37.6	36.8	38.1	37.9
Utah	743	734	751	775	29.7	30.3	31.6	33.4
Vermont	272	262	248	238	43.9	42.2	40.1	38.6
Virginia	2,638	2,578	2,584	2,463	34.9	34.5	35.0	33.9
Washington	2,543	2,257	2,137	2,161	40.6	36.4	34.9	35.6
West Virginia	940	1,152	1,051	989	52.1	63.6	58.1	54.8
Wisconsin	2,490	2,331	2,372	2,246	44.9	42.4	43.3	41.3
Wyoming	302	290	297	315	59.6	57.4	59.2	63.1

Source: Deaths are from the National Center for Health Statistics. Rates are National Safety Council estimates based on data from the National Center for Health Statistics and the U.S. Bureau of the Census. See Technical Appendix for comparability.
[a] Deaths for each state are by place of occurrence and exclude nonresident aliens.
[b] Latest official figures.
[c] Starting in 2005, Massachusetts changed the classification of most poisonings from undetermined to unintentional.

FATAL OCCUPATIONAL INJURIES BY STATE

In general, the states with the largest number of persons employed have the largest number of work-related fatalities. The four largest states—California, Florida, New York, and Texas—accounted for about 28% of the total 2007 fatalities in the United States. Each state's industry mix, geographic features, age of population, and other characteristics of the workforce must be considered when evaluating state fatality profiles.

FATAL OCCUPATIONAL INJURIES BY STATE AND EVENT OR EXPOSURE, UNITED STATES, 2006–2007

State	2006 Total[a]	2007							
		Total[b]	Transpor-tation[c]	Contact with Objects & Equipment	Falls	Assaults & Violent Acts[d]	Exposure to Harmful Substances or Environments	Fires & Explosions	All Other
Total	5,840	5,488	2,234	916	839	835	488	151	25
Alabama	100	99	42	13	18	15	8	3	—
Alaska	45	30	17	4	—	—	5	—	—
Arizona	112	88	30	17	9	20	10	—	—
Arkansas	78	87	42	18	9	7	8	3	—
California	537	407	148	58	78	66	37	17	—
Colorado	137	119	58	21	18	11	11	—	—
Connecticut	38	38	8	—	9	10	6	—	5
Delaware	15	10	4	—	3	—	—	—	—
Dist. of Columbia	7	13	—	—	5	5	—	—	—
Florida	360	362	136	45	70	62	42	5	—
Georgia	201	171	68	31	25	22	16	8	—
Hawaii	30	23	4	3	4	7	5	—	—
Idaho	38	30	14	6	5	3	—	—	—
Illinois	207	182	57	24	29	34	32	6	—
Indiana	148	127	62	18	20	13	10	4	—
Iowa	71	88	51	18	5	9	3	—	—
Kansas	85	100	47	23	8	13	9	—	—
Kentucky	147	112	57	21	10	19	—	4	—
Louisiana	118	134	70	17	13	15	17	—	—
Maine	20	21	11	3	—	5	—	—	—
Maryland	106	82	33	7	18	14	7	—	—
Massachusetts	66	74	27	5	11	18	7	6	—
Michigan	157	120	35	27	27	17	11	—	—
Minnesota	78	72	24	16	9	11	7	5	—
Mississippi	96	92	34	16	14	12	13	—	—
Missouri	167	155	73	23	27	20	7	4	—
Montana	45	54	37	5	4	5	3	—	—
Nebraska	57	63	24	17	13	6	—	—	—
Nevada	49	68	28	10	7	17	5	—	—
New Hampshire	13	14	4	4	3	—	—	—	—
New Jersey	88	106	40	11	27	17	10	—	—
New Mexico	59	43	20	9	5	3	5	—	—
New York	234	219	71	35	43	53	12	5	—
North Carolina	168	158	72	27	31	18	9	—	—
North Dakota	31	23	10	7	—	4	—	—	—
Ohio	193	164	57	37	23	26	16	4	—
Oklahoma	91	104	50	20	6	16	9	—	—
Oregon	87	69	29	13	9	13	4	—	—
Pennsylvania	240	220	93	36	36	36	12	6	—
Rhode Island	10	5	—	—	3	—	—	—	—
South Carolina	95	114	45	12	25	15	7	10	—
South Dakota	37	21	12	3	—	6	—	—	—
Tennessee	153	147	66	32	18	25	4	—	—
Texas	489	527	192	85	86	78	66	17	—
Utah	60	78	38	19	7	3	5	6	—
Vermont	14	10	4	3	—	—	—	—	—
Virginia	165	141	53	22	21	25	16	—	—
Washington	87	88	36	25	6	11	4	—	6
West Virginia	79	61	18	17	4	10	6	5	—
Wisconsin	91	103	45	20	14	12	10	—	—
Wyoming	36	48	34	7	—	—	3	—	—

Source: U.S. Department of Labor, Bureau of Labor Statistics.
Note: Dashes (—) indicate no data or data that do not meet publication criteria.
[a]Data for 2006 revised and total includes five deaths for which state of occurrence could not be determined.
[b]Data for 2007 preliminary and total includes four deaths for which state of occurrence could not be determined.
[c]Includes highway, nonhighway, air, water, and rail fatalities, and fatalities resulting from being struck by a vehicle.
[d]Includes violence by persons, self-inflicted injury, and attacks by animals.

NONFATAL OCCUPATIONAL INCIDENCE RATES BY STATE

NONFATAL OCCUPATIONAL INJURY AND ILLNESS INCIDENCE RATES[a] BY STATE, PRIVATE INDUSTRY, 2006

State	Total Recordable Cases	Cases with Days away from Work[b]	Cases with Job Transfer or Restriction	Other Recordable Cases
Private Industry[c]	**4.4**	**1.3**	**1.0**	**2.1**
Alabama	4.7	1.2	1.1	2.4
Alaska	6.2	2.3	0.7	3.3
Arizona	4.4	1.3	1.0	2.2
Arkansas	4.4	1.0	1.0	2.4
California	4.3	1.2	1.3	1.8
Colorado	—	—	—	—
Connecticut	4.8	1.5	1.0	2.3
Delaware	3.8	1.4	0.6	1.9
Dist. of Columbia	2.0	0.7	0.2	1.1
Florida	4.4	1.2	1.1	2.1
Georgia	4.0	1.0	0.9	2.1
Hawaii	4.8	2.6	0.4	1.8
Idaho	—	—	—	—
Illinois	4.1	1.2	1.0	2.0
Indiana	5.4	1.2	1.5	2.7
Iowa	6.0	1.3	1.6	3.0
Kansas	5.1	1.1	1.2	2.8
Kentucky	5.2	1.5	1.3	2.4
Louisiana	3.0	1.0	0.5	1.5
Maine	7.0	1.8	2.1	3.1
Maryland	3.8	1.5	0.5	1.8
Massachusetts	3.9	1.6	0.5	1.8
Michigan	5.0	1.1	1.4	2.5
Minnesota	5.0	1.3	1.1	2.6
Mississippi	—	—	—	—
Missouri	4.7	1.1	1.0	2.5
Montana	6.9	2.0	0.9	4.0
Nebraska	5.0	1.3	1.0	2.7
Nevada	5.5	1.4	1.5	2.6
New Hampshire	—	—	—	—
New Jersey	3.6	1.5	0.6	1.6
New Mexico	4.5	1.3	1.1	2.1
New York	3.0	1.4	0.2	1.4
North Carolina	4.0	1.1	1.0	1.9
North Dakota	—	—	—	—
Ohio	—	—	—	—
Oklahoma	4.7	1.3	1.1	2.3
Oregon	5.3	1.7	1.1	2.4
Pennsylvania	—	—	—	—
Rhode Island	5.2	2.0	0.6	2.5
South Carolina	3.8	1.1	0.9	1.8
South Dakota	—	—	—	—
Tennessee	4.8	1.3	1.2	2.3
Texas	3.7	1.0	1.0	1.7
Utah	5.2	1.0	1.2	2.9
Vermont	5.5	1.6	0.9	3.0
Virginia	3.5	1.0	0.7	1.8
Washington	6.6	2.2	1.0	3.4
West Virginia	5.1	2.5	0.4	2.2
Wisconsin	5.5	1.5	1.3	2.7
Wyoming	4.8	1.9	0.5	2.4

Source: Bureau of Labor Statistics, U.S. Department of Labor.
Note: Because of rounding, components may not add to totals. Dashes (—) indicate data not available.
[a]Incidence rates represent the number of injuries and illnesses per 100 full-time workers using 200,000 hours as the equivalent.
[b]Days-away-from-work cases include those that result in days away from work with or without job transfer or restriction.
[c]Data cover all 50 states.

NONFATAL OCCUPATIONAL INJURY AND ILLNESS INCIDENCE RATES BY STATE, PRIVATE INDUSTRY, 2006

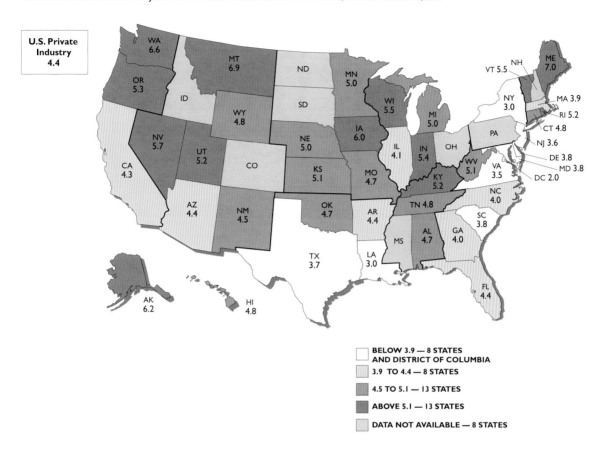

U.S. Private
Industry
4.4

WA 6.6
MT 6.9
ND
MN 5.0
OR 5.3
ID
WY 4.8
SD
WI 5.5
MI 5.0
NV 5.7
UT 5.2
CO
NE 5.0
IA 6.0
IL 4.1
IN 5.4
OH
CA 4.3
AZ 4.4
NM 4.5
KS 5.1
MO 4.7
OK 4.7
AR 4.4
TN 4.8
KY 5.2
WV 5.1
VA 3.5
NC 4.0
SC 3.8
MS
AL 4.7
GA 4.0
TX 3.7
LA 3.0
FL 4.4
AK 6.2
HI 4.8

VT 5.5
NH
ME 7.0
NY 3.0
MA 3.9
RI 5.2
CT 4.8
PA
NJ 3.6
DE 3.8
MD 3.8
DC 2.0

☐ **BELOW 3.9 — 8 STATES
AND DISTRICT OF COLUMBIA**

▨ **3.9 TO 4.4 — 8 STATES**

▨ **4.5 TO 5.1 — 13 STATES**

■ **ABOVE 5.1 — 13 STATES**

▨ **DATA NOT AVAILABLE — 8 STATES**

MOTOR-VEHICLE DEATHS BY STATE

MOTOR-VEHICLE DEATHS BY STATE, UNITED STATES, 2004–2007

State	Motor-Vehicle Traffic Deaths (Place of Accident)				Total Motor-Vehicle Deaths[a] (Place of Residence)			
	Number		Mileage Rate[b]		Number		Population Rate[b]	
	2007	2006	2007	2006	2005[c]	2004	2005	2004
Total U.S.[a]	43,100	44,600	1.4	1.5	45,343	44,933	15.3	15.3
Alabama	1,086	1,208	1.8	2.0	1,188	1,259	26.1	27.9
Alaska	83	74	1.7	1.5	93	119	14.0	18.1
Arizona	1,068	1,289	1.7	2.2	1,200	1,125	20.2	19.6
Arkansas	650	665	2.0	2.1	696	779	25.1	28.4
California	3,967	4,197	1.2	1.3	4,427	4,417	12.2	12.3
Colorado	554	535	1.1	1.1	673	700	14.4	15.2
Connecticut	297	325	0.9	1.0	293	336	8.4	9.6
Delaware	118	147	1.3	1.5	119	141	14.1	17.0
Dist. of Columbia	54	41	1.5	1.1	38	46	6.5	7.9
Florida	3,220	3,382	1.6	1.7	3,526	3,294	19.8	19.0
Georgia	1,648	1,703	1.5	1.5	1,686	1,497	18.5	16.8
Hawaii	134	161	1.3	1.6	141	142	11.1	11.3
Idaho	252	267	1.7	1.8	283	249	19.8	17.9
Illinois	1,248	1,254	1.2	1.2	1,469	1,513	11.5	11.9
Indiana	898	899	1.3	1.2	975	1,006	15.6	16.2
Iowa	445	439	1.4	1.4	468	418	15.8	14.2
Kansas	416	468	1.4	1.6	498	500	18.1	18.3
Kentucky	864	913	1.8	1.9	1,003	992	24.0	24.0
Louisiana	985	992	2.2	2.2	1,029	1,022	22.8	22.7
Maine	186	185	1.2	1.2	192	180	14.6	13.7
Maryland	615	651	1.1	1.2	628	671	11.2	12.1
Massachusetts	441	430	0.8	0.8	484	532	7.5	8.3
Michigan	1,084	1,084	1.0	1.0	1,231	1,307	12.2	12.9
Minnesota	508	494	0.9	0.9	642	652	12.5	12.8
Mississippi	884	911	2.1	2.2	965	915	33.2	31.6
Missouri	991	1,096	1.4	1.6	1,203	1,111	20.7	19.3
Montana	276	263	2.5	2.4	236	241	25.2	26.0
Nebraska	256	269	1.3	1.4	287	282	16.3	16.1
Nevada	373	432	1.7	2.1	459	422	19.0	18.1
New Hampshire	129	127	1.0	0.9	162	165	12.4	12.7
New Jersey	724	770	1.0	1.0	760	771	8.7	8.9
New Mexico	413	471	1.6	2.0	461	480	23.9	25.3
New York	—	1,435	—	1.0	1,530	1,586	7.9	8.2
North Carolina	1,680	1,559	1.7	1.5	1,666	1,691	19.2	19.8
North Dakota	111	111	1.4	1.5	130	117	20.5	18.4
Ohio	1,258	1,238	1.1	1.1	1,404	1,383	12.2	12.1
Oklahoma	754	765	1.6	1.6	833	765	23.5	21.7
Oregon	455	477	1.3	1.3	512	501	14.1	14.0
Pennsylvania	1,491	1,525	1.4	1.4	1,771	1,595	14.3	12.9
Rhode Island	69	81	0.8	1.0	87	99	8.1	9.2
South Carolina	1,075	1,045	2.2	2.1	1,071	1,034	25.2	24.7
South Dakota	146	191	1.6	2.3	176	189	22.7	24.5
Tennessee	1,205	1,287	1.7	1.8	1,308	1,386	22.0	23.5
Texas	3,460	3,467	1.5	1.5	3,780	3,864	16.5	17.2
Utah	299	287	1.2	1.1	319	321	12.8	13.3
Vermont	66	87	0.8	1.1	82	83	13.2	13.4
Virginia	1,026	961	1.3	1.2	969	1,016	12.8	13.6
Washington	569	630	1.0	1.1	762	669	12.1	10.8
West Virginia	431	410	2.1	2.0	403	414	22.2	22.9
Wisconsin	737	712	1.2	1.2	870	815	15.7	14.8
Wyoming	149	195	1.6	2.1	155	121	30.5	23.9

Source: Motor-Vehicle Traffic Deaths are provisional counts from state traffic authorities; Total Motor-Vehicle Deaths are from the National Center for Health Statistics (see also page 167).
[a]Includes both traffic and nontraffic motor-vehicle deaths. See definitions of motor-vehicle traffic and nontraffic accidents on page 199.
[b]The mileage death rate is deaths per 100,000,000 vehicle miles; the population death rate is deaths per 100,000 population. Death rates are National Safety Council estimates.
[c]Latest year available. See Technical Appendix for comparability.

MILEAGE DEATH RATES, 2007
MOTOR-VEHICLE TRAFFIC DEATHS PER 100,000,000 VEHICLE MILES

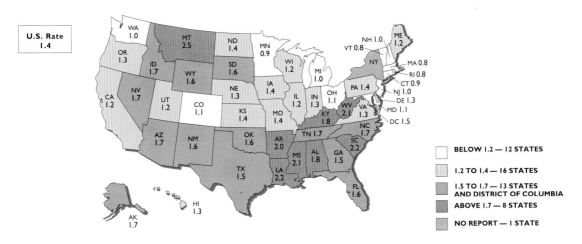

REGISTRATION DEATH RATES, 2007
MOTOR-VEHICLE TRAFFIC DEATHS PER 10,000 MOTOR VEHICLES

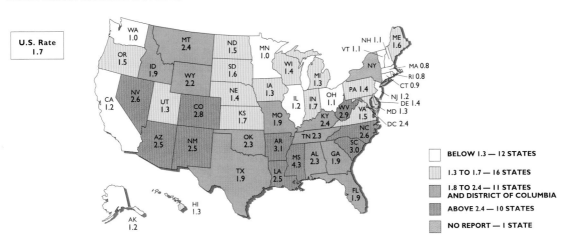

POPULATION DEATH RATES, 2007
MOTOR-VEHICLE TRAFFIC DEATHS PER 100,000 POPULATION

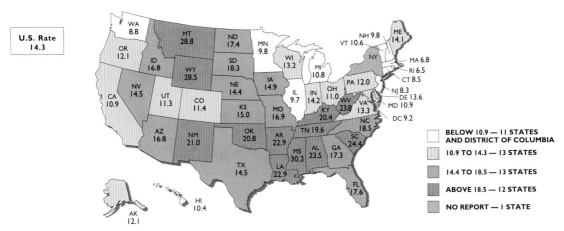

Source: Rates estimated by National Safety Council based on data from state traffic authorities, National Center for Health Statistics, Federal Highway Administration, and the U.S. Census Bureau.

NATIONAL SAFETY COUNCIL

INJURY FACTS®

INTERNATIONAL DATA

Road traffic accidents represent the largest burden of unintentional injury and deaths across the world.

This section on international injury and fatalities includes data for occupational and motor-vehicle injuries as well as general unintentional injury and mortality. The two primary data sources used in this section are the World Health Organization and International Labor Organization.

The charts on pages 177 through 180 show graphically the burden of unintentional injuries and death in 2005 for the world overall as well as six geographic regions. As measured in disability adjusted life years (DALYs), the African Region has the highest average unintentional DALY rate in the world with 3,212 per 100,000 population. This contrasts sharply with the Region of the Americas with the lowest average unintentional DALY rate of 1,282. Overall the World has an average unintentional DALY rate of 2,080.

Looking at specific causes, road traffic accidents are the leading cause of unintentional DALYs for each region in the world. The overall DALY rate for road traffic accidents is 651. The 15 to 29 year olds followed closely by 0 to 4 year olds are the age groups with the highest burden of unintentional injuries. These age groups have DALY rates of 2,628 and 2,529, respectively.

The charts on pages 181 through 185 provide the unintentional injury deaths and death rates for 53

countries. The most current year of mortality data available is reported for motor-vehicle, falls, drowning, poisonings, and overall unintentional injury deaths. Looking at overall age trends across the world, the 65 and older age group has the highest rate of unintentional injury deaths per 100,000 population while the 5 to 14 year old age group has the lowest. Death rates for all causes except poisonings peak for the 65 and older age group. The poisoning death rate peaks for the 45 to 64 age group. Because of differences in record keeping, comparisons among countries are not recommended.

The charts on pages 186 and 187 detail the occupational deaths by country for the last five years. Because of the wide range of recordkeeping standards used in the world, countries with similar recordkeeping practices are grouped together. Although comparison among countries is not recommended even within these country groupings, trends over the past five years are evident. Of the forty countries listed, fully 26 show improvement in the occupational death rate, 4 countries have remained stable, while 10 countries have reported at least a slight increase.

As part of the Global Burden of Disease project the World Health Organization (WHO) makes mortality and burden of disease projections based on 2002 mortality estimates. These projections are used in this section to compare the impact that unintentional injuries are having in six regions of the world and overall.

Burden of disease refers to the overall impact of diseases and injuries at the individual or societal level. The WHO quantifies the burden of disease using an estimate of disability-adjusted life years (DALY), which are the sum of the years of life lost due to premature mortality and the years lost due to disability. The DALY is a health gap measure that combines the potential years of life lost due to premature death and the equivalent years of 'healthy' life lost due to disability. In other words, one DALY represents the loss of one year of equivalent full health.

The WHO DALYs are developed using a set of statistical models to project trends based on economic and social development, and using the historically observed relationships of these with cause-specific mortality rates. Years of life lost are calculated from projections of mortality by cause, age, and sex. Years lived with disabilities are calculated by applying the ratio of years lived with disability to years of life lost for 2002.

This section presents unintentional injury DALY rates (per 100,000 population) for the world overall and for six regions: Africa, Americas, Mediterranean, European, South East Asian, and Western Pacific.

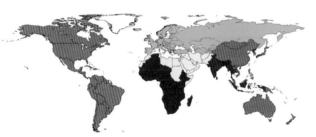

WORLD

As illustrated in the chart below, the burden of unintentional injuries in the world per 100,000 population is greatest among the 15 to 29 age group followed closely by the 0 to 4 age group. The 15 to 29 age group has a DALY rate of 2,628 and the 0 to 4 age group has a rate of 2,529 compared to an average DALY rate of 2,080 across all age groups. Looking at causes, road traffic accidents has the highest DALY rate of 651. Road traffic accidents are the leading unintentional DALY cause for all age groups under 70. Starting with the 70–79 age group, falls represent the leading cause of DALYs.

WORLD: DISABILITY ADJUSTED LIFE YEARS (DALY) RATE, 2005

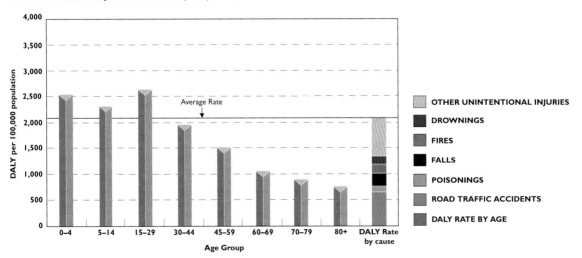

Source: National Safety Council analysis of World Health Organization Burden of Disease Project data.

INTERNATIONAL BURDEN OF UNINTENTIONAL INJURY AFRICAN REGION

The African Region represented by 46 countries has the highest average unintentional DALY rate in the world with 3,212 per 100,000 population. Although road traffic accidents are the most prevalent cause overall, fires represent the top cause for the 0–4 age group, while falls are the leading cause for individuals 80 and older.

AFRICAN REGION: DISABILITY ADJUSTED LIFE YEARS (DALY) RATE, 2005

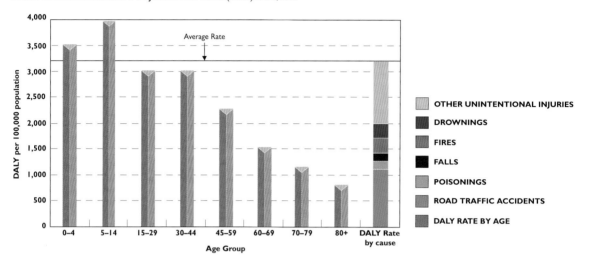

REGION OF THE AMERICAS

The Americas represented by 35 countries has the lowest average unintentional DALY rate in the world with 1,282 per 100,000 population. DALY rates spike for the 15–29 age group with 1,922 but quickly drop back down to average for the 30–44 age group. Road traffic accidents are the leading cause for each age group under 70. Starting with the 70–79 age group, falls represent the leading cause of DALYs.

REGION OF THE AMERICAS: DISABILITY ADJUSTED LIFE YEARS (DALY) RATE, 2005

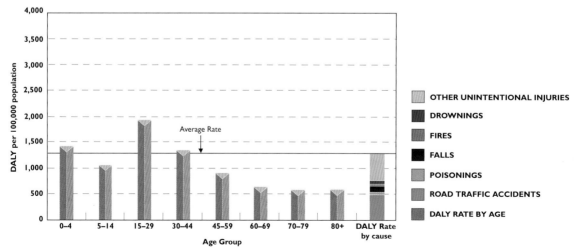

Source: National Safety Council analysis of World Health Organization Burden of Disease Project data.

The Eastern Mediterranean Region represented by 21 countries has the second highest DALY rate behind the African Region with 2,717 per 100,000 population. Road traffic accidents are the predominate cause among all but the oldest age group. Falls represent the second leading cause for the 0–14 and 45–79 age ranges and the leading cause for the 80 and above age group.

EASTERN MEDITERRANEAN REGION: DISABILITY ADJUSTED LIFE YEARS (DALY) RATE, 2005

EUROPEAN REGION

The European Region represented by 52 countries has the second lowest DALY rate behind the Region of the Americas with 1,554 per 100,000 population. Looking at the age groups there is no one dominate cause. Road traffic accidents are the leading cause among 5–44 year olds, poisoning is the leading cause for 45–69 year olds, while falls are the leading cause for 0–4 and 70 and older age groups.

EUROPEAN REGION: DISABILITY ADJUSTED LIFE YEARS (DALY) RATE, 2005

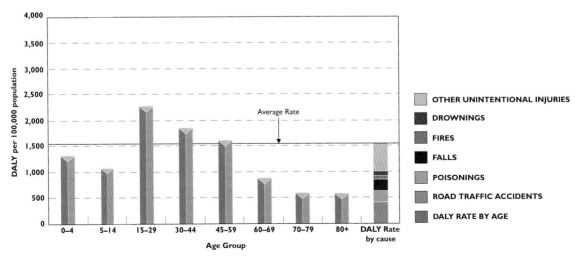

Source: National Safety Council analysis of World Health Organization Burden of Disease Project data.

INTERNATIONAL BURDEN OF UNINTENTIONAL INJURY
SOUTH EAST ASIAN REGION

The South East Asian Region is represented by 11 countries including India. Although road traffic accidents are the most prevalent cause overall, fires and falls represent the top cause for the 0–4 age group, while falls are the leading cause for individuals 70 and older.

SOUTH EAST ASIAN REGION: DISABILITY ADJUSTED LIFE YEARS (DALY) RATE, 2005

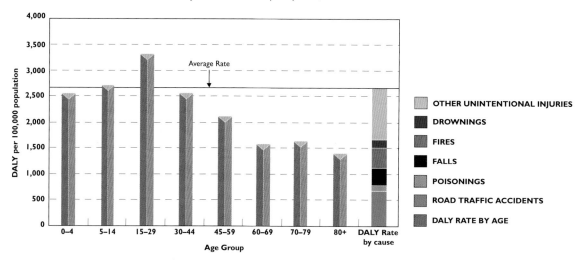

WESTERN PACIFIC REGION

The Western Pacific Region is represented by 27 countries including China. Although road traffic accidents are the most prevalent cause overall, drowning represent the top cause for the 0–14 age group, while falls are the leading cause for individuals 70 and older.

WESTERN PACIFIC REGION: DISABILITY ADJUSTED LIFE YEARS (DALY) RATE, 2005

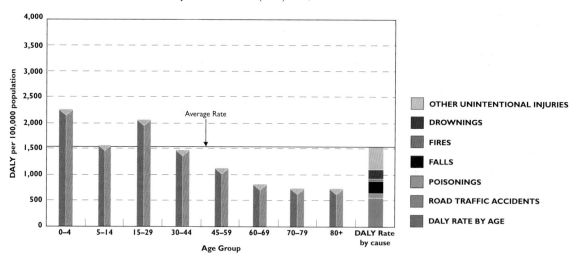

Source: National Safety Council analysis of World Health Organization Burden of Disease Project data.

The term "Accidents and Adverse Effects" used in the International Classification of Diseases system (ICD) refers to all causes of unintentional injury deaths, including transportation accidents, unintentional poisonings, falls, fires, burns, natural and environmental factors, drowning, suffocation, medical and surgical complications and misadventures, and other causes such as those involving machinery, firearms, or electric

current. The data presented in the table below are identified by codes V01–X59, Y85–Y86 of the tenth ICD revision (except were noted).

The tables on pages 181 through 185 show the number of injury deaths and the unadjusted death rates for 53 countries for which mortality data and population estimates were obtained.

UNINTENTIONAL INJURY DEATHS AND DEATH RATES BY AGE GROUP, LATEST YEAR AVAILABLE

Country	Year	Deaths		Deaths per 100,000 Population[a]						
		Total	% Male	All Ages	0 to 4	5 to 14	15 to 24	25 to 44	45 to 64	65+
Argentina	2005	10,514	71.3%	26.8	18.9	8.9	25.0	24.5	29.6	66.9
Australia	2003	4,956	63.3%	24.9	9.9	3.9	23.5	21.1	17.3	79.4
Austria	2006	2,526	61.3%	30.5	5.0	2.7	20.3	14.0	24.0	103.2
Belarus[b]	2003	12,063	77.8%	122.2	32.0	11.2	55.0	140.2	214.6	132.8
Brazil	2004	57,565	79.9%	30.9	13.8	10.2	32.0	34.3	38.7	79.9
Canada	2004	8,986	60.3%	28.1	5.2	4.0	21.7	18.0	21.5	104.1
Chile	2005	4,772	77.3%	29.8	10.7	5.4	21.5	28.6	38.2	101.9
Colombia	2005	10,733	78.1%	24.9	19.6	8.6	24.0	25.3	30.7	81.7
Costa Rica	2005	1,174	75.7%	29.2	8.0	8.5	22.4	26.5	36.1	153.6
Croatia	2006	1,840	62.9%	41.4	7.3	4.9	29.0	23.9	34.9	122.9
Cuba	2005	4,609	58.7%	40.7	10.0	8.2	17.5	21.3	26.3	231.6
Czech Republic	2005	4,270	63.0%	41.7	7.8	5.3	25.9	25.8	40.6	130.1
Dominican Republic	2004	1,582	79.6%	17.7	5.8	4.7	19.2	24.8	21.9	42.1
Ecuador	2005	4,965	77.7%	37.2	21.8	12.5	30.0	41.7	56.2	9.7
El Salvador	2005	2,323	79.3%	34.6	11.8	10.2	27.6	42.9	56.1	138.3
Estonia	2005	1,109	76.3%	82.4	25.8	11.5	46.2	76.4	137.1	104.9
Finland	2006	3,082	67.1%	58.5	3.1	2.3	25.0	30.0	77.4	156.0
France	2005	24,786	54.6%	40.6	5.8	2.7	22.6	17.8	25.4	157.1
Germany	2006	18,755	56.9%	22.8	4.1	2.2	14.5	10.7	15.2	69.9
Hong Kong, China	2006	790	70.5%	11.5	0.5	1.4	4.3	9.0	9.3	42.1
Hungary	2005	5,061	63.8%	50.2	6.7	4.1	21.9	29.4	53.0	151.5
Israel	2004	1,323	63.7%	19.4	6.3	4.9	16.9	14.1	16.5	83.6
Japan	2006	39,720	60.7%	31.5	6.6	2.3	10.1	8.8	20.3	104.4
Kazakhstan[b]	2006	16,887	76.7%	110.3	47.2	22.1	68.3	155.9	172.5	139.6
Kyrgyzstan	2006	2,571	76.8%	49.8	44.4	12.2	21.7	66.8	105.3	82.0
Latvia	2006	2,360	75.4%	103.1	19.3	11.8	36.4	95.5	179.2	139.0
Lithuania	2006	3,554	75.8%	104.7	21.1	14.8	48.5	95.4	186.6	143.2
Luxembourg	2005	147	60.5%	32.1	10.9	3.5	28.3	25.5	26.7	93.2
Mexico	2005	34,960	76.0%	32.9	25.2	8.7	29.3	33.2	43.1	121.3
Netherlands	2006	3,588	51.1%	21.9	3.4	2.4	8.8	7.4	11.0	106.7
New Zealand	2004	1,138	61.6%	27.8	14.8	5.1	32.6	20.7	20.1	90.8
Nicaragua	2005	1,184	81.1%	21.6	10.6	7.2	22.8	25.8	31.0	105.1
Norway	2005	1,835	57.1%	39.7	3.5	2.6	23.2	22.4	27.9	156.0
Panama	2004	825	79.5%	26.6	22.1	9.0	23.5	27.3	32.3	83.9
Paraguay	2004	1,380	70.4%	22.3	11.3	9.3	25.8	28.0	32.1	47.8
Poland	2006	15,816	72.6%	41.5	6.2	5.1	24.9	32.3	55.6	96.3
Portugal	2003	3,927	70.1%	37.5	9.0	7.5	31.5	28.8	32.9	92.0
Puerto Rico	2005	1,120	76.3%	28.6	2.3	2.4	28.4	30.0	29.8	0.6
Republic of Korea	2006	15,633	68.8%	32.0	9.9	5.4	12.0	17.6	41.6	144.6
Romania	2007	9,369	75.7%	43.5	21.5	13.3	27.5	33.7	61.8	77.7
Russian Federation[b]	2006	211,086	76.7%	148.1	33.4	17.9	81.3	175.7	221.0	171.8
Slovakia	2005	2,085	77.6%	38.7	11.5	4.7	20.9	31.6	63.4	73.3
Slovenia	2006	895	64.6%	44.6	5.6	4.2	31.6	22.8	33.2	152.1
South Africa	2005	12,141	68.6%	25.6	26.1	8.3	18.4	33.8	29.9	70.2
Spain	2005	12,515	69.0%	28.8	5.3	3.6	24.0	21.8	22.5	76.4
Sweden	2005	3,061	57.3%	33.9	2.0	1.8	13.6	12.7	22.6	130.8
Switzerland[b]	2005	2,098	56.3%	28.2	4.1	3.5	15.1	11.5	18.3	110.7
Ukraine[b]	2005	54,791	78.8%	116.8	34.9	16.5	53.6	130.4	203.1	107.3
United Kingdom	2006	13,816	56.2%	22.8	3.8	2.3	15.5	14.0	14.7	79.1
United States of America	2005	117,809	64.8%	39.7	13.5	6.0	37.4	36.8	40.1	100.0
Uruguay	2004	1,101	69.1%	32.3	29.1	9.0	23.5	22.6	33.8	91.4
Uzbekistan	2005	6,342	75.5%	24.2	36.6	11.2	13.7	31.7	34.5	41.2
Venezuela	2005	8,518	77.1%	33.7	29.0	11.2	31.5	40.2	40.8	92.2

Source: National Safety Council tabulations of World Health Organization data.
[a] Population estimates based on data from the World Health Organization and the U.S. Census Bureau (International Data Base)
[b] Data include deaths due to all external causes, including self-harm and assault.

INTERNATIONAL MOTOR-VEHICLE DEATHS AND DEATH RATES

The International Classification of Diseases system (ICD) identifies motor-vehicle traffic accidents by codes V02–V04, V09, V12–V14, V19–V79, V86–V89 of the tenth ICD revision. A motor vehicle is a mechanically or electrically powered device used in the transportation of persons or property on a land highway. A motor-vehicle traffic accident involves a motor vehicle in transport (i.e., in motion or on a roadway) on a public highway.

MOTOR-VEHICLE DEATHS AND DEATH RATES BY AGE GROUP, LATEST YEAR AVAILABLE

Country	Year	Deaths Total	% Male	Deaths per 100,000 Population[a] All Ages	0 to 4	5 to 14	15 to 24	25 to 44	45 to 64	65+
Argentina	2005	3,285	76.2%	8.4	2.4	3.1	9.2	10.3	11.0	11.3
Australia	2003	1,617	72.7%	8.1	3.8	2.4	15.7	8.4	6.3	11.0
Austria	2006	421	74.6%	5.1	1.3	1.3	9.2	4.6	4.8	6.9
Belarus[b]	2003	2,241	23.9%	22.7	2.4	3.6	23.7	28.2	28.3	23.4
Brazil	2004	25,281	82.2%	13.6	2.3	3.0	18.3	17.9	16.5	18.0
Canada	2004	2,834	70.8%	8.9	1.2	2.3	16.1	8.6	8.0	13.1
Chile	2005	1,118	80.9%	7.0	1.8	1.2	7.4	9.2	9.1	10.3
Colombia	2005	4,830	79.2%	11.2	2.6	3.0	12.8	13.9	14.2	30.2
Costa Rica	2005	501	83.8%	12.5	2.1	3.9	12.9	14.1	18.4	31.8
Croatia	2006	526	77.0%	11.8	3.4	3.0	19.1	10.5	12.8	15.1
Cuba	2005	1,158	78.8%	10.2	2.3	3.2	9.8	11.6	11.9	16.9
Czech Republic	2005	809	73.5%	7.9	1.1	3.0	11.9	8.5	7.4	9.8
Dominican Republic	2004	1,197	81.3%	13.4	1.8	3.0	16.4	19.9	16.4	27.1
Ecuador	2005	745	78.9%	5.6	1.5	1.0	6.1	7.8	8.7	0.9
El Salvador	2005	1,461	81.6%	21.8	4.0	5.9	15.9	29.2	40.9	78.9
Estonia	2005	177	75.7%	13.1	4.6	7.2	15.2	16.2	14.3	10.7
Finland	2006	329	72.6%	6.2	0.7	1.1	11.7	5.4	5.9	9.5
France	2005	5,136	74.5%	8.4	1.3	1.3	17.5	9.2	7.0	10.1
Germany	2006	4,250	73.2%	5.2	1.0	1.0	10.2	5.2	4.4	6.1
Hong Kong, China	2006	153	62.7%	2.2	0.0	0.7	1.3	2.0	1.7	6.9
Hungary	2005	1,275	75.6%	12.6	2.1	2.4	14.2	14.6	14.4	15.0
Israel	2004	352	77.0%	5.2	0.9	1.5	9.6	5.8	5.2	7.3
Japan	2006	8,297	68.4%	6.6	1.3	1.0	6.7	3.8	5.9	14.4
Kazakhstan[b]	2006	4,896	27.0%	32.0	8.1	9.6	31.3	47.8	39.0	27.6
Kyrgyzstan	2006	534	77.2%	10.3	2.5	3.1	7.0	15.9	17.9	17.0
Latvia	2006	415	74.7%	18.1	2.9	4.6	20.9	20.9	20.7	19.1
Lithuania	2006	794	72.8%	23.4	6.6	5.8	30.7	27.3	26.7	21.9
Luxembourg	2005	46	58.7%	10.1	3.6	3.5	18.9	12.7	8.0	9.2
Mexico	2005	10,689	78.3%	10.1	3.2	2.7	13.0	12.9	12.9	17.8
Netherlands	2006	690	70.7%	4.2	1.0	1.4	6.6	3.6	3.4	8.7
New Zealand	2004	469	68.2%	11.5	4.2	2.1	25.4	11.0	9.9	14.9
Nicaragua	2005	439	82.2%	8.0	2.7	2.3	8.4	11.7	12.7	24.2
Norway	2005	238	68.5%	5.1	1.0	0.8	11.1	5.0	4.7	6.9
Panama	2004	392	83.9%	12.6	1.5	2.2	15.3	16.4	17.4	28.0
Paraguay	2004	415	78.3%	6.7	0.9	1.5	9.4	9.4	11.1	12.8
Poland	2006	4,696	76.9%	12.3	1.7	2.4	15.1	12.8	13.9	17.0
Portugal	2003	1,724	79.5%	16.5	3.4	3.6	24.5	17.8	15.5	21.3
Puerto Rico	2005	426	80.5%	10.9	0.4	1.3	20.1	13.1	11.0	0.1
Republic of Korea	2006	7,609	72.8%	15.6	4.3	3.2	9.1	10.6	22.0	52.6
Romania	2007	2,497	73.5%	11.6	1.9	3.6	12.1	11.2	13.5	17.6
Russian Federation[b]	2006	38,241	27.2%	26.8	4.2	6.5	31.5	34.4	26.7	28.0
Slovakia	2005	625	76.6%	11.6	2.3	2.4	12.7	12.5	14.5	14.5
Slovenia	2006	279	82.4%	13.9	5.6	2.6	25.5	16.2	10.5	15.2
South Africa	2005	5,404	73.3%	11.4	3.8	4.8	9.6	18.0	15.0	15.0
Spain	2005	4,617	78.9%	10.6	1.5	2.1	17.0	11.0	10.1	13.6
Sweden	2005	424	73.6%	4.7	0.2	0.7	7.8	5.2	4.3	6.3
Switzerland[b]	2005	398	24.4%	5.4	1.6	1.3	9.4	4.4	4.6	9.2
Ukraine[b]	2005	9,893	23.8%	21.1	3.8	5.1	24.2	26.3	23.7	19.6
United Kingdom	2006	3,269	76.0%	5.4	1.1	1.4	11.0	6.2	4.0	6.0
United States of America	2005	45,343	69.8%	15.3	3.8	3.6	25.9	16.7	14.9	20.1
Uruguay	2004	347	76.7%	10.2	0.4	3.1	11.1	9.5	15.5	16.8
Uzbekistan	2005	2,247	79.2%	8.6	3.2	3.8	5.1	13.3	13.7	18.3
Venezuela	2005	3,185	79.1%	12.6	3.7	3.6	13.5	17.4	17.4	25.8

Source: National Safety Council tabulations of World Health Organization data.
[a]Population estimates based on data from the World Health Organization and the U.S. Census Bureau (International Data Base).
[b]Data include deaths due to all transportation-related causes, ICD–10 codes V01–V99.

INTERNATIONAL FALL-RELATED DEATHS AND DEATH RATES

"Accidental falls" are identified by codes W00–W19 in the tenth revision of the International Classification of Diseases system.

FALL-RELATED DEATHS AND DEATH RATES BY AGE GROUP, LATEST YEAR AVAILABLE

Country	Year	Deaths Total	% Male	Deaths per 100,000 Population[a] All Ages	0 to 4	5 to 14	15 to 24	25 to 44	45 to 64	65+
Argentina	2005	319	78.1%	0.8	0.3	0.2	0.3	0.7	1.0	3.0
Australia	2003	717	53.8%	3.6	0.2	0.1	1.0	1.0	1.6	21.6
Austria	2006	954	53.1%	11.5	0.3	0.0	0.9	2.1	7.4	53.4
Belarus	2003	1,181	77.1%	12.0	2.2	1.0	3.5	12.3	20.8	18.9
Brazil	2004	6,617	69.7%	3.5	0.7	0.5	0.9	2.3	5.0	29.2
Canada	2004	2,229	48.5%	7.0	0.4	0.2	0.4	0.8	3.1	45.1
Chile	2005	725	56.4%	4.5	0.3	0.0	0.6	1.8	4.2	37.5
Colombia	2005	1,138	80.8%	2.6	0.9	0.5	0.9	1.9	4.2	19.8
Costa Rica	2005	82	90.2%	2.0	0.0	0.1	0.9	1.3	4.4	12.8
Croatia	2006	729	44.7%	16.4	0.5	0.0	0.5	1.0	7.6	82.4
Cuba	2005	1,754	44.9%	15.5	0.9	0.1	1.1	1.5	4.7	135.4
Czech Republic	2005	1,474	43.7%	14.4	0.8	0.0	0.4	2.3	6.0	84.6
Dominican Republic	2004	30	53.3%	0.3	0.2	0.0	0.0	0.0	0.5	4.4
Ecuador	2005	501	79.4%	3.7	2.3	0.6	2.3	3.7	6.4	1.4
El Salvador	2005	299	71.2%	4.5	1.0	0.6	1.3	3.0	7.1	44.5
Estonia	2005	127	65.4%	9.4	0.0	0.0	2.9	5.7	14.0	23.7
Finland	2006	1,178	54.5%	22.4	0.0	0.2	1.1	3.2	16.9	102.3
France	2005	5,333	48.4%	8.7	0.5	0.1	0.5	1.3	4.7	43.2
Germany	2006	8,381	45.4%	10.2	0.5	0.1	0.5	1.0	4.3	44.5
Hong Kong, China	2006	172	69.2%	2.5	0.5	0.3	0.8	1.1	1.8	12.1
Hungary	2005	2,102	49.2%	20.8	0.0	0.2	0.4	2.7	14.1	103.0
Israel	2004	87	50.6%	1.3	0.4	0.2	0.5	0.8	0.8	7.5
Japan	2006	6,601	59.6%	5.2	0.3	0.2	0.7	0.9	3.1	19.2
Kazakhstan	2006	575	81.0%	3.8	2.8	1.0	2.6	4.9	5.5	4.8
Kyrgyzstan	2006	87	82.8%	1.7	1.4	1.4	0.7	2.2	2.5	2.1
Latvia	2006	314	71.7%	13.7	1.0	1.4	2.8	9.2	19.1	33.8
Lithuania	2006	555	75.1%	16.4	0.0	0.5	1.9	9.4	31.2	37.4
Luxembourg	2005	44	65.9%	9.6	0.0	0.0	0.0	5.0	11.6	36.7
Mexico	2005	2,333	78.5%	2.2	1.1	0.3	0.8	1.5	3.9	14.8
Netherlands	2006	1,264	45.3%	7.7	0.2	0.1	0.3	0.9	2.4	47.1
New Zealand	2004	355	47.3%	8.7	0.4	0.2	2.0	1.6	2.8	61.1
Nicaragua	2005	84	76.2%	1.5	0.5	0.2	0.8	1.3	3.3	18.3
Norway	2005	353	51.3%	7.6	0.0	0.3	0.7	1.1	5.2	40.0
Panama	2004	76	68.4%	2.4	0.9	0.6	0.5	1.5	2.7	20.6
Paraguay	2004	33	75.8%	0.5	0.6	0.3	0.4	0.3	1.5	0.7
Poland	2006	3,668	53.0%	9.6	0.5	0.1	1.1	2.5	7.7	50.1
Portugal	2003	858	52.1%	8.2	0.5	0.5	0.7	1.7	5.1	37.2
Puerto Rico	2005	185	68.6%	4.7	0.4	0.0	0.7	1.4	5.3	0.2
Republic of Korea	2006	3,419	60.1%	7.0	1.4	0.4	0.6	2.1	7.5	47.1
Romania	2007	1,327	79.7%	6.2	1.0	0.6	1.5	3.8	10.1	14.7
Russian Federation	2006	11,394	74.1%	8.0	1.7	0.6	3.6	7.7	11.3	15.4
Slovakia	2005	472	74.2%	8.8	0.8	0.3	1.2	3.6	14.3	32.2
Slovenia	2006	437	47.8%	21.8	0.0	0.0	1.2	2.8	10.6	113.5
South Africa	2005	103	78.6%	0.2	0.1	0.1	0.1	0.2	0.4	1.2
Spain	2005	1,763	58.1%	4.1	0.4	0.1	1.0	1.5	2.5	16.8
Sweden	2005	788	51.6%	8.7	0.2	0.0	0.4	0.3	4.6	42.8
Switzerland	2005	1,100	46.2%	14.8	0.3	0.4	1.0	1.9	5.0	80.1
Ukraine	2005	3,368	79.7%	7.2	1.2	0.5	2.8	6.2	12.2	11.4
United Kingdom	2006	3,985	48.1%	6.6	0.2	0.2	0.6	1.1	3.6	32.9
United States of America	2005	19,656	51.7%	6.6	0.2	0.1	0.6	1.1	3.6	43.0
Uruguay	2004	38	73.7%	1.1	0.0	0.2	0.2	0.8	1.5	4.0
Uzbekistan	2005	444	79.1%	1.7	1.9	1.1	1.2	1.9	2.4	3.3
Venezuela	2005	702	63.2%	2.8	0.8	0.4	0.7	1.5	3.0	32.1

Source: National Safety Council tabulations of World Health Organization data.
[a] Population estimates based on data from the World Health Organization and the U.S. Census Bureau (International Data Base).

INTERNATIONAL DROWNING DEATHS AND DEATH RATES

The International Classification of Diseases system (ICD) identifies drowning by codes W65–W74, which include cases of unintentional drowning and submersion while in or following a fall in a bathtub, swimming pool, or natural body of water. Other specified and unspecified cases of drowning and submersion are also included.

UNINTENTIONAL DROWNING DEATHS AND DEATH RATES BY AGE GROUP, LATEST YEAR AVAILABLE

Country	Year	Deaths		Deaths per 100,000 Population[a]						
		Total	% Male	All Ages	0 to 4	5 to 14	15 to 24	25 to 44	45 to 64	65+
Argentina	2005	563	81.7%	1.4	3.8	1.0	1.8	1.1	1.1	1.1
Australia	2003	192	75.0%	1.0	2.2	0.3	1.0	0.9	1.0	1.3
Austria	2006	69	65.2%	0.8	1.0	0.3	0.4	0.6	0.9	1.9
Belarus	2003	1,047	80.8%	10.6	4.2	3.6	8.6	14.8	12.1	9.9
Brazil	2004	6,431	85.9%	3.4	2.9	3.0	4.7	3.5	2.9	3.2
Canada	2004	251	80.1%	0.8	1.2	0.5	0.9	0.7	0.8	1.0
Chile	2005	488	87.7%	3.1	3.0	1.2	3.5	2.9	3.4	5.7
Colombia	2005	1,019	80.5%	2.4	4.5	2.1	3.3	1.6	1.4	3.4
Costa Rica	2005	146	83.6%	3.6	2.4	3.2	4.2	4.0	3.2	4.4
Croatia	2006	78	67.9%	1.8	0.0	0.2	1.0	1.2	2.2	4.0
Cuba	2005	263	90.5%	2.3	1.7	2.6	2.4	2.4	1.9	2.8
Czech Republic	2005	202	74.8%	2.0	0.6	0.8	1.8	1.5	2.7	3.0
Dominican Republic	2004	31	58.1%	0.3	0.4	0.2	0.2	0.4	0.5	0.6
Ecuador	2005	376	82.4%	2.8	3.9	1.7	3.1	2.7	2.6	0.4
El Salvador	2005	310	84.8%	4.6	1.8	2.3	6.7	6.6	4.4	4.7
Estonia	2005	59	84.7%	4.4	4.6	0.7	3.8	4.9	6.2	3.6
Finland	2006	135	77.8%	2.6	1.0	0.2	0.9	2.1	4.2	4.1
France	2005	933	71.0%	1.5	1.3	0.3	0.7	1.0	1.9	3.6
Germany	2006	418	71.3%	0.5	0.7	0.4	0.2	0.3	0.6	0.9
Hong Kong, China	2006	56	76.8%	0.8	0.0	0.3	1.0	0.7	0.6	2.1
Hungary	2005	192	81.8%	1.9	1.3	0.7	1.5	2.0	2.5	2.1
Israel	2004	44	84.1%	0.6	0.6	0.3	0.7	0.5	0.7	1.5
Japan	2006	6,038	53.4%	4.8	1.1	0.6	0.9	0.9	2.6	17.3
Kazakhstan	2006	1,131	80.8%	7.4	9.2	5.3	6.4	8.9	7.9	5.3
Kyrgyzstan	2006	270	74.4%	5.2	16.4	2.5	1.8	5.6	6.2	3.9
Latvia	2006	237	81.0%	10.4	8.7	4.1	4.2	11.7	13.4	13.4
Lithuania	2006	335	78.2%	9.9	3.3	4.8	3.6	9.7	16.6	11.8
Luxembourg	2005	2	50.0%	0.4	3.6	0.0	0.0	0.0	0.0	1.5
Mexico	2005	2,198	83.8%	2.1	3.1	1.3	2.6	1.8	1.9	3.1
Netherlands	2006	88	76.1%	0.5	0.9	0.3	0.2	0.2	0.9	1.0
New Zealand	2004	57	77.2%	1.4	1.8	1.3	1.7	1.6	0.8	1.4
Nicaragua	2005	196	87.2%	3.6	1.2	2.1	5.3	4.1	4.1	6.5
Norway	2005	82	84.1%	1.8	1.0	0.5	1.8	1.4	1.8	4.0
Panama	2004	126	85.7%	4.1	6.7	2.9	3.2	4.0	3.6	7.4
Paraguay	2004	99	78.8%	1.6	1.7	1.0	2.3	1.5	1.8	1.6
Poland	2006	1,031	82.3%	2.7	0.9	1.1	2.5	2.6	4.0	2.4
Portugal	2003	167	74.9%	1.6	1.3	0.8	1.6	1.3	1.7	2.6
Puerto Rico	2005	37	81.1%	0.9	0.4	0.5	0.7	1.3	1.1	0.0
Republic of Korea	2006	757	78.2%	1.5	0.6	0.9	1.2	1.1	2.1	3.9
Romania	2007	992	79.0%	4.6	2.8	4.5	4.1	3.2	6.2	6.1
Russian Federation	2006	12,212	83.6%	8.6	3.7	4.9	6.9	10.8	10.2	7.3
Slovakia	2005	138	80.4%	2.6	3.1	0.8	1.8	2.1	4.4	2.4
Slovenia	2006	25	72.0%	1.2	0.0	0.0	0.0	0.3	1.7	4.4
South Africa	2005	147	73.5%	0.3	1.3	0.5	0.1	0.1	0.1	0.3
Spain	2005	494	81.6%	1.1	1.1	0.2	0.8	0.8	1.2	2.4
Sweden	2005	99	82.8%	1.1	0.0	0.5	0.3	0.7	1.5	2.6
Switzerland	2005	35	60.0%	0.5	0.3	0.7	0.6	0.0	0.6	0.8
Ukraine	2005	4,182	84.5%	8.9	4.3	5.7	6.8	10.9	11.7	6.5
United Kingdom	2006	214	72.0%	0.4	0.5	0.1	0.5	0.3	0.5	0.4
United States of America	2005	3,582	78.7%	1.2	2.7	0.6	1.5	1.0	1.0	1.3
Uruguay	2004	71	83.1%	2.1	2.3	1.7	3.3	1.6	1.9	2.5
Uzbekistan	2005	1,042	67.5%	4.0	15.5	3.3	1.7	2.9	2.7	3.2
Venezuela	2005	590	83.4%	2.3	3.8	2.0	3.5	1.8	1.7	1.7

Source: National Safety Council tabulations of World Health Organization data.
[a] Population estimates based on data from the World Health Organization and the U.S. Census Bureau (International Data Base).

INTERNATIONAL POISONING DEATHS AND DEATH RATES

The International Classification of Diseases system (ICD) identifies unintentional poisonings by codes X40–X49, which include cases of accidental poisoning by drugs, medicaments, biological substances, alcohol, solvents, gases, vapors, and pesticides. Other accidental poisonings by unspecified chemicals and noxious substances are also included.

UNINTENTIONAL POISONING DEATHS AND DEATH RATES BY AGE GROUP, LATEST YEAR AVAILABLE

| Country | Year | Deaths | | Deaths per 100,000 Population[a] | | | | | | |
		Total	% Male	All Ages	0 to 4	5 to 14	15 to 24	25 to 44	45 to 64	65+
Argentina	2005	365	64.4%	0.9	1.2	0.4	1.9	0.8	0.5	1.3
Australia	2003	668	67.7%	3.4	0.3	0.0	2.9	6.3	3.2	2.4
Austria	2006	38	52.6%	0.5	0.0	0.0	0.2	0.4	0.4	1.2
Belarus	2003	3,737	78.2%	37.8	5.1	0.5	6.7	45.1	80.5	30.6
Brazil	2004	249	68.7%	0.1	0.2	0.0	0.1	0.1	0.2	0.2
Canada	2004	954	71.4%	3.0	0.1	0.0	1.6	4.5	4.3	2.2
Chile	2005	109	70.6%	0.7	0.3	0.2	0.4	0.8	0.8	2.0
Colombia	2005	127	74.8%	0.3	0.4	0.1	0.3	0.3	0.3	0.8
Costa Rica	2005	6	83.3%	0.1	0.5	0.0	0.1	0.2	0.0	0.4
Croatia	2006	111	81.1%	2.5	0.0	0.2	2.4	4.5	1.9	2.5
Cuba	2005	36	66.7%	0.3	0.6	0.0	0.1	0.2	0.5	1.0
Czech Republic	2005	314	70.4%	3.1	0.4	0.2	1.7	2.9	5.7	2.6
Dominican Republic	2004	2	100.0%	0.0	0.0	0.0	0.0	0.0	0.0	0.2
Ecuador	2005	163	85.3%	1.2	0.3	0.2	0.7	1.5	2.8	0.3
El Salvador	2005	25	76.0%	0.4	0.0	0.0	0.2	0.5	0.7	2.3
Estonia	2005	262	77.5%	19.5	1.5	0.7	15.7	22.7	35.4	10.7
Finland	2006	861	74.8%	16.3	0.0	0.0	7.5	14.5	33.8	13.1
France	2005	1,016	55.0%	1.7	0.2	0.1	0.8	1.6	1.5	4.6
Germany	2006	758	75.2%	0.9	0.1	0.0	0.7	1.6	1.0	0.6
Hong Kong, China	2006	149	86.6%	2.2	0.0	0.0	0.8	3.8	2.6	0.7
Hungary	2005	154	68.8%	1.5	0.2	0.0	1.7	1.7	2.1	1.6
Israel	2004	89	82.0%	1.3	0.0	0.0	1.1	3.0	1.6	0.4
Japan	2006	873	68.3%	0.7	0.1	0.0	0.4	0.9	0.9	0.9
Kazakhstan	2006	3,598	77.2%	23.5	5.0	1.4	9.8	38.2	38.9	29.6
Kyrgyzstan	2006	648	77.9%	12.5	2.5	0.4	2.7	17.1	39.2	24.0
Latvia	2006	448	76.8%	19.6	0.0	0.5	5.8	23.4	39.1	13.2
Lithuania	2006	745	76.9%	21.9	2.6	0.8	3.2	23.6	47.2	20.0
Luxembourg	2005	12	91.7%	2.6	0.0	0.0	5.7	5.0	0.9	1.5
Mexico	2005	882	70.6%	0.8	0.6	0.3	0.7	1.1	1.0	2.0
Netherlands	2006	114	73.7%	0.7	0.0	0.1	0.6	1.2	0.7	0.8
New Zealand	2004	48	64.6%	1.2	0.0	0.3	1.4	2.2	1.0	0.6
Nicaragua	2005	17	70.6%	0.3	0.3	0.0	0.5	0.5	0.0	0.6
Norway	2005	316	72.8%	6.8	0.0	0.0	7.9	10.9	9.1	3.4
Panama	2004	26	65.4%	0.8	0.9	0.2	0.5	0.4	1.3	4.8
Paraguay	2004	15	53.3%	0.2	0.5	0.1	0.2	0.2	0.5	0.3
Poland	2006	2,087	83.2%	5.5	0.2	0.3	1.2	5.4	11.9	4.5
Portugal	2003	74	63.5%	0.7	0.4	0.5	0.3	1.2	0.4	0.8
Puerto Rico	2005	160	86.9%	4.1	0.0	0.0	3.2	8.5	4.2	0.0
Republic of Korea	2006	296	65.9%	0.6	0.0	0.1	0.1	0.3	0.7	3.3
Romania	2007	1,037	70.9%	4.8	3.4	0.4	1.3	3.1	8.1	10.0
Russian Federation	2006	55,303	77.8%	38.8	3.8	1.2	14.4	51.9	65.0	32.7
Slovakia	2005	162	80.2%	3.0	0.0	0.0	1.2	3.6	6.2	1.3
Slovenia	2006	28	71.4%	1.4	0.0	0.5	2.3	0.3	2.2	2.2
South Africa	2005	1,140	56.1%	2.4	12.9	0.4	0.5	1.7	1.9	3.1
Spain	2005	885	77.9%	2.0	0.0	0.1	1.4	3.8	1.4	1.5
Sweden	2005	295	78.3%	3.3	0.0	0.0	2.9	4.1	5.2	2.6
Switzerland	2005	32	53.1%	0.4	0.0	0.0	0.6	0.4	0.4	0.8
Ukraine	2005	14,066	78.6%	30.0	4.1	0.9	4.9	34.9	63.0	20.2
United Kingdom	2006	1,281	70.4%	2.1	0.0	0.1	1.8	3.8	2.5	1.2
United States of America	2005	23,618	67.3%	8.0	0.2	0.1	5.9	13.2	12.3	2.5
Uruguay	2004	21	71.4%	0.6	0.4	0.7	0.4	0.2	1.0	1.1
Uzbekistan	2005	426	76.8%	1.6	0.9	0.3	0.8	2.9	2.9	2.6
Venezuela	2005	82	69.5%	0.3	0.9	0.2	0.3	0.2	0.3	0.8

Source: National Safety Council tabulations of World Health Organization data.
[a]Population estimates based on data from the World Health Organization and the U.S. Census Bureau (International Data Base).

OCCUPATIONAL DEATHS

Counts and rates of fatal work-related injuries are shown on this page and the next. Comparisons between countries should be made with caution and take into account the differences in sources, coverage, and kinds of cases included.

OCCUPATIONAL DEATHS BY COUNTRY, 2003–2007

Country	Deaths					Source of Data	Maximum Period[a]	Coverage		
	2003	2004	2005	2006	2007			Worker Types[b]	% of Total Employment[c]	Activities Excluded
Injuries Only—Compensated Cases										
France	661	626	474	537	—	IR	varies	E	75	P
Injuries Only—Reported Cases										
Austria	103	132	124	107	—	IR	none	E, SE	71	none
Azerbaijan	52	72	54	81	128	LR	—	E	—	—
Belarus	214	248	235	228	214	C	same year	E	—	none
Czech Republic	199	185	163	152	188	AR	none	E, SE	95	AF, Pol
Hungary	133	160	125	123	118	LR	90 days	E, SE	98	none
Japan	1,628	1,620	1,514	1,472	1,357	LR	—	E	—	none
Latvia	41	61	56	53	58	S	none	E	—	none
Moldova, Rep. of	43	38	49	38	54	C	none	E	52	none
Norway	49	38	48	31	38	LR	none	E	100	none
Poland	515	490	468	493	479	LR	6 months	E, SE	76	Agr
Puerto Rico	29	55	51	—	—	C		E, SE	97	—
Singapore	55	51	44	62	63	LR	none	E	33	none
Slovakia	94	79	76	95	97	C	none	IE	98	none
Spain	722	695	662	682	613	IR	—	—	—	—
Sweden	56	57	67	68	—	IR	none	E, SE	97	none
Taiwan, China	401	366	382	—	—	LR	—	—	—	—
Ukraine	1,128	1,068	989	972	1,069	LR	4 months	E	71	AF
United Kingdom	174	179	173	—	—	LR	1 year	E, SE	92	SF, AT
United States	5,575	5,764	5,734	5,840	—	C	none	E, SE	100	none
Injuries and Commuting Accidents—Compensated Cases										
Croatia	47	38	62	76	74	IR	immediate	E, SE	84	none
Germany	1,029	949	863	—	—	IR	none	E, SE	100	none
Italy	976	930	918	938	987	IR	none	I	76	none
Injuries and Commuting Accidents —Reported Cases										
Hong Kong, China	171	187	187	187	—	LR	none	E	77	none
Kyrgyzstan	26	41	24	22	—	LR	none	E	33	none
Lithuania	118	94	118	108	—	LR	none	E, SE	64	AF
Romania	423	432	531	416	344	LR	same year	E, SE	61	AF, P
Russian Federation	3,540	3,290	3,090	2,900	2,986	S	none	E	5	Low
Slovenia	40	21	21	32	--	LR	1 month	I	85	none
Injuries and Diseases—Compensated Cases										
Australia[d]	196	168	166	177	—	IR	3 years	E	83	AF
Canada	963	928	1,097	976	—	IR	none	E, SE	85	AF
Finland	43	44	51	46	—	IR	1 year	E	85	none
Malta	12	12	6	8	7	IR	—	E, SE	—	none
Switzerland	46	67	45	51	—	IR	same year	IE	88	none
Injuries and Diseases—Reported Cases										
Iceland	4	2	3	6	—	AR	none	E	—	none
Sri Lanka	42	42	52	84	77	LR	1 year	E	35	M,E,TSC,C
Turkey	811	843	1,096	1,601	—	IR	—	IE	25	none
Injuries, Diseases, and Commuting Accidents—Compensated Cases										
Costa Rica	55	50	60	—	—	IR	none	I	56	none
Estonia	31	34	24	28	21	IR	1 year	I	100	AF, Pol
Israel	88	88	82	84	76	IR	same year	E, SE	100	none
South Korea[e]	1,408	1,417	1,288	1,238	1,267	IR	—	I	45	none
Syrian Arab Republic	174	205	612	—	—	LR	—	I	46	none
Thailand	787	861	1,444	808	741	IR	—	I	16	none
Injuries, Diseases, and Commuting Accidents—Reported Cases										
Bahrain	21	13	29	25	22	IR	none	E, SE	100	none
Bulgaria	114	130	130	169	—	AR	—	E, SE	35	none
Jordan	70	52	63	87	—	IR	none	E	—	AF
Mexico	1,427	1,364	1,367	1,328	1,279	IR	none	IE	32	none
New Zealand	88	80	105	97	—	IR	1 year	E, SE	100	none

Source: International Labour Office. (2006). Yearly Data of Total and Economically Active Population, Employment, Unemployment, Hours of Work, Wages, Labour Cost, Consumer Price Indices, Occupational Injuries, Strikes and Lockouts: 1969–2005. Data available at http://laborsta.ilo.org
Note: Dash (—) indicates data not available.
[a]Maximum period between accident and death for death to be counted.

[b]Types of workers included in the data.
[c]Workers covered by the statistics as a percentage of total employment; latest year available.
[d]Excluding Victoria and Australian Capital Territory.
[e]Establishments with 10 or more workers.

Source of Data	Worker Types	Economic Activities			
AR = Administrative reports	E = Employees	AF = Armed forces	D = Domestic services	PA = Public administration
C = Census	I = Insured persons	Agr = Agriculture	E = Electricity, gas, and water	Pol = Police
IR = Insurance records	IE = Insured employees	ASO = Air, sea, offshore accidents	Low = Activities with low rates of injuries	SF = Sea fishing
LR = Labor inspectorate records	SE = Self-employed	AT = Air transport	M = Manufacturing	TSC = Transport, storage, and communications
S = Survey		C = Construction	P = Public sector	

The International Labour Organization (ILO) estimates that approximately 270 million work-related injuries occur worldwide every year. The annual death toll has exceeded 350,000 worldwide and is expected to increase even further in the foreseeable future.

Source: International Labour Organization. (2005). Global Estimates of Fatal Work Related Diseases and Occupational Accidents, World Bank Regions 2005. *[http://www.ilo.org/public/english/protection/safework/accidis/globest_2005/index.htm, accessed 10/3/08].*

OCCUPATIONAL DEATH RATES BY COUNTRY, 2003–2007

Country	Coverage[a]	2003	2004	2005	2006	2007
Deaths per 100,000 Employed Persons						
Injuries Only						
Azerbaijan	RC	6	8	6	8	13
Belarus	RC	5.6	6.4	6.1	5.8	5.4
Hungary	RC	3.39	4.1	3.2	3.13	3.01
Moldova, Rep. of	RC	5.6	4.9	6.4	4.7	7.1
Norway	RC	2.1	1.7	2.1	1.3	1.6
Poland	RC	4.9	4.7	4.4	4.6	4.3
Sweden	RC	1.3	1.4	1.6	1.6	—
Ukraine	RC	9.4	8.9	8.4	8.3	9.3
United Kingdom	RC	0.7	0.7	0.6	—	—
United States	RC	4	4	4	4	—
Injuries and Commuting Accidents						
Croatia	CC	3.4	2.7	4.3	5	4.7
Germany	CC	2.83	2.57	2.38	—	—
Hong Kong, China	RC	7.2	7.7	7.5	7.3	—
Kyrgyzstan	RC	5	8	5	5	—
Lithuania	RC	11.3	9	10.9	9.6	—
Romania	RC	7	7	9	7	6
Russian Federation	RC	13.1	12.9	12.4	11.9	12.4
Injuries and Diseases						
Australia	CC	2.4	2	1.9	2	—
Canada	CC	6.1	5.8	6.8	5.9	—
Finland	CC	2.1	2.1	2.4	2.2	—
Malta	CC	8.2	8.1	4	5.2	4.5
Injuries, Diseases, and Commuting Accidents						
Israel	CC	3.6	3.3	3	3	2.6
Bahrain	RC	10	5	10	8	7
Deaths per 100,000 Workers Insured						
Injuries Only						
France	CC	3.7	3.5	—	—	—
Austria	RC	3.86	5	4.6	3.9	—
Czech Republic	RC	4.5	4.2	3.7	3.4	4.1
Slovakia	RC	4.66	3.91	3.72	4.6	4.1
Spain	RC	5.27	4.89	4.5	4.4	3.8
Taiwan, China	RC	5	4.4	4.5	—	—
Injuries and Commuting Accidents						
Italy	CC	5	5	5	5	—
Slovenia	RC	5.1	2.6	2.6	3.8	—
Injuries and Diseases						
Switzerland	CC	1.3	1.9	1.3	1.4	—
Turkey	RC	14.4	13.6	15.8	20.5	—
Injuries, Diseases, and Commuting Accidents						
Costa Rica	CC	7	6.1	6.4	—	—
Estonia	CC	5.22	5.71	3.95	4.3	3.2
Thailand	CC	11.19	11.66	18.7	10.1	9.1
Bulgaria	RC	5.2	6	5.8	7.2	—
Mexico	RC	12	11	11	10	9
Deaths per 1,000,000 Hours Worked						
Injuries Only						
Japan	RC	0.01	0.01	0.01	0.01	0.01
Injuries and Diseases						
Sri Lanka	RC	0.01	0.007	0.009	0.0135	0.012
Injuries, Diseases, and Commuting Accidents						
Jordan	RC	0.062	0.039	0.025	0.055	—
South Korea	CC	0.06	0.06	0.05	0.05	0.04

See source and limitations of data on page 186.
Note: Dash (—) indicates data not available.
[a]*Includes reported cases (RC) and compensated cases (CC) of occupational fatalities.*

NATIONAL SAFETY COUNCIL

INJURY FACTS®

This appendix gives a brief explanation of some of the sources and methods used by the National Safety Council (NSC) Statistics Department in preparing the estimates of deaths, injuries, and costs presented in this book. Because many of the estimates depend on death certificate data provided by the states or the National Center for Health Statistics (NCHS), it begins with a brief introduction to the certification and classification of deaths.

Certification and classification. The medical certification of death involves entering information on the death certificate about the disease or condition directly leading to death, antecedent causes, and other significant conditions. The death certificate is then registered with the appropriate authority and a code is assigned for the underlying cause of death. The underlying cause is defined as "(a) the disease or injury which initiated the train of morbid events leading directly to death, or (b) the circumstances of the accident or violence which produced the fatal injury" (World Health Organization [WHO], 1992). Deaths are classified and coded on the basis of a WHO standard, the *International Statistical Classification of Diseases and Related Health Problems*, commonly known as the International Classification of Diseases or ICD (WHO, 1992). For deaths due to injury and poisoning, the ICD provides a system of "external cause" codes to which the underlying cause of death is assigned. (See pages 18–19 of *Injury Facts®* for a condensed list of external cause codes.)

Comparability across ICD revisions. The ICD is revised periodically and these revisions can affect comparability from year to year. The sixth revision (1948) substantially expanded the list of external causes and provided for classifying the place of occurrence. Changes in the classification procedures for the sixth revision as well as the seventh (1958) and eighth (1968) revisions classified as diseases some deaths previously classified as injuries. The eighth revision also expanded and reorganized some external cause sections. The ninth revision (1979), provided more detail on the agency involved, the victim's activity, and the place of occurrence. The tenth revision, which was adopted in the United States effective with 1999 data, completely revised the transportation-related categories. Specific external cause categories affected by the revisions are noted in the historical tables.

The table at the end of this appendix (page 186) shows the ICD-9 codes, the ICD-10 codes, and a comparability ratio for each of the principal causes of unintentional-injury death. The comparability ratio represents the net effect of the new revision on statistics for the cause of death. The comparability ratio was obtained by classifying a sample of death certificates under both ICD-9 and ICD-10 and then dividing the number of deaths for a selected cause classified under ICD-10 by the number classified to the most nearly comparable ICD-9 cause. A comparability ratio of 1.00 indicates no net change due to the new classification scheme. A ratio less than 1.00 indicates fewer deaths assigned to a cause under ICD-10 than under ICD-9. A ratio greater than 1.00 indicates an increase in assignment of deaths to a cause under ICD-10 compared to ICD-9.

The broad category of "accidents" or "unintentional injuries" under ICD-9 included complications and misadventures of surgical and medical care (E870–E879) and adverse effects of drugs in therapeutic use (E930–E949). These categories are not included in "accidents" or "unintentional injuries" under ICD-10. In 1998, deaths in these two categories numbered 3,228 and 276, respectively.

Under ICD-9, the code range for falls (E880–E888) included a code for "fracture, cause unspecified" (E887). A similar code does not appear in ICD-10 (W00–W19), which probably accounts for the low comparability ratio (0.8409). In 1998, deaths in code E887 numbered 3,679.

Beginning with 1970 data, tabulations published by NCHS no longer include deaths of nonresident aliens. In 2005, there were 976 such accidental deaths, of which 368 were motor-vehicle related.

Fatality estimates. The Council uses four classes and three venues to categorize unintentional injuries. The four classes are Motor Vehicle, Work, Home, and Public. Each class represents an environment and an intervention route for injury prevention through a responsible authority such as a police department, an employer, a home owner, or public health department. The three venues are Transportation, Work, and Home & Community.

Motor vehicle. The Motor-Vehicle class can be identified by the underlying cause of death (see the table on page 194).

Work. The National Safety Council adopted the Bureau of Labor Statistics' Census of Fatal Occupational Injuries (CFOI) figure, beginning with the 1992 data year, as the authoritative count of unintentional work-related deaths. The CFOI system is described in detail in Toscano and Windau (1994).

The 2-Way Split. After subtracting the Motor-Vehicle and Work figures from the unintentional-injury total (ICD-10 codes V01–X59, Y85–Y86), the remainder belong to the Home and Public classes. The Home class can be identified by the "place of occurrence" subclassification (code .0) used with most nontransport deaths; the Public class is the remainder. Missing "place of occurrence" information, however, prevents the direct determination of the Home and Public class totals. Because of this, the Council allocates nonmotor-vehicle, nonwork deaths into the Home and Public classes based on the external cause, age group, and cases with specified "place of occurrence." This procedure, known as the 2-Way Split, uses the most recent death certificate data available from the NCHS and the CFOI data for the same calendar year. For each cause-code group and age group combination, the Motor-Vehicle and Work deaths are subtracted and the remainder, including those with "place of occurrence" unspecified, are allocated to Home and Public in the same proportion as those with "place of occurrence" specified.

The table on page 194 shows the ICD-10 cause-codes and CFOI event codes for the most common causes of unintentional-injury death. The CFOI event codes (BLS, 1992) do not match exactly with ICD cause codes, so there is some error in the allocation of deaths among the classes.

State reporting system. The Council operates a reporting system through which participating states send tabulations of unintentional-injury death data by age group, class, and type of event or industry. This is known as the Injury Mortality Tabulation reporting system. These data are used to make current year estimates based on the most recent 2-Way Split and CFOI data.

Linking up to current year. The benchmark data published by NCHS are usually two years old and the CFOI data are usually one year old. The link-relative technique is used to make current year estimates from these data using the state vital statistics data. This method assumes that the change in deaths from one year to the next in states reporting for both years reflects the change in deaths for the entire nation. The ratio is calculated and multiplied times the benchmark figure resulting in an estimate for the next year. It may be necessary to repeat the process, depending on the reference year of the benchmark. For example, the 2005 NCHS and CFOI data were used this year for a 2-Way Split and state data were used to make estimates for 2006 and 2007 Home and Public classes using the link-relative technique. CFOI data for 2006 and 2007 were also available so it was not necessary to make Work estimates.

Revisions of prior years. When the figures for a given year are published by NCHS, the 2-Way Split based on those figures and the CFOI become the final estimate of unintentional-injury deaths by class, age group, and type of event or industry. Subsequent years are revised by repeating the link-relative process described above. For example, in the current edition of *Injury Facts*®, the 2005 NCHS and CFOI data were used to produce final estimates using the 2-Way Split, the 2006 estimates were revised using more complete state data and 2006 CFOI figures, and the new 2007 estimates were made with the state data available in the late summer of 2008 together with 2007 CFOI data.

Nonfatal injury estimates. The Council uses the concept of "disabling injury" to define the kinds of injuries included in its estimates. See page 23 for the definition of disabling injury and the National Health Interview Survey (NHIS) injury definitions.

Injury to death ratios. There is no national injury surveillance system that provides disabling injury estimates on a current basis. The National Health Interview Survey, a household survey conducted by the NCHS (see page 23), produces national estimates using its own definition of injury (Schiller, Adams, & Coriaty Nelson, 2005). For this reason, the Council uses injury-to-death ratios to estimate nonfatal disabling injuries for the current year. Complete documentation of the procedure, effective with the 1993 edition, may be found in Landes, Ginsburg, Hoskin, and Miller (1990).

The resulting estimates are not direct measures of nonfatal injuries and should not be compared with prior years.

Population sources. All population figures used in computing rates are estimates taken from various reports published by the Bureau of the Census, U.S. Department of Commerce, on their Internet web site (www.census.gov). *Resident* population is used for computing rates.

Costs (pp. 4–7). The procedures for estimating the economic losses due to fatal and nonfatal unintentional injuries were extensively revised for the 1993 edition of *Accident Facts*®. New components were added, new benchmarks adopted, and a new discount rate assumed. All of these changes resulted in significantly higher cost estimates. For this reason, it must be re-emphasized that the cost estimates should not be compared to those in earlier editions of the book.

The Council's general philosophy underlying its cost estimates is that the figures represent income not received or expenses incurred because of fatal and nonfatal unintentional injuries. Stated this way, the Council's cost estimates are a measure of the economic impact of unintentional injuries and may be compared to other economic measures such as gross domestic product, per capita income, or personal consumption expenditures. (See page 91 and "lost quality of life" [p. 193] for a discussion of injury costs for cost-benefit analysis.)

The general approach followed was to identify a benchmark unit cost for each component, adjust the benchmark to the current year using an appropriate inflator, estimate the number of cases to which the component applied, and compute the product. Where possible, benchmarks were obtained for each class: Motor Vehicle, Work, Home, and Public.

Wage and productivity losses include the value of wages, fringe benefits, and household production for all classes, and travel delay for the Motor Vehicle class.

For fatalities, the present value of after-tax wages, fringe benefits, and household production was computed using the human capital method. The procedure

incorporates data on life expectancy from the NCHS life tables, employment likelihood from the Bureau of Labor Statistics household survey, and mean earnings from the Bureau of the Census money income survey. The discount rate used was 4%, reduced from 6% used in earlier years. The present value obtained is highly sensitive to the discount rate; the lower the rate, the greater the present value.

For permanent partial disabilities, an average of 17% of earning power is lost (Berkowitz & Burton, 1987). The incidence of permanent disabilities, adjusted to remove intentional injuries, was computed from data on hospitalized cases from the National Hospital Discharge Survey (NHDS) and nonhospitalized cases from the National Health Interview Survey and National Council on Compensation Insurance data on probabilities of disability by nature of injury and part of body injured.

For temporary disabilities, an average daily wage, fringe benefit, and household production loss was calculated and this was multiplied by the number of days of restricted activity from the NHIS.

Travel delay costs were obtained from the Council's estimates of the number of fatal, injury, and property damage crashes and an average delay cost per crash from Miller et al. (1991).

Medical expenses, including ambulance and helicopter transport costs, were estimated for fatalities, hospitalized cases, and nonhospitalized cases in each class.

The incidence of hospitalized cases was derived from the NHDS data adjusted to eliminate intentional injuries. Average length of stay was benchmarked from Miller, Pindus, Douglass, and Rossman (1993b) and adjusted to estimate lifetime length of stay. The cost per hospital day was benchmarked to the National Medical Expenditure Survey (NMES).

Nonhospitalized cases were estimated by taking the difference between total NHIS injuries and hospitalized cases. Average cost per case was based on NMES data adjusted for inflation and lifetime costs.

Medical cost of fatalities was benchmarked to data from the National Council on Compensation Insurance

(1989) to which was added the cost of a premature funeral and coroner costs (Miller et al., 1991).

Cost per ambulance transport was benchmarked to NMES data and cost per helicopter transport was benchmarked to data in Miller et al. (1993a). The number of cases transported was based on data from Rice and MacKenzie (1989) and the National Electronic Injury Surveillance System.

Administrative expenses include the administrative cost of private and public insurance, which represents the cost of having insurance, and police and legal costs.

The administrative cost of motor-vehicle insurance was the difference between premiums earned (adjusted to remove fire, theft, and casualty premiums) and pure losses incurred, based on data from A. M. Best. Workers' compensation insurance administration was based on A. M. Best data for private carriers and regression estimates using Social Security Administration data for state funds and the self-insured. Administrative costs of public insurance (mainly Medicaid and Medicare) amount to about 4% of the medical expenses paid by public insurance, which were determined from Rice and MacKenzie (1989) and Hensler et al. (1991).

Average police costs for motor-vehicle crashes were taken from Miller et al. (1991) and multiplied by the Council's estimates of the number of fatal, injury and property damage crashes.

Legal expenses include court costs, and plaintiff's and defendant's time and expenses. Hensler et al. (1991) provided data on the proportion of injured persons who hire a lawyer, file a claim, and get compensation. Kakalik and Pace (1986) provided data on costs per case.

Fire losses were based on data published by the National Fire Protection Association in the *NFPA Journal*. The allocation into the classes was based on the property use for structure fires and other NFPA data for nonstructure fires.

Motor-vehicle damage costs were benchmarked to Blincoe and Faigin (1992) and multiplied by the Council's estimates of crash incidence.

Employer costs for work injuries is an estimate of the productivity costs incurred by employers. It assumes each fatality or permanent injury resulted in 4 person-months of disruption, serious injuries 1 person-month, and minor to moderate injuries 2 person-days. All injuries to nonworkers were assumed to involve 2 days of worker productivity loss. Average hourly earnings for supervisors and nonsupervisory workers were computed and then multiplied by the incidence and hours lost per case. Property damage and production delays (except motor-vehicle related) are not included in the estimates but can be substantial.

Lost quality of life is the difference between the value of a statistical fatality or statistical injury and the value of after-tax wages, fringe benefits, and household production. Because this does not represent real income not received or expenses incurred, it is not included in the total economic cost figure. If included, the resulting *comprehensive costs* can be used in cost-benefit analysis because the total costs then represent the maximum amount society should spend to prevent a statistical death or injury.

Work deaths and injuries (p. 48). The method for estimating total work-related deaths and injuries is discussed above. The breakdown of deaths by industry division for the current year is obtained from the CFOI and state Injury Mortality Tabulation figures using the link-relative technique (also discussed above).

The estimate of nonfatal disabling injuries by industry division is made by multiplying the estimate of employment for each industry division by the BLS estimate of the incidence rate of cases involving days away from work for each division (e.g., BLS, 2008) and then adjusting the results so that they add to the work-injury total previously established. The "private sector" average incidence rate is used for the government division, which is not covered in the BLS survey.

Employment. The employment estimates for 1992 to the present were changed for the 1998 edition. Estimates for these years in prior editions are not comparable. The total employment figure used by the Council represents the number of persons in the civilian labor force, aged 16 and older, who were wage or salary workers, self-employed, or unpaid family workers, plus active duty military personnel resident in the U.S. The total employment estimate is a combination of three figures—total civilian employment from the Current Population Survey (CPS) as published in *Employment and Earnings*, plus the difference between total resident population and total civilian population, which represents active duty military personnel.

Employment by industry is obtained from an unpublished Bureau of Labor Statistics table titled "Employed and experience unemployed persons by detailed industry and class of worker, Annual Average [year] (based on CPS)."

Time lost (p. 51) is the product of the number of cases and the average time lost per case. Deaths average 150 workdays lost in the current year and 5,850 in future years; permanent disabilities involve 75 and 565 days lost in current and future years, respectively; temporary disabilities involve 17 days lost in the current year only. Off-the-job injuries to workers are assumed to result in similar lost time.

Off-the-job (p. 52) deaths and injuries are estimated by assuming that employed persons incur injuries at the same rate as the entire population.

Motor-Vehicle (pp. 86–117). Estimates of miles traveled, registered vehicles and licensed drivers are published by the Federal Highway Administration in *Highway Statistics* and *Traffic Volume Trends*.

SELECTED UNINTENTIONAL-INJURY CODE GROUPINGS

Manner of Injury	ICD-9 Codes[a]	ICD-10 Codes[b]	Comparability Ratio[c]	OI & ICM[d] Event Codes
Unintentional Injuries	E800–E869, E880–E929[e]	V01–X59, Y85–Y86	1.0305 (1.0278–1.0333)[f]	00–60, 63–9999
Railway accident	E800–E807	V05, V15, V80.6, V81(.2–.9)	n/a	44
Motor-vehicle accident	E810–E825	V02–V04, V09.0, V09.2, V12–V14, V19.0–V19.2, V19.4–V19.6, V20–V79, V80.3–V80.5, V81.0–V81.1, V82.0–V82.1, V83–V86, V87.0–V87.8, V88.0–V88.8, V89.0, V89.2	0.9754 (0.9742–0.9766)	41, 42, 43 with source = 82, 83
Water transport accident	E830–E838	V90–V94	n/a	45
Air transport accident	E840–E845	V95–V97	n/a	46
Poisoning by solids and liquids	E850–58, E860–66	X40–X49	n/a	344
Poisoning by gases and vapors	E867–E869			341
Falls	E880–E888	W00–W19	0.8409 (0.8313–0.8505)	1
Fires and burns	E890–E899	X00–X09	0.9743 (0.9568–0.9918)	51
Drowning	E910	W65–W74	0.9965 (0.9716–1.0213)	381
Suffocation by ingestion or inhalation	E911–E912	W78–W80	n/a	382
Mechanical suffocation	E913	W75–W77, W81–W84	n/a	383, 384, 389
Firearms	E922	W32–W34	1.0579 (1.0331–1.0828)	0220, 0222, 0229 with source = 911[g]

Source: National Safety Council.
Note: n/a means comparability ratio not calculated or does not meet standards of reliability or precision.
[a]*WHO (1977).*
[b]*WHO (1992).*
[c]*Hoyert, Arias, Smith, et al. (2001). Table III.*

[d]*BLS (1992).*
[e]*The National Safety Council has used E800–E949 for unintentional injuries. The code group in the table omits complications and misadventures of surgical and medical care (E870–E879) and adverse effects of drugs in therapeutic use (E930–E949).*
[f]*Figures in parentheses are the 95% confidence interval for the comparability ratio.*
[g]*Struck by flying object where the source of injury was a bullet.*

Berkowitz, M., & Burton, J.F., Jr. (1987). *Permanent Disability Benefits in Workers' Compensation.* Kalamazoo, MI: W.E. Upjohn Institute for Employment Research.

Blincoe, L.J., & Faigin, B.M. (1992). *Economic Cost of Motor Vehicle Crashes*, 1990. Springfield, VA: National Technical Information Service.

Bureau of Labor Statistics [BLS]. (1992). *Occupational Injury & Illness Classification Manual.* Itasca, IL: National Safety Council.

Bureau of Labor Statistics [BLS]. (2008, October 23). *Workplace Injuries and Illnesses in 2007.* Press release USDL-08-1498.

Hensler, D.R., Marquis, M.S., Abrahamse, A.F., Berry, S.H., Ebener, P.A., Lewis, E.D., Lind, E.A., MacCoun, R.J., Manning, W.G., Rogowski, J.A., & Vaiana, M.E. (1991). *Compensation for Accidental Injuries in the United States.* Santa Monica, CA: The RAND Corporation.

Hoyert, D.L., Arias, E., Smith, B.L., Murphy, S.L., & Kochanek, K.D. (2001). Deaths: final data for 1999. *National Vital Statistics Reports, 49*(8).

Kakalik, J.S., & Pace, N. (1986). *Costs and Compensation Paid in Tort Litigation.* R-3391-ICJ. Santa Monica, CA: The RAND Corporation.

Landes, S.R., Ginsburg, K.M., Hoskin, A.F., & Miller, T.A. (1990). *Estimating Nonfatal Injuries.* Itasca, IL: Statistics Department, National Safety Council.

Miller, T., Viner, J., Rossman, S., Pindus, N., Gellert, W., Douglass, J., Dillingham, A., & Blomquist, G. (1991). *The Costs of Highway Crashes.* Springfield, VA: National Technical Information Service.

Miller, T.R., Brigham, P.A., Cohen, M.A., Douglass, J.B., Galbraith, M.S., Lestina, D.C., Nelkin, V.S., Pindus, N.M., & Smith-Regojo, P. (1993a). Estimating the costs to society of cigarette fire injuries. *Report to Congress in Response to the Fire Safe Cigarette Act of 1990.* Washington, DC: U.S. Consumer Product Safety Commission.

Miller, T.R., Pindus, N.M., Douglass, J.B., & Rossman, S.B. (1993b). *Nonfatal Injury Incidence, Costs, and Consequences: A Data Book.* Washington, DC: The Urban Institute Press.

Rice, D.P., & MacKenzie, E.J. (1989). *Cost of Injury in the United States: A Report to Congress.* Atlanta, GA: Centers for Disease Control and Prevention.

Schiller, J.S., Adams, P.F., & Coriaty Nelson Z. (2005). Summary health statistics for the U.S. population: National health interview survey, 2003. *Vital and Health Statistics, Series 10, No. 224.* Hyattsville, MD: National Center for Health Statistics.

Toscano, G., & Windau, J. (1994). The changing character of fatal work injuries. *Monthly Labor Review, 117*(10), 17–28.

World Health Organization. (1977). *Manual of the International Statistical Classification of Diseases, Injuries, and Causes of Death.* Geneva, Switzerland: Author.

World Health Organization. (1992). *International Statistical Classification of Diseases and Related Health Problems—Tenth Revision.* Geneva, Switzerland: Author.

The following organizations may be useful for obtaining more current data or more detailed information on various subjects in *Injury Facts*®.

American Association of Poison Control Centers
3201 New Mexico Avenue, Suite 330
Washington, DC 20016
(202) 362-7217
www.aapcc.org
info@aapcc.org

Bureau of Labor Statistics
U.S. Department of Labor
2 Massachusetts Avenue, NE
Washington, DC 20212
(202) 691-5200
www.bls.gov
blsdata_staff@bls.gov

Bureau of the Census
U.S. Department of Commerce
Public Information Office
Washington, DC 20233-0001
(800) 321-1995
www.census.gov

Bureau of Justice Statistics
810 7th Street, NW
Washington, DC 20531
(202) 307-0765
www.ojp.usdoj.gov/bjs
askbjs@usdoj.gov

Bureau of Transportation Statistics
U.S. Department of Transportation
400 7th Street, SW, Room 3430
Washington, DC 20590
(800) 853-1351
www.bts.gov
answers@bts.gov

Centers for Disease Control and Prevention
1600 Clifton Road
Atlanta, GA 30333
(800) 311-3435
www.cdc.gov

Chemical Safety Board
2175 K Street, NW, Suite 400
Washington, DC 20037
(202) 261-7600
www.chemsafety.gov
info@csb.gov

Eno Transportation Foundation
1634 I Street, NW, Suite 500
Washington, DC 20006
(202) 879-4700
www.enotrans.com

Environmental Protection Agency, U.S.
1200 Pennsylvania Avenue, NW
Washington, DC 20460
(202) 272-0167
www.epa.gov

European Agency for Safety and Health at Work
Gran Via, 33
E-48009 Bilbao, Spain
Phone: +34 944-794-360
Fax: +34 944-794-383
http://europe.osha.eu.int
information@osha.eu.int

Federal Aviation Administration
U.S. Department of Transportation
National Aviation Safety Data Analysis Center
800 Independence Avenue, SW
Washington, DC 20591
(866) 835-5322
www.faa.gov

Federal Bureau of Investigation
935 Pennsylvania Avenue, NW
Washington, DC 20535-0001
(202) 324-3000
www.fbi.gov

Federal Highway Administration
U.S. Department of Transportation
400 7th Street, SW
Washington, DC 20590
(202) 366-0660
www.fhwa.dot.gov
execsecretariat.fhwa@fhwa.dot.gov

Federal Motor Carrier Safety Administration
U.S. Department of Transportation
400 7th Street, SW
Washington, DC 20590
(800) 832-5660
www.fmcsa.dot.gov

Federal Railroad Administration
U.S. Department of Transportation
1120 Vermont Avenue, NW
Washington, DC 20590
(202) 493-6000
www.fra.dot.gov

Federal Transit Administration
400 7th Street, SW
Washington, DC 20590
www.fta.dot.gov

FedStats
Gateway to official statistical information available to the public from more than 100 federal agencies.
www.fedstats.gov

FirstGov
Gateway to federal, state, local, tribal, and international government websites.
www.firstgov.gov

Insurance Information Institute
110 William Street
New York, NY 10038
(212) 346-5500
www.iii.org

Insurance Institute for Highway Safety
1005 N. Glebe Road, Suite 800
Arlington, VA 22201
(703) 247-1500
www.highwaysafety.org

International Hunter Education Association
P.O. Box 490
Wellington, CO 80549-0490
(970) 568-7954
www.ihea.com
info@ihea.com

International Labour Office
4, rue des Morillons
CH-1211 Geneva 22
Switzerland
Phone: +41-22-799-6111
Fax: +41-22-798-8685
www.ilo.org
ilo@ilo.org

Mine Safety and Health Administration
1100 Wilson Boulevard, 21st Floor
Arlington, VA 22209-3939
(202) 693-9400
www.msha.gov

Motorcycle Safety Foundation
2 Jenner Street, Suite 150
Irvine, CA 92718-3812
(714) 727-3227
www.msf-usa.org

National Academy of Social Insurance
1776 Massachusetts Avenue, NW, Suite 615
Washington, DC 20036-1904
(202) 452-8097
www.nasi.org
nasi@nasi.org

National Center for Education Statistics
U.S. Department of Education
1990 K Street, NW
Washington, DC 20006
(202) 502-7300
http://nces.ed.gov

National Center for Health Statistics
3311 Toledo Road, Room 2217
Hyattsville, MD 20782
(301) 458-4000
www.cdc.gov/nchs

National Center for Injury Prevention and Control
Office Of Communication Resources, Mail Stop K65
4770 Buford Highway, NE
Atlanta, GA 30341-3724
(770) 488-1506
www.cdc.gov/ncipc
ohcinfo@cdc.gov

National Clearinghouse for Alcohol and Drug Information
P.O. Box 2345
Rockville, MD 20847-2345
(301) 468-2600 or (800) 729-6686
www.health.org

National Climatic Data Center
151 Patton Avenue
Asheville, NC 28801-5001
(828) 271-4800
www.ncdc.noaa.gov/oa/ncdc.html
ncdc.info@noaa.gov

National Collegiate Athletic Association
700 W. Washington Street
P.O. Box 6222
Indianapolis, IN 46206-6222
(317) 917-6222
www.ncaa.org

National Council on Compensation Insurance
901 Peninsula Corporate Circle
Boca Raton, FL 33487
(800) NCCI-123 (800-622-4123)
www.ncci.com

National Fire Protection Association
P.O. Box 9101
Batterymarch Park
Quincy, MA 02269-0910
(617) 770-3000 or (800) 344-3555
www.nfpa.org
osds@nfpa.org

National Highway Traffic Safety Administration
U.S. Department of Transportation
400 7th Street, SW
Washington, DC 20590
(888) 327-4236
www.nhtsa.dot.gov
    National Center for Statistics and Analysis (NPO-121)
    (202) 366-4198 or (800) 934-8517
    NCSAweb@nhtsa.dot.gov

National Institute for Occupational Safety and Health
Clearinghouse for Occupational Safety and Health
    Information
4676 Columbia Parkway
Cincinnati, OH 45226
(800) 356-4674
www.cdc.gov/niosh
eidtechinfo@cdc.gov

National Spinal Cord Injury Association
6701 Democracy Boulevard, Suite 300-9
Bethesda, MD 20817
(301) 214-4006
www.spinalcord.org
info@spinalcord.org

National Sporting Goods Association
1601 Feehanville Drive, Suite 300
Mt. Prospect, IL 60056
(800) 815-5422
www.nsga.org
info@nsga.org

National Transportation Safety Board
490 L'Enfant Plaza East, SW
Washington, DC 20594
(202) 314-6000
www.ntsb.gov

Occupational Safety and Health Administration
U.S. Department of Labor
Office of Statistics
200 Constitution Avenue, NW
Washington, DC 20210
(800) 321-OSHA (6742)
www.osha.gov

Prevent Blindness America
211 W. Wacker Dr., Suite 1700
Chicago, IL 60606
(800) 331-2020
www.preventblindness.org
info@preventblindness.org

Transportation Research Board
500 5th Street, NW
Washington, DC 20001
(202) 334-2934
www.nas.edu/trb

U.S. Coast Guard
2100 2nd Street, SW
Washington, DC 20593-0001
(800) 368-5647
www.uscgboating.org
uscginfoline@gcrm.com

U.S. Consumer Product Safety Commission
National Injury Information Clearinghouse
Washington, DC 20207-0001
(301) 504-7921
www.cpsc.gov
clearinghouse@cpsc.gov

World Health Organization
20, avenue Appia
CH-1211 Geneva 27
Switzerland
Phone: +41-22-791-2111
Fax: +41-22-791-3111
www.who.int
info@who.int

Accident is that occurrence in a sequence of events that produces unintended injury, death, or property damage. *Accident* refers to the event, not the result of the event (see *Unintentional injury*).

Death from accident is a death that occurs within one year of the accident.

Disabling injury is an injury causing death, permanent disability, or any degree of temporary total disability beyond the day of the injury.

Fatal accident is an accident that results in one or more deaths within one year.

Home is a dwelling and its premises within the property lines including single-family dwellings and apartment houses, duplex dwellings, boarding and rooming houses, and seasonal cottages. Excluded from *home* are barracks, dormitories, and resident institutions.

Incidence rate, as defined by OSHA, is the number of occupational injuries and/or illnesses or lost workdays per 100 full-time employees (see formula on page 61).

Injury is physical harm or damage to the body resulting from an exchange, usually acute, of mechanical, chemical, thermal, or other environmental energy that exceeds the body's tolerance.

Motor vehicle is any mechanically or electrically powered device not operated on rails, upon which or by which any person or property may be transported upon a land highway. The load on a motor vehicle or trailer attached to it is considered part of the vehicle. Tractors and motorized machinery are included while self-propelled in transit or used for transportation. *Nonmotor vehicle* is any road vehicle other than a motor vehicle, such as a bicycle or animal-drawn vehicle, except a coaster wagon, child's sled, child's tricycle, child's carriage, and similar means of transportation; persons using these latter means of transportation are considered pedestrians.

Motor-vehicle accident is an unstabilized situation that includes at least one harmful event (injury or property damage) involving a motor vehicle in transport (in motion, in readiness for motion, or on a roadway but not parked in a designated parking area) that does not result from discharge of a firearm or explosive device and does not directly result from a cataclysm. [See Committee on Motor Vehicle Traffic Accident Classification (1997), *Manual on Classification of Motor Vehicle Traffic Accidents*, ANSI D16.1-1996, Itasca, IL: National Safety Council.]

Motor-vehicle traffic accident is a motor-vehicle accident that occurs on a trafficway — a way or place, any part of which is open to the use of the public for the purposes of vehicular traffic. *Motor-vehicle nontraffic accident* is any motor-vehicle accident that occurs entirely in any place other than a trafficway.

Nonfatal injury accident is an accident in which at least one person is injured and no injury results in death.

Occupational illness is any abnormal condition or disorder other than one resulting from an occupational injury caused by exposure to environmental factors associated with employment. It includes acute and chronic illnesses or diseases that may be caused by inhalation, absorption, ingestion, or direct contact (see also page 61).

Occupational injury is any injury such as a cut, fracture, sprain, amputation, etc., which results from a work accident or from a single instantaneous exposure in the work environment (see also page 61).

Pedalcycle is a vehicle propelled by human power and operated solely by pedals; excludes mopeds.

Pedestrian is any person involved in a motor-vehicle accident who is not in or upon a motor vehicle or nonmotor vehicle. Includes persons injured while using a coaster wagon, child's tricycle, roller skates, etc. Excludes persons boarding, alighting, jumping, or falling from a motor vehicle in transport who are considered occupants of the vehicle.

Permanent disability (or permanent impairment) includes any degree of permanent nonfatal injury. It includes any injury that results in the loss or complete loss of use of any part of the body or in any permanent impairment of functions of the body or a part thereof.

Property damage accident is an accident that results in property damage but in which no person is injured.

Public accident is any accident other than motor-vehicle that occurs in the public use of any premises. Includes deaths in recreation (swimming, hunting, etc.), in transportation except motor-vehicle, public buildings, etc., and from widespread natural disasters even though some may have happened on home premises. Excludes accidents to persons in the course of gainful employment.

Source of injury is the principal object such as tool, machine, or equipment involved in the accident and is usually the object inflicting injury or property damage. Also called *agency* or *agent*.

Temporary total disability is an injury that does not result in death or permanent disability but that renders the injured person unable to perform regular duties or activities on one or more full calendar days after the day of the injury.

Total cases include all work-related deaths and illnesses and those work-related injuries that result in loss of consciousness, restriction of work or motion, or transfer to another job, or require medical treatment other than first aid.

Unintentional injury is the preferred term for accidental injury in the public health community. It refers to the *result* of an accident.

Work hours are the total number of hours worked by all employees. They are usually compiled for various levels, such as an establishment, a company, or an industry. A work hour is the equivalent of one employee working one hour.

Work injuries (including occupational illnesses) are those that arise out of and in the course of gainful employment regardless of where the accident or exposure occurs. Excluded are work injuries to private household workers and injuries occurring in connection with farm chores that are classified as home injuries.

Workers are all persons gainfully employed, including owners, managers, other paid employees, the self-employed, and unpaid family workers but excluding private household workers.

Work/Motor-vehicle duplication includes *work injuries* that occur in *motor-vehicle accidents* (see *Work injuries* and *Motor-vehicle accident*).